D1594407

The Scent of Snowflowers

a chronicle of faith,
hope and survival
in war-ravaged
Budapest

the Scent

FELDHEIM PUBLISHERS Jerusalem/New York

R.L. Klein

For the convenience of the reader, a number of Hungarian words and names which appear in this book have been transliterated phonetically.

First published 1989
Hardcover edition: ISBN 0-87306-498-4
Paperback edition: ISBN 0-87306-499-2

Feldheim Publishers Ltd.
POB 6525/Jerusalem, Israel

Philipp Feldheim Inc.
200 Airport Executive Park
Spring Valley, NY 10977

Library of Congress Cataloging-in-Publication Data

Klein, R. L. (Rivka Leah)
The scent of snowflowers / by R. L. Klein,
p. cm.
ISBN 0-87306-498-4. — ISBN 0-87306-499-2 (pbk.)
I. Klein, R. L. (Rivka Leah) 2. Jews—Hungary—Budapest—Biography. 3. Holocaust, Jewish (1939-1945)—Personal narratives. Hungarian. 4. Budapest (Hungary)—Biography. I.Title.
DS135.H93K54 1989
943.9'1200492402—dc20 89-32592
CIP

10 9 8 7 6 5 4 3 2

Printed in Israel

In tribute to
KARCSI and MAGDI BITTER,
the righteous young Gentile couple
who went above and beyond the boundaries
of human kindness and courage,
by putting their own lives in jeopardy
to save ours.

ACKNOWLEDGMENTS

First and foremost, my profound gratitude goes to my husband Yankl, whose confidence in me, far and beyond my capabilities, launched me on this project. And it goes without saying that without his constant encouragement and patience, this book would never have been written.

A very special thanks to my children, my "sounding boards," my constant help and inspiration, my great source of strength when the past's echoes were too much to bear. May they always remain a source of *naches* to us.

I would like to express my heartfelt thanks to Chaya Sora Fogel for her enthusiastic encouragement and devoted assistance in typing and helping me with English usage, and clearing the path to the publisher's desk. In spite of her very busy schedule, she always found the time to help when I needed it. Her contribution was invaluable.

And last but certainly not least, my appreciation to Feldheim Publishers and its staff, and especially to Marsi Tabak, Feldheim's editor-in-chief, and Debbie Ismailoff, for their great empathy and expertise in editing my book.

This story is true and all individuals whose permission I received to use their names appear here under those names. Others, whose permission I was unable to obtain, appear under fictitious names and every effort was made to conceal their true identity; any similarity between these fictitious names and those of persons living or dead is therefore purely coincidental. The names of many martyred relatives and friends are recorded here for posterity. ה׳ יקום דמם.

As for me, I have prayerfully turned to
Thee, O Lord, and on the morning that
is to be, my prayer will have come to
meet Thee.

Psalms 88:14

In Szombathely, next door to the shul,
Next door to the shul, stood the house.
But across the seas, and over the oceans
I still hear the laughter once echoed in its walls,
This house I visit in my dreams so often
With heart pounding, torn to shreds,
Only to awaken in the morning
Clenching bitter tears tightly in my hands.
For in my dreams I had sauntered up to those old walls,
And peered into the earth-shattering Silence.
And then I wonder, I wonder on those dreadful nights:
How ever can I dream of my old house,
Dream and yet not lose my mind?
But of this I have no doubt, for this I know perfectly well:
Though cruel elements did tear me from my old house,
They could not tear my old house from my heart
Nor could they erase it, erase it from the face of the earth,
For the blueprint of our parents' dear old house
Is etched on us from the moment of our birth.
Oh! but is this a blessing or a curse? a doublebladed sword,
For if every one of us is to build on the old foundation,
If so build we must, oh! what then, dear Lord, what then?
How will this human tragedy ever stop?
Unless of course, You watched, my Lord, the holocaust from above
And thundered in disgust: "ENOUGH! ENOUGH! NO MORE!"
And then destroyed hatred on the spot,
So in the future might every house be built
On the foundation of Tolerance, Justice, and Brotherly Love,
On which was built that house.
The house, the house, oh my parents' dear old house.
There. Next door to the shul,
Next door to the shul, which is no more.

Book One

1

ON A COLD WINTER EVENING in the year nineteen forty-one, Jacob Klein disembarked from the Budapest Express which had brought him from the pretty little border town of Ujhely, his home. He was a young man barely out of his teens, with a new beard sprouting from his sharp-planed face in wisps. The threadbare suit he wore hung loosely from his lanky frame. His eyes darted left and right. It was his first time in the big city and he looked around nervously, trying to figure out which way to turn. The crowd of passengers seemed to be heading toward a trolley station, so he followed them.

He'd guessed right. In a few seconds he spotted the trolley to Dob Utca, which was in the heart of the Jewish quarter, where his parents had obtained a furnished room for him. They hoped that there, among the masses in the Hungarian capital, their son might escape the horrible fate that had befallen the Hungarian Jews. The anti-Semitic government had just passed a new law declaring the Jews unfit for army duty. Instead, every able-bodied Jewish male was drafted into one of the new all-Jewish units called *munkatabor.* These were slave-labor units in every respect, where the laborers were subjected to torments and humiliations by their Gentile officers and to subhuman working conditions. Clearly, being drafted was a fate to be avoided at all costs.

Technically, Jacob was not yet a draft-dodger as he still had six months before he'd be of age to report for duty. His plan, however, was to register under his younger brother's name in order to evade the draft for a few more years. Looking at the sea of faces surrounding him, he imagined that everyone could see his intentions, that at any moment someone would point an accusing finger at him. He knew that draft evasion was a crime carrying severe penalties, involving imprisonment and unspeakable tortures, and as he took his first steps into his new life of subterfuge, he was filled with terror.

To still his turbulent heart as he followed the crowd into the trolleycar, Jacob recited in his mind his father's firm advice: "Don't, my son, don't for a moment feel guilty about disregarding the law of the land. The authorities have renounced you. They don't claim you anymore as their son. All that Hungary is doing now is plotting your downfall. From now on, your law should be the law of survival. Let only our holy Torah and your conscience guide you. And if you succeed in escaping this decree, be sure to help others who are trying to do the same."

Intellectually, he agreed with his father's words, but his heart was not at peace with his actions.

Deep in thought, tired and hungry, he arrived at his new apartment. He found his landlady to be a pleasant, middle-aged woman whose husband was in the work-camp and who supported herself and her teenaged sons by taking in boarders. She showed him the room which he was to share with another boarder. It was very small, and was sparsely furnished with two narrow iron cots, two battered chests of drawers and a closet divided by a faded sheet. Being one of thirteen children, though, he didn't mind the furnishings or the idea of having a roommate. In fact, he looked forward to the company and felt surprisingly at home immediately.

His roommate came in a few moments later. He was about Jacob's own age, a thin freckle-faced boy with a sunny disposition, and the two got to talking right away. Jacob wanted to know the arrangements and the local situation and his roommate, Yitzchok, was a veritable fount of information. Life in Budapest, Jacob learned, was no longer easy for the Jews. The only work to be found was in the black market, and then only if one had connections. And without some source of income, there was no guarantee of avoiding starvation. Their landlady, for example, could accommodate her boarders with meals only on Friday nights and Saturdays. The rest of the week they all got by on bread, butter and a few vegetables.

Talking about food made Jacob realize how hungry he was, and he suggested to his new acquaintance that they share his package from home. Feeling relaxed among his own, he began to talk about his family and his trip, adding that he had gone for two days without eating a thing. He had been too excited and worried to eat on the day before his trip, he explained, and on the train he had been afraid that everyone was watching him, waiting to point him out to the first policeman they saw: "Look at that Jew. He's up to no good!"

Yitzchok protested that Jacob surely needed to keep the food for himself, but Jacob insisted that they share it. Eventually, each convinced of the other's sincerity, the two new friends made themselves a very hearty supper.

Afterwards, Jacob wrote home to let his family know of his safe arrival, addressing the letter to the prearranged address. He smiled to himself as he recalled the one he'd hastily mailed from Miskolc, when the train had stopped there for a few minutes. He had hurried out to the station to mail the fabricated letter in which he bade farewell to his parents and begged their forgiveness for running away from home. Tears had formed in his eyes as he thought, I hope this letter will protect my parents when I fail to show up together with my classmates at the draft board. The letter he now wrote was likewise filled with misinformation, but his parents would know he was well.

Although it wasn't late when he finished, Yitzchok had already gone to bed, and Jacob prepared to do the same. He would need all his strength the next day to face the policemen's inquiring eyes when he registered his new address at the precinct. He climbed onto his cot and tried to warm himself under the covers, but the thought of facing the authorities sent shivers through his body. He was afraid that despite his exhaustion, he would not be able to sleep. He harbored very strong feelings of hatred and mistrust for the police. Awful memories, from far back in his childhood, awakened in his mind. He could still remember the border police bursting into his parents' house — which was located two houses away from the Hungarian-Czechoslovakian border — at all hours of the day or night, and he could still hear the voices which never failed to frighten him out of his wits: "We came to inspect your premises for smugglers and contraband."

They never found anything, but that didn't discourage them. Every month or so they'd be back. They blew in like a tornado, and in no time his home looked as if it had been hit by one. They turned the whole house upside-down and then left, swaggering out as arrogantly as they had entered.

Within moments after they were gone, it seemed, everything was back in its proper place, and his home was once again the warm, comforting fortress he depended on. Immediately the search seemed to be forgotten. In the supportive and closely-knit Jewish community in which his family lived, no one allowed himself to believe that anything could go seriously wrong. Even later, when warning signs of more serious trouble appeared, everyone turned a blind eye. Their entire existence was built on a foundation of false security. The truth was too frightening to face.

His mind roiling with these memories, Jacob could not remain in bed. He threw back the covers and started pacing the floor, hoping he wouldn't wake Yitzchok, who was sleeping deeply. As he paced, he remembered himself as a seventeen-year-old yeshiva student in a city far away from home. His landlord there was an old man with failing eyesight and Jacob would read the newspaper aloud to him every night. One evening, he opened the paper and read: "David Klein indicted for illegal possession of foreign currency. To serve prison sentence immediately."

He stared at the article, unbelieving. "That's my father!" he cried. "He's in prison!" A wail rose in his throat. "Those anti-Semites! They even managed to smear *him*, the most honest of men."

No one could talk him out of returning home. Determined, but with no money of his own, he ventured out on foot. After two exhausting days of walking almost nonstop, he reached Ujhely at last.

A horrifying sight greeted him on his arrival at home. Suitcases, cartons and bundles cluttered every surface, and all his aunts and uncles were sitting around the table discussing how to resettle his family! Jacob gaped at the scene. His home and fortress was crumbling before his eyes. He heard his uncle say that his mother and oldest sister were to stay in the house. As for the rest of them, each aunt and uncle offered to keep a child or two in their home until the father and breadwinner would return to gather his family together again.

No one noticed Jacob standing there silently watching. But when shy little Litzi reluctantly started to follow their Aunt Leah out of the room, Jacob could hold his tongue no longer. He ran to the table and pounded his fist on it with full force. "Stop, Litzi!" he shouted. "No one is to leave this house!"

Everyone looked up in astonishment. "When did he come in?" they asked one another, and then they dismissed him with, "Oh, he doesn't know what he's saying. He's just upset."

Aunt Leah tugged at Litzi to come along, but by that time Jacob was at the door, locking it and pocketing the key. "Don't worry, Mama, we'll all stay together. Not one of us is to leave here. You'll see — I'm going to run the business, to support us until Papa returns." He felt in total control.

Stunned silence followed his outburst. Then suddenly his mother was hugging him, and telling the excited children to unpack, assuring them that everything would be alright.

Turning to him she sobbed, "Let me tell you how it happened. The mailman delivered a letter from your Aunt Rachel in America with a fifty-dollar bill in it, and right away the police came in. I'm sure they knew about the letter, because they came in a moment after it was delivered. They could easily have taken the money, but all they cared about was the opportunity for causing pain and disgrace to a Jew. They found the bill in your father's vest pocket and that was enough 'evidence' for them to make it into a big crime. You know the rest."

Jacob relived these terrifying memories as he paced the floor, and when they were over, a warm glow shone in his tired brown eyes. "And I really did it," he whispered to himself. "I *did* keep the family all together and we were able to weather that whole horrible year. I *did* make Mama's plight easier to bear."

He thought of their happiness when their father was released, of the year or two of peace, and then of the new unbearable law. And finally, he heard his parents' parting words: "May the God of Abraham, Isaac and Jacob be with you, my son, and bless you. He will surely watch over you and protect you."

Jacob felt his eyelids getting heavy. Glancing out the window he was surprised to find the courtyard aglow in the rays of the rising sun. Wearily, he threw himself onto the bed and fell asleep.

He awoke only a few hours later, but he felt rested and ready to start the day. He managed to register his new address at the police station with surprisingly little difficulty, and a great burden was lifted from his chest. Then, with renewed confidence and vigor, he began the very necessary search for work. He made his way to his first stop, the office of Mr. Chaim Stern, full of hope and anticipation.

Stern looked him over approvingly. "So you are Duvid Klein's son. I know you from our correspondence. I remember when you were managing your father's coat factory and I sent fabric to you. When was that, Jacob?"

"Three years ago."

"And now you say you're twenty? Don't tell me that you were only seventeen when that tragedy happened to your father! Your hard work and efficiency made me think that you were much older than that!"

"Thank you," Jacob answered.

"I'm really glad to meet you, son," Stern said, "and I'm ready to do anything in my power to help you now."

"Well," Jacob began, "I'm on my own now. I decided to evade the draft, and I'm staying in Budapest to hide out. So I really could use some help. I appreciate your offer."

Suddenly the older man looked extremely perturbed. "Now, you take my advice, young man," he said sharply. "You have just informed me of something which should have been strictly your own secret. Heed my words and be more discreet! Do you have any idea how much trouble you could make for yourself if you're not careful?" Jacob paled visibly at these words and Stern's heart went out to him. "As far as I'm concerned, son, you have my full support. Of course your secret is safe with me. Now, I understand you to mean that you're looking for a business opportunity, yes?"

Jacob nodded, grateful but too embarrassed to know what to say. "Good," Stern said with a smile. "Mrs. Mermelstein will explain how we operate." He indicated a quiet young woman who was waiting in the corridor. "Mrs. Mermelstein, this is Jacob Klein — the newest member of our little enterprise."

"How do you do?" she said shyly.

"Hello," Jacob managed to say. Then, finding his usual voice, he thanked his new employer enthusiastically and went to receive his instructions from Mrs. Mermelstein.

By the end of the day, Jacob was very excited. He ran home to write to his parents to tell them how well things were going. His immediate success was far better than he had dreamed possible. Full of hope for the future and in an excellent mood, he mailed the letter and went off with Yitzchok to find a place for supper.

2

If the Lord does not build on a house, then its builders have labored in vain upon it;
If the Lord will not keep a city, the watchman has watched in vain.

Psalms 127:1

AUTUMN OF 1942 came early to Szombathely. It blew in on top of a whirlwind, accompanied by a torrent of rain. Estie Einhorn stood at the window watching the rain, listening to the rattling windowpanes and the happy sounds of her children responding to Rivka Leah's story hour.

This was only the second day of the storm and the wild chestnut tree outside her window was already stripped of leaves. A shiver passed through her. "It's freezing in here," she said aloud. "The children must be very cold!" She threw her coat over her shoulders and stepped out into the driving rain, hurrying toward the bin where the kindling was stored for the winter. "*Ribbono shel Olam*!" she exclaimed, dismayed at the sight of the meager stock of wood. "All I need is to start heating the house at the beginning of September. At this rate we'll have no wood left when real winter comes!" She blinked at the almost empty bin as a thought swiftly passed through her mind. "Tomorrow will be the day," she said aloud.

She piled the wood into the fireplace and lit it. "Come, *kinderlach*," she called to her children. "Come see the surprise I have for you!" Six happy, laughing children came running in from the other room and skidded to a halt before the crackling fire. From the oldest, who was eleven, to the two-year-old baby, they "oohed" and "ahhed" and danced with the leaping flames.

As Rivka Leah followed the children in to see the fire, Estie caught her eye and nodded toward the kitchen. The two sisters-in-law sat down at the kitchen table. The atmosphere was charged with Estie's pent-up tension. "I must face the facts, Leichi," she said at last. "We have no income. None at all. Shimon is in work-camp, the store has been shut down, and our savings will only last us at best another month or two..." She got up, wringing her apron in distress, and began to pace. Tears glistened in her eyes.

Rivka Leah had never seen Estie so close to crying before. A hard knot formed in her chest. She hadn't realized that their savings were that low. They had been living on them for the last three months, ever since her brother had been drafted to the work-camp. Could they really be down to their last few forints?

Estie turned to lean on the sink. She didn't want her young sister-in-law to see her crying. Then, in a choked voice she said, "I can delay it no longer. Maybe tomorrow I'll take the train to Budapest."

Rivka Leah knew what she meant. They had discussed the possibility many times, but until now it had never seemed real. Estie would make the four-hour trip by train to Budapest, and there find some sort of work. With God's help, she'd be back for Shabbos with enough money to keep them going. And when that too would run out? Rivka Leah shuddered to think what that would mean. Estie would return to Budapest for another week and another until this horrid war ended and Shimon came back home. That's what so many women were doing, women in similar circumstances with mouths to feed and no other source of income.

Rivka Leah sank into a chair and looked around blankly. The thought of being left responsible for their home and the children gripped her heart and left her unable to think. She was still mostly a child herself. She wasn't ready for anything like this, she thought. The sparse but spotlessly clean kitchen; the warm supper in the pots; the fire; the children, secure in the comfort of their mother's love; every glance she took reminded her of how much she appreciated Estie and how inadequate she was to replace her.

Estie turned back to face her and Rivka Leah could see that she hadn't even allowed herself to cry. Her beautiful, young face was drawn and pale. Her eyes had lost their secure, calm look. It frightened Rivka Leah. Estie had always been so strong, solid as a rock. Rivka Leah was reduced to utter despair. She blinked a couple of times, knowing Estie needed reassurance, but not knowing what to say.

"Estie, I'll watch your children. I promise I will take care of them as well as you would." The words sounded hollow and meaningless to her ears. "I love those children as if they were my own!"

"Yes, yes, of course you do," Estie said with a small ironic smile. She placed a gentle hand on Rivka Leah's shoulder. "I know you love them with all the love your heart possesses, but then, what could you know of a *mother's* love?" She read the hurt in her sister-in-law's eyes and immediately regretted her remark. "I know I can trust you. Let's talk about this another time," she said and quickly left the room.

Toward the middle of the month, Estie knew that her procrastination was only prolonging her misery. "It's no use," she told herself. "There is nothing to be done about it. If other Jewish mothers can do it, so can I." Rivka Leah heard her muttering this under her breath day after day until at last, one Monday morning, she kissed her children good-bye and gave Rivka Leah a parting hug. Her suitcase had stood in the hall for weeks, all packed and ready to go. She picked it up, took the packet of food Rivka Leah had wrapped for her and, with only the briefest backward glance, left the house and headed for the station. Rivka Leah and the children watched her tearfully from the window.

The travelers were mostly women, women whose husbands and sons had been drafted into the all-Jewish work camps. From the towns and villages all over Hungary, every able-bodied Jewish male over the age of twenty had been conscripted and sent to the *munkatabors* — the forced-labor camps. Their formerly pampered Jewish wives and mothers were now forced out of their sheltered homes as their husbands and sons, the traditional breadwinners, were called away to work without reimbursement. To make matters worse, wholesale businesses owned by Jews had been shut down. Liquor stores, largely in the hands of Jewish proprietors, had had their licenses revoked. This was followed in quick succession with more and more discriminatory activities against the Jews by the government, until all means of self-support were wrested from their hands. For these women, there remained no alternative. It was a question of bringing home the daily bread or starving with their families!

For those who dared, Budapest still offered an opportunity for some sort of livelihood. Because of the war in Europe, food and other commodities were scarce in the city, and so the downtrodden, penniless women who had never before left hearth and home journeyed to Budapest in the hope of finding work in the black market. Those who were fortunate enough to find employment traveled back and forth from their towns to the city as smugglers. These women transported slaughtered geese and ducks, dairy products, anything and everything they could sell at a profit on the flourishing black market.

They learned to act like hard-driving businessmen, tough and even aggressive, to eke out a living so their families could stay afloat. All their lives they had been law-abiding citizens and they had always had high morals and respect for the law. Now, beneath their tough facades, they were left feeling miserable. They went about their business guiltridden and terrified, for they knew that selling things on the black market was illegal and carried a stiff penalty by law. Nevertheless, the urgent needs of their loved ones made them risk their very lives.

The women became extremely clever at concealing the contraband in their packages and on their persons, hidden from the ever-prying eyes of police officers who were constantly after them to confiscate their goods. These blue-coated "patriots" of the government, it was well-known, appropriated the merchandise for themselves and the women only rarely were made to answer for their crimes. Robbed and terrified, they had to go home empty-handed, all their risk-taking for nought. But the next day, bright and early, they were back on the trains, carrying their heavy packages, with renewed hope and determination that this time they would succeed.

Estie sat with them in the first compartment, alongside the window, trembling in her seat. Her head was buried in her hands and her large brown eyes were red-rimmed. Alone and far from Rivka Leah and the children, she broke down and cried over her misfortune. She hadn't seen her Shimon for three months and there was no knowing when he would return from the work-camp. Now she had left her precious children at home in the care of her sister-in-law. Rivka Leah was her husband's orphaned sister, who had been their ward for the past few years. The children loved her more like an older sister than an aunt, and Rivka Leah truly loved them in return. It was a blessing to have someone like her to leave the children with. But no matter how hard she tried, Estie couldn't block out the memory of her children's heart-rending cries upon her departure.

The train came to a sudden halt, jolting her out of her thoughts. She sprang to her feet, dried her eyes automatically and, gripping her tattered suitcase, fell in line with the moving crowd. She soon arrived at Kozinsky Utca, a street of old and dilapidated houses in the Jewish quarter. In the front downstairs window of most of them was a sign announcing "Rooms to Let." Unable to decide, she walked aimlessly up and down the block. Estie, she admonished herself, what difference does it make which house you choose? You'll be lonely and miserable wherever you go, so decide already! But she could not.

"Looking for lodging?" a woman asked, tapping her on the shoulder. Estie turned abruptly to look into the friendly face of a young woman who was returning from her shopping. She appeared to be in her early thirties, just like Estie herself, and her openness and warmth made Estie feel she could trust her. She nodded gratefully.

"If you want a furnished room, I know there's one in this house," the woman said. "I rent here and I can assure you the rooms are decent. The landlady is really nice too." And then she added almost pleadingly, "She needs the money. Her husband is in the work-camp and taking in boarders is her only way of supporting her large family."

"Thank you," Estie said. She followed the woman to the rear of the nearest building, through a large courtyard paved with red cobblestones and teeming with children.

"It's on the second floor," the woman said, leading her toward the narrow, winding staircase. "This your first try?" she asked. Without waiting for an answer, she went on. "It's the same story with all of us, you know. Well, here we are." They had reached a paint-chipped door indistinguishable from the others they had passed. "Miriam," she called, "please come to the door. I have someone with me. She's looking for a room."

Another young woman, a baby on one arm and a toddler tugging at her skirts, answered the door. Her face looked prematurely aged with worry, but she must have once been a pretty girl, Estie thought. "Please come in," the woman said. "I have an excellent room for you. It's right near the bathroom in the hallway."

"I'll take it," Estie said without any questions.

She opened the door to her new room and tossed her coat on the chair. Fully clothed, she threw herself, weeping, onto the bed.

It was much later when she opened her eyes and looked around the room. Her gaze fell on the faded bedsheets and from there wandered to the streaked and stained walls of the narrow room. There was no window. No window! she thought, breaking out in a cold sweat, chills running up and down her spine. "Why am I panicking?" she asked herself, and suddenly she knew. She sat down heavily on the wooden chair and closed her eyes. A long-forgotten episode from the past flooded her mind. "Yes, Bubbie, no window. No window to let the sun in. No sun, no sunshine. This is the end."

She was a child again, a pale little four-year-old with long honey-colored braids and a starched pinafore, her face dominated by large brown eyes. She was the one and only granddaughter of her grandparents, a much-loved visitor to their home in the country. With her parents and grandparents, she sat on the open whitewashed terrace, dining on roast chicken, boiled potatoes and fresh salad.

After supper, her grandmother rose and, taking Estie's hand in her own, whispered in her ear, "Come, I want to show you something which you cannot see in the city where you live." They headed for the open field, walking among the stalks of growing corn. "Look, Estie! This is the way the corn grows," her grandmother said. "Would you like some for tomorrow's lunch?" They broke off a few beautiful ears of corn and gathered them in her grandmother's upturned apron.

As they crossed the field, her grandmother pointed to a colorful patch of wildflowers. "Come, let's pick some to make a bouquet for your Mama. Do you know that tomorrow is her birthday?" Estie skipped merrily from the daisies to the cornflowers, to the big beautiful red poppies, selecting the most perfect blossoms for her mother. Then, hand in hand, they headed home, singing all the way.

When they reached the front yard, her grandmother halted. She turned her face to the sky. "Do you see the sunset, *mamaleh*? The sun is going to sleep now." But Estie started to cry. "What's the matter?" her grandmother asked. "Did I frighten you? Don't you like the lovely sunset?"

"No, no!" Estie cried. "I don't want the sun to go to sleep!"

"But my dear, it is time for all of us to sleep, and for the sun too. It's been a long day." She picked Estie up in her arms and crooned to her until she had calmed down; then she carried her into the house and tucked her into bed. "Sleep, my dear," Bubbie whispered. "The sun is asleep now, but soon it will be morning and you'll both be awake to start a new day."

In the morning, when Estie awoke, she found her grandmother sitting next to her bed, knitting. "Look, Estie," she said, pointing to the window. The sun's rays shone through the curtains, making a bright bridge of light from one end of the room to the other. "You see, the sun is awake and has come to see you. Come, say hello to it. And from now on, don't forget to look for it every morning when you open your eyes."

"But what should I do when it's cloudy?" Estie asked.

Smiling, her grandmother replied, "Just look for it the next day. The clouds always go away sooner or later."

With a start Estie came back to herself. Many years had passed since then, and the little girl had grown into a woman, but in a secret place in her heart, the little girl still lived, searching for the bright bridge of sunshine her grandmother had promised her. Her panic returned and she had a horrifying feeling that this time the clouds would never go away. "My Bubbie is dead, and so is my golden bridge. And so is the little girl who lived inside me. Dead forever."

Estie could not find the energy to unpack or undress for bed. Knowing she needed sleep, she lay down under the covers, but sleep eluded her. She tossed and turned, recalling the circumstances which had brought her to her strange new surroundings.

Their personal troubles had started with a knock at the

door. There stood their neighbor and supposed friend, matter-of-factly informing them that he wanted their apartment and the attached store. Seeing their shock and despair, he said, "I am sorry to do this to you, but you know as well as I do that if I don't take the place, the landlord will only give it to some other Aryan brother. He is an anti-Semite and he won't have Jews in his houses any longer. So you see, it might as well be mine."

The question of why their business and the roof over their heads should be taken away from them by force never entered their minds. Robbery of the helpless Jew was already commonplace. It was so taken for granted that it seemed almost to have been legalized.

Their eviction was only the first devastating blow they sustained and their morale, along with their livelihood, was rapidly destroyed. They had hardly settled into their new apartment when the license for their delicatessen was revoked by the government, leaving them more desolate and despairing than ever. And then Shimon's draft notice had arrived.

"Now we have an apartment to live in, but where will I get the money to pay the rent?" she had asked him in the few hours before he had to leave. "With no income of our own, how on earth will we survive? We need clothes, and firewood, and food! What about food?"

He looked at her, his anguish barely masked, without giving an answer. They had only three hours to pack and make arrangements before the transport would take all the men of the town to the *munkatabor,* the labor camp. Three hours was not enough time to make half the arrangements they had to make, and no time was left at all to say the things they wanted to say. There was no knowing when he'd return, or what state he'd be in when he did; no knowing what condition the family would be in, or where. Thirteen years of marriage, of love and trust, of working together to build a home. In the rush, even their eyes couldn't spare a moment to express how they felt. The minutes flew as they worked frantically. Would he need his heavy overcoat or would he be back before winter? Shimon ran next door to consult with the neighbors about financial arrangements and when he returned, he asked Estie to listen carefully to what he had to say.

"Listen to me, Estie. Everyone agrees — the only jobs are in Budapest. Try to find work here, but if you cannot, you must go." He saw her start, but he held her gaze. "Estie, you are more fortunate than most. You have been such a wonderful mother that I'm sure our children will be able to manage during this difficult time if you must go away — even little Rechie. And besides, you have Rivka Leah right here to watch them."

Estie could not understand how he could be so callous, but then she saw that he was only trying to be strong for her sake. His confidence in her, though, was genuine. "I'll do what I have to," she assured him.

"I'm certain that, with God's help, you'll do very well," he said, his voice conveying the anguish he felt for his wife and all that she would have to endure.

Those were the only meaningful words of farewell they had had time for. "I hope I'll do well, Shimon," she whispered now, shivering at the memory of his leaving, and of herself leaving only a few months later. She rubbed her eyes to erase the painful images. She could only pray that his confidence in her was not misplaced, for everything now depended on her. "Well, Estie, this is it," she told herself soberly, "and it's time to do what must be done and to stop dwelling on it."

The night had passed but the only evidence of this was the muffled noise of traffic rising from the street below. She left the depressing, windowless room and headed for the police station, to register her temporary stay in the city as mandated by law. By the time she arrived, long lines had already formed at the window bearing the sign "Register for Change of Address."

She took her place at the end of the line and looked around at the mass of faces, some of which seemed vaguely familiar. They were the faces of her fellow travelers on the train to

Budapest. Pity engulfed her at the thought of the staggering number of women who were sharing her tragic fate. She shuddered. How many of them, she wondered, are also sharing my grief? How many had to tear themselves away from their sobbing and protesting children? The cries of her own still reverberated in her mind: "Oh, Mama, it's bad enough that Papa had to leave us. Can't you, at least, stay? Please, Mama, don't go!" Her heart ached with longing for them.

"Next! Hey, next!" a rough voice suddenly shouted. "Come on, move up!"

Estie had no idea how long she'd been standing there, lost in her misery. "I'm sorry," she apologized. She handed the policeman her documents and he looked her over, comparing her face to her likeness. "Home address?" he barked from across the desk. "Length of stay?"

If only I were still at my "home address," she cried inwardly. She heard herself say, "A week, sir. Perhaps two." She watched the policeman stamp and sign her papers and finally blot the wet signature, a superior smirk on his face. Then he double-checked her face with the photograph and slammed her papers down on the desk. To her relief, she once again heard the gruff voice ring out, "Next!"

Thank God I'm through, she told herself, sighing deeply and hurrying out of the dreadful place. Outside, the sun was high in the cloudless autumn sky. "I've lost half a day already," she said aloud, and then she caught herself. "Lost from what? I've no idea where to start." She looked up and down the busy street until her gaze fell on a brightly painted sign: "Korn's Cafeteria."

"Go to Korn's Cafeteria," her landlady had told her. "That's where everyone goes. That's where they pick up information about business opportunities and such." It was the only lead she had, and besides, she was hungry. She couldn't remember when she'd eaten last. With renewed determination, she headed straight for the cafeteria.

Once inside, Estie paused for a moment to take in the scene. Korn's was packed with people, and alive with the hustle and bustle of the lunch-hour crowd. At first glance, the atmosphere seemed casual and relaxed, but the easy flow of words between patrons, the jocular banter, was misleading. Without pausing in their conversations, the diners repeatedly shot nervous glances toward the door. The pitch of their voices revealed to Estie that behind the casual facade, the cafeteria throbbed with tension and sheer animal fear.

Her eyes scanned the room for an empty chair. She soon found one and moved toward it in a daze. With rapt attention, she listened to the conversations going on around her, momentarily forgetting her hunger in her desperation to pick up a hint of information. The waitress, a pretty Jewish girl with long dark hair and warm brown eyes, stopped by her table.

"Coffee and some hot farina, please."

The girl returned quickly with her order and placed the tray in front of her. "First time in the city?" she asked good-naturedly.

"Uh-huh," Estie answered in surprise. "How does everyone know?"

"They all have the same look when they first come in here," the girl said, avoiding Estie's eyes. Then she was gone.

Estie continued to visit Korn's religiously, as her landlady advised her, but without getting any smarter at all. The long days dragged into long sleepless nights and she was no closer to a source of income than she had been when she arrived. Her melancholy days were relieved only by the letters she received — letters from Shimon giving her courage, and from her children, telling her that they were managing and that she needn't worry.

Then, all too soon, it was Thursday, and the only thing being discussed at the restaurant was going home for the weekend. A terrible yearning for her children engulfed her and a feeling of failure clutched her heart. You'll never get anywhere if you just sit here waiting for someone to come over and give you work, she chastised herself. Ask somebody what to do! Take the initiative!

Before she could change her mind, she extended her hand to the woman at the next table and said, "Hello, I'm Estie Einhorn, from Szombathely." Without ceremony she proceeded to tell the woman of her plight, and asked for any possible assistance.

The woman was about to answer, when a man leaped up from a table nearby. "Excuse me," he said, "but I couldn't help overhearing your name. Are you Shimon Einhorn's wife?"

"Yes, I am," Estie replied, tears welling up in her eyes. "Shimon is in the work-camp. Do you know him?"

"Yes, and I knew your father-in-law, the *Dayan* of Szombathely. I was a student in his yeshiva. What a genius! What a *tzaddik*! What unlimited knowledge he possessed! Just the other day, I was speaking about him with a fellow alumnus. How we mourned his untimely death." Estie could only nod her agreement, for her emotions were so close to the surface that she dared not speak.

"It's ironic," the man went on, "for now we can thank God he's not here for the Gentiles to humiliate. But you need work, not speeches, right? When you finish your breakfast I'll try to help you make some contacts. May I join you at your table?"

"Please do," Estie said breathlessly, hardly believing her luck.

He took a chair and looked at her with unmasked pity. "Not only did Shimon and I learn together in his father's yeshiva, but he was my *chavrusa*. We became very close friends right from the start. Oh, excuse me, I haven't even introduced myself. My name is Aaron Goldstein."

"Aaron Goldstein! I've heard so much about you from my husband," she said, beginning to lose her shyness. "Shimon likes to talk about the pranks you used to play together."

"Yes, those were the days," Aaron sighed."We were carefree youths, alright. But let's get back to the subject — finding you some work. When you're done here, I'll take you to see some people." She finished very quickly, relieved to have someone to help take care of things. They paid their bills and left.

Outside, it was much quieter. "Good," Aaron said. "Now we can hear ourselves talk. Mrs. Einhorn, have you heard of a man called Chaim Stern?"

"No, the name is not familiar to me."

"But you must have heard of the firm Obudai Freudiger?"

"Are you talking about the giant Jewish textile manufacturer?"

"Yes, that's the one. Stern heads the distribution department there. He alone decides who gets what. And believe me, he could be a millionaire, if he chose to."

"How's that?"

"Merely by selling the merchandise directly to the Aryan wholesalers or to the Jewish tailors. Instead, he gives the merchandise on consignment to people like us to sell for a profit. That profit pays our rent and feeds our families. And he does this just out of the goodness of his heart."

"But how does this prevent him from being a millionaire?" Estie interrupted, confused.

"You know, there's a big demand for textiles now with the war on. Almost all of the textiles Hungary produces are bought up by the Germans to clothe their vast armies, and so the little that's left is in such demand that our customers would gladly pay highly inflated black-market prices for it. Now do you see how much money Mr. Stern could make if he sold his goods directly himself?"

"I do see," she said, impressed. "He gives you the goods at list price and you sell them at the black-market price. But officially you are just salesmen, or middlemen."

"That's right! That's exactly what we are. Do you think you could do this kind of work?"

"Of course," Estie replied excitedly. "But do you think Mr. Stern would take me on?"

"I'll do everything I can."

"Thank you, Mr. Goldstein. Thank you so very much," she said, overwhelmed with gratitude.

"Don't thank me. I haven't done anything yet. And besides, it isn't so easy: you still have to find your own customers to sell to." Aaron checked his wristwatch and said, "I have just enough time before my train leaves to talk to Mr. Stern on your behalf, and at this hour he's usually still in his office."

"Is it far from here?" Estie asked, excited now at the prospect of finding work at last.

"No, no," Aaron assured her, "it's only about a ten-minute walk."

They walked in silence, Aaron contemplating how best to present the situation to Stern for maximum effect, and Estie stifling her excitement and the feeling that her heart would jump through her mouth if she dared open it. Soon they reached the building.

"Don't worry," Aaron said. "I'm sure he'll help you if he can." He led her to a bench in the hall outside Stern's office. "I think it would be better if you waited here while I speak with him alone." Estie nodded her agreement.

After a seemingly endless wait, she heard the office door opening. "Mr. Goldstein," she said, leaping to her feet. "Mr. Goldstein, what did he say? Will he take me on?"

"Everything's been arranged," he said with a smile, opening the door wide.

"Come in, please," she heard her new employer say in a soft, pleasant tone. He was a thin, bespectacled man of middle age, with a ready smile and a fatherly manner. "Please be seated, Mrs. Einhorn, and make yourself comfortable."

She sat on the edge of the chair nervously, watching the man rummage through his desk drawers and choose a batch of fabric samples to give her.

"This will do," he said, handing her a swatch of beige wool. "I'm going to write down the quantity of yardage available, and the legal and suggested black-market prices. We will deliver the goods directly to whomever you sell them to. I understand that our friend Aaron Goldstein has explained our procedure to you?"

"Yes, yes," Estie said. "He certainly has. And thank you very much, Mr. Stern."

"I wish you all the luck in the world, Mrs. Einhorn," he said, rising from his chair and escorting her to the door.

Aaron was waiting for her in the hall. "Now I understand what you meant about Mr. Stern being able to be a millionaire," she whispered. The gap between the legal and black-market prices was surprisingly large. "This will be just enough to keep my family going, and if you count all those whom he helps, it really adds up!"

Aaron agreed. "The nicest part of it is that Stern is so businesslike. He makes you forget that this is actually a handout."

Thus Estie Einhorn became yet another of the many beneficiaries of this noble man's philanthropy for the downtrodden victims of their government's and fellow citizens' prejudices.

On the way home, she spoke to her husband in her heart: Shimon, I didn't let you see how afraid and miserable I was when you first suggested I go to Budapest, but now I see how well you knew me. Without your encouragement and faith, I would never have been able to go through with this.

She arrived at the rooming house in a much cheerier mood than when she'd left, and immediately began a letter to her husband, overflowing with love and encouragement. "And Shimon," she concluded, "always remember: this nightmare will pass, and soon we'll be home together as the happy family we were before."

By the following Thursday, she had realized her goal. Her pockets were lined with the money they so desperately needed for food and rent. She ran to the post office to telegraph Rivka Leah and the children. "With God's help," she wrote, "I'll be home tomorrow."

3

THE DAYS PASSED SLOWLY and, in the hustle and bustle, I found myself yearning for the time when I had been a simple young girl with relatively few responsibilities. Now I had become the surrogate mother — as well as father — to the six small children of my brother Shimon and his wife Estie.

A lump forms in my throat when I remember the very first night after Estie left for Budapest, when Rifky, the oldest of the children, had a nightmare. She came into my room in the middle of the night and crept into my bed, shivering with fright. She could hardly bear to tell me her dream. Instead, out of earshot of her younger brothers and sisters, she lowered her defenses and hurled question after question at me, deep philosophical questions about hatred and war, questions to which I had no answers. To hear these age-old questions coming from the lips of a child so young filled me with despair, and I clenched my fists in impotent rage.

Oh, Rifky, I cried to myself, what can I tell you? Your questions are as old as history itself. There are no easy answers. None at all.

My heart went out to the child and I held her close. "Rifky," I said aloud, "I couldn't sleep tonight either. I'm also afraid, you know. How on earth will I be able to take care of everything here? I don't even know how to cook! I couldn't possibly manage, unless, of course...you were to help me. I said to myself, 'Rifky is a big girl. She's almost eleven. Maybe she can help me.' Would you, Rifky? We — the two big girls — we two could run the house together." I stopped abruptly and held my breath. It was not a performance I was putting on for her sake. I meant every word of it.

She regarded me with surprise. Her eyes were dark gray and enormous in her tiny, thin face. She reached out to take my hand. I felt her hand tightening as we began to talk, making plans together. She clung to me tightly as we spoke far into the night. Slowly, I felt her grip relax as she drifted off to sleep, but not before she agreed that she would represent her mother to her younger siblings. In her mother's absence, she would be the one to settle all the quarrels among them. Furthermore, she decided to enlist everyone's help: her brother Shia would be assigned to seeing that all the children's homework was done, just as their father had done before he was called away. With Rifky taking the role of mother and Shia that of father, Zeesy, the six-year-old, would be the big sister, and Pinky, the five-year-old, would act as the big brother. Faigie and Rechie, aged three and two respectively, were the babies, and babies they would remain. "And you," she decided with indisputable eleven-year-old logic, "you will be the grandmother!" Then she fell asleep.

As I covered her with a warm blanket and tucked her in, I was fully convinced that my observations had been correct. She was a child in years, but her childhood had left her during these last few months. I hoped that giving her these grown-up responsibilities would somehow compensate for her lost childhood and help keep her spirits up.

I still could not fall asleep, so I found my brother's most recent letter and began examining it for some hint, some message, some true feeling between the lines, but all I could sense was apathy and despair.

"Oh, those beasts! What have they done to you, Shimon?" I whispered into the dark. "Where is your laughter? Where are your jokes?" All at once, the stories that had come to us through the grapevine, of the horrors of the work-camp, became real to me, and now I believed everything I had heard. I asked myself, Why did my brother go? Why did all of them go like mindless sheep when they were called? Why didn't they all run away and hide somewhere? But no matter how much I pondered this, I could not find an answer. I trembled and wept miserably beneath the covers.

How could it be, I wondered, that after living with oppression for thousands of years, we Jews still had not learned how to defend ourselves? Why did we remain so innocent, so trusting? Were we merely fools?

No. Not fools. It was because we ourselves were so trustworthy that we so readily placed our trust in others; because we were so honest and open that we never suspected others of dishonesty and deceit. Maybe we *were* fools after all.

My oldest sister, Nechy, didn't have any answers either. She had come to visit the day before and I had asked her, "Where does the army find all those beastly men to be appointed as overseers and torturers in the work-camps?" She had replied that it was only natural. Beasts had but to smell blood and power and out they came. Her response had shocked me. All I could do was look at her blankly, so innocent was I and so unaware of the ways of the world. Could it be that normal people could turn into beasts overnight, or was it that such beasts lurked among us always, only waiting for the right moment to appear?

"What's the use of thinking about it?" Nechy had said, nervously checking her wristwatch. "We can't do anything about it now, anyway." My questions had made her uncomfortable. I urged her to go back home and leave me to my fruitless contemplations. It was unkind of me to subject her to this when her own husband was in the camps.

I finally laid my questions aside and fell into a sleep so deep that I overslept the next morning. At first I flew into a panic, but when I rushed out of my room, I was pleasantly surprised to find that the children were all dressed and fed and ready for school. Even the little ones had eaten breakfast and were playing contentedly in a corner.

"Rifky told us to tiptoe," Zeesy volunteered, "so that you could sleep. We were playing house and I was the big sister and helped a lot."

"And I am the big brother," said Pinky.

Then Rifky, the eleven-year-old little mother, bent her head solicitously to me and asked, "Do you feel all right, Leichi? I was worried."

The children quickly put on their coats as Shia, the little father, hurried them out of the house, so as not to be late for school.

Waving good-bye to them from the doorway, I thought to myself: No matter what Estie says, I am sure that when I have children of my own, I will never love them more than I love these. At least, that is what I thought at the time.

All week long, the children and I counted the days, marking them off on the calendar each night. I was as anxious as they were to see Estie home, and to give her back her responsibilities. I was already anticipating the freedom I would have over the weekend to go out with my friends. But on Thursday afternoon, we received word that Estie would not be returning for Shabbos.

I dreaded the moment the children would come home from school. The news was sure to throw them into an uproar. But they took it quite calmly, and without protest began counting the days all over again. I congratulated myself, attributing their easy acceptance to my skill in handling them, despite my ignorance and lack of experience with children. Then all at once I recalled an episode from my own childhood and my bubble of pride was deflated.

"They are all liars," my friend Kato had said crossly. The two of us were in the schoolyard, some distance from the other children.

"Who?" I asked with alarm, seeing her agitation.

"You won't believe me if I tell you," she said. "Our own mothers!" I frowned at her in disbelief, but she was adamant. "Don't tell me it's not so," she insisted, "because I heard them myself! Just listen and you'll agree with me." She was so agitated that there was no way she could have kept her story to herself.

"Yesterday afternoon," she began, "I was sitting in my room doing my homework. Suddenly I heard voices coming from the garden. My mother's friends were visiting and they were all working on their needlecrafts and discussing their problems — which means us. They call it 'child-rearing.' I heard my mother say, straight out, that it's perfectly natural for children to fight and to be mean to each other, and that if anybody were to tell her about children who never quarreled, she would know that there was something awfully wrong in that house. All the other mothers agreed with her. Now, tell me, does a day go by in your house without the children being scolded for fighting?" I had to admit that she was right about the scolding. "You see, they were all lying," Kato concluded triumphantly.

"You are the one who is lying!" I screamed at her in anger. "Mothers don't tell lies!" The schoolbell began to ring and all the children started running to their classes. Kato grabbed my shoulder and made me stay behind. She placed her hand on her heart and solemnly swore that every word she'd related was true.

I was terribly confused. Learning was over for me that day. The only thing I could think of was how happy I was that my own mother had not been at Kato's house with all the two-faced, lying ones.

Now, watching my nieces and nephews walking about silently, all being extra-helpful and obedient, I understood those mothers very well. They knew exactly what they were talking about. Silently I begged their forgiveness for ten years of thinking them two-faced. I found myself wishing for my nieces and nephews to quarrel or disobey me; in a word, to be carefree children again. I wished desperately for a way to bring back those innocent, rebellious days of just a short while ago.

My day centered around the children. Rifky, Shia, Zeesy and Pinky went to school while the two little ones, Faigie and Rechie, stayed home with me. At first, my heart went out to the younger ones, imagining how they must be missing their parents, but fortunately they knew me well and loved me and adjusted easily. I soon realized, though, that the older ones were hit much harder by the upheaval in their lives, for besides missing their parents, they were old enough to feel the impact of the daily growing anti-Semitism. They were visibly frightened. It terrified us all to see the Gentiles united in their hatred of us. More often than not, one or another of the children came home bruised and bloodied, having suffered a beating at the hands of the Christian children in the neighborhood. One day, Rifky came home with a bloody nose. She didn't complain about the pain. What hurt her was that the boy had taunted her. "Cry, Jew," he had baited. "Go see if your ever-loving Jewish mother can kiss that pain away."

"Of course she could have, if she were here," I said, frantically trying to comfort her. "Here, let me substitute Mama's kisses until she comes home." I racked my brain in desperation for a way to calm her.

Suddenly the mailman appeared and came to my rescue. He held out two letters. "Oh, look!" I cried jubilantly. "A letter from your Papa, and another from your Mama! Isn't that wonderful!" Handing Rifky her father's letter, I asked her to read it aloud for all of us to hear.

As I watched my beautiful, eleven-year-old "grown-up" niece read her father's letter in a firm, clear voice, her eyes swimming with unshed tears and a smile warming her little girl's lips, a terrible truth became clear to me. I thought, She is not a child anymore. She's more an adult, a woman determined to hide her pain and cheer up her little ones.

She folded the letter neatly and put it back into the envelope. "It *is* wonderful!" she said smiling. "Everything is all right. Papa is well."

"But when is he going to come home?" Pinky begged.

Then they all started shouting, "When? When? When?"

Oh, no! I cried to myself. Once again I was at a loss, searching for an answer that might satisfy them.

Then I heard Rifky saying, "What a shame. Papa forgot to write about it. But I'm sure he'll be home soon."

Following Rifky's lead, I directed everyone's attention to Shia. "Come, Shia," I said, handing my sister-in-law's letter to him. "Now it's your turn. Let's see if you can read us your Mama's letter."

"If I can read?" he said indignantly, puffing out his chest. "Why, you know I'm the best reader in my class." Then in a proud, unwavering voice, he began reciting his mother's letter. Missing in him was the air of maturity his sister possessed, and I was deeply grateful that this little eight-year-old was still a child. All of a sudden his face flushed crimson, and he started jumping up and down. "Mama's coming home! Mama's coming home!"

"Mama's coming home!" the walls echoed back. Needless to say, I did not have to search any further for a balm to heal Rifky's wounds. Within a few minutes they were all busily coloring "Welcome Home" signs.

After supper they helped me spruce up the place. They worked tirelessly, polishing every corner and all the while singing and dancing like little elves. No chore was too difficult, no task performed well enough for their mother, the homecoming queen.

Estie arrived home in the middle of the night and even Rechie, the baby, was still awake and waiting up for her. The children ran to the door, jumping all over her, nearly knocking her down. They kept pulling and pushing each other, just to be close to her.

"So these are my angelic children that you've been raving

about, Leichi," she called over the tops of their heads. "Are you sure we're talking about the same kids? Well, one thing's for sure — they are the most beautiful children in the whole world, just as you said."

"How could they *not* be, with such a beauty for a mother?" I responded, swallowing my tears of emotion.

It was only much later, when they had all fallen asleep, that she joined me for a cup of tea and some long-awaited words.

"How did you manage?" she asked anxiously. "Was it very hard? How did they really behave?"

"Hard to manage?" I repeated. "Are you kidding? Just the opposite. If anything, they were *too* good. I couldn't take it! I kept begging them to be *normal*." She looked at me oddly and I started to blush.

"You didn't *want* them to be so good?" Her large dark eyes opened wide in astonishment. I didn't know what to say. I didn't want to tell her that I thought they had behaved so well because they were unhappy.

"Of course I want them to be good children. It just seemed better that they act the same as always..." I assured her that I would encourage this good behavior, but I was especially pleased to see that all weekend they were very boisterous and rowdy — in short, exceedingly normal.

Our lives now revolved around Estie's return each weekend. Thursday nights were holidays for the children, while Sundays were dreaded, for that was when their mother had to leave them again. The biggest treats of all were the letters from their father, but they brought me no joy for I sensed the bitterness and despair in them. Fortunately, the children were too young to understand.

One Shabbos afternoon, while the children were napping and Estie and I were sitting in the parlor, she turned to me and asked, "Leichi, do you remember the fellow I told you about, the one who works for Mr. Stern? I met him my second week in the city and he made such a good impression on me then. I bump into him often and I must say I like him more and more each time I do. I was thinking that he'd be a perfect match for you."

This took me completely by surprise. I told Estie that I didn't think it was a very good time to get married, but she persisted.

"I'd like you to meet him," she said earnestly. "Please don't say no. To tell you the truth, I'm surprised myself. It came up so unexpectedly. I had supper with him and his father in the restaurant and I was so impressed with him that I invited him here to the house."

"Well, that's really nice of you," I said indignantly. "You pick up a stranger in the city and invite him here just like that? You *could* have asked me first." I was deeply hurt by what she'd done.

"I really did mean to ask you, Leichi, but I wanted to meet his parents before I said anything, and once we were all talking, the invitation just slipped out. I'm really sorry about that," she added soothingly, "but it wouldn't have happened if he hadn't seemed to be such a special person."

"Does Shimon know anything about this?" I asked, still unmoved.

"You *know* I wouldn't do anything without your brother's approval," she replied. "I wrote to him about the fellow, and for the past few weeks, both he and I have been gathering information about him and his family."

"And I suppose they're doing the same," I said, unsympathetically.

Opening her pocketbook, Estie produced a letter. "Here, read this. It's from Shimon," she said, handing it to me.

Dearest Leichi,

I'm sure this shidduch *will come as a shock to you — as it did to me — but Leichi, I really want you to consider it. I'd like you to meet this boy. Estie is very impressed with him and I trust her judgment. I only wish I had his courage. You see, he's managed to avoid the work-camp. It would come as a great relief to me if you would meet him and see if he's the one for you. Estie and I would both be overjoyed to see you married. Knowing how your mind works, I can just hear you asking, 'And who will tend to the children when Estie goes to Budapest?' Remember that Surie, my sister-in-law from Kassau, could come and help us out.*

I know what a difficult decision this is for a young girl to make on her own, especially in times like these. I realize that Estie and I can never take the place of our dear departed parents and advise you as they would have, but please keep in mind that we love you dearly and want only the best for you. I urge you, dear sister, to consider and discuss it with Nechy and Estie.

With much love,
Shimon

P.S. I'd consider it a personal favor if you would just give him a chance.

So, while my Gentile contemporaries were daydreaming of knights on white horses who would come to offer their hearts and their castles, I daydreamed about a boy who put up a fight to avoid falling into the brutal hands of the anti-Semites. For this reason, even before I met him, I greatly respected him. If anyone had suggested becoming serious about a boy while the storms of war raged all around us, I would have called him insane. And yet, when this tall, skinny young man came through the door and my eyes met his — warm, intelligent, laughing eyes — the first thought that came into my mind was: "*Klein, Rivka Leah Klein.* It sounds good."

To my own astonishment, it didn't take more than six weeks until we were engaged to be married.

To make the transition easier for the children, Estie invited her sister, Surie, to our house immediately after my engagement. It was a very wise idea. Not only did it give the children time to get accustomed to her, but it eased my feelings of guilt about leaving them. Now I was free to come and go at will and attend to my personal affairs without worrying about their welfare.

Jacob and I decided to buy our furniture in Budapest,

where we were planning to live, so he did all of the furniture shopping. We agreed that we would buy our kitchenware once we moved to our apartment. That left only one exciting purchase for me to make alone: my wedding gown. There was very little else I bought for myself, due to the bad times and inflated prices, but I felt that in spite of everything I had to have my very own wedding gown.

On the Thursday before the wedding, I went to the seamstress and tried on the gown together with the veil. It was truly a masterpiece, I thought. Standing before the mirror, I just couldn't get enough of my own image. My long black hair was a stunning contrast to all those endless yards of white silk and lace.

"It looks like you don't want to take it off," Gisella, the seamstress, said, "but remember, you agreed to abide by my terms. I am to dress you on the day of your wedding, so you cannot take the gown home just yet."

"I guess it's alright with me," I replied, turning crimson at the thought of how vain I must have looked to her. "Anyway, with Paula and Mathilda in the house cooking and baking for the wedding already, I don't know where to put *myself*, let alone a gown such as this. But please, Gisella, be prompt to the wedding. You know that the *chuppah* will start at one o'clock sharp."

"Don't worry, I'll be on time," she said with a smile. I floated out of her house in a daze.

By tradition and for economic reasons, weddings and other ceremonies were celebrated in private homes. Paula and Mathilda were two women who made their living by preparing food for these affairs, and they were now cooking 'round the clock. With barely a week until the wedding, our house became a veritable hive of activity.

The kitchen especially was in a fearful mess, and the constant bickering of the two cooks was exasperating, so I fled to Nechy's house around the corner. Her place was invitingly clean and quiet, offering a peaceful haven for me to think and daydream and to imagine myself all dressed up in my beautiful gown, with its billows of lace and tulle. It never ceased to surprise me that the lovely young girl of my daydreams was actually me. Then, full of guilt over the few moments of happiness stolen in the midst of those perilous times, I hurried back to the chaos of my brother's house.

Since it was Thursday, Estie was due to return from Budapest, and Surie and I worked frantically to finish sewing the children's wedding outfits for them to show off to their mother. Then, amid all the hectic preparations, with so much yet to do, Surie noticed that Mathilda was leaving! "Oh, my heavens!" Surie cried. "Where is she going? That's all I need! Five days until the wedding and so much of the cooking left to be done! That bad-tempered Paula must have driven her off."

I ran to her, calling, "Mathilda! Please stay! Where are you going?"

She brushed past me without answering and collided with the mailman in the doorway. He handed her a telegram. "It's for you," she said, passing it to me. "It's from Ujhely, from your fiancé, I suppose."

"From Ujhely!" I began to tremble. "Yes, it must be from him!" I ripped clumsily at the envelope.

"Open it! Come on!" Surie urged. "Let's see what it says!" Her face was pale with anxiety. Telegrams always have that effect on their recipients.

I stood there hardly able to breathe, my fears suffocating me. Inwardly I cried, He's been caught, I know it... dragged to the work-camps.... What will they do to him?

"Open it! Open it up!" Surie and Mathilda prodded.

I forced my hands to unfold the telegram. It read:

EVERYBODY, EVERYTHING, ALRIGHT. SENDING LOVE. MADE TELEPHONE APPOINTMENT POST OFFICE. 5 P.M. MUST TALK. BE PROMPT. UNCLE YIDEL.

We breathed a collective sigh of relief as we realized all was well. But the telegram from my future father-in-law's brother, Yidel, was not without its ominous overtones.

4

IT WAS A PERFECT June day. The streets were full of people strolling and laughing leisurely under the balmy skies. Here and there we met some of our friends, but they hurried past, glancing at us surreptitiously. No one had to tell me: I knew without a doubt that Mathilda had spread the news of our telegram all over town.

Nechy accompanied me to the post office. We arrived there way ahead of time and nervously waited for the clock to strike five. (Few private homes in Szombathely had telephones installed and most calls came through the post office, by prior arrangement.) My name was called at last. I was told to pick up the phone in booth number 2 and as soon as I did, a jovial voice came across the line.

"Hello, is this Rivka Leah Einhorn? Let me introduce myself. I am Yidel Klein, your future uncle."

"Hello," I replied anxiously. "Yes, it's me, it's Rivka Leah. How are you, uncle?"

"Fine, fine. Let me say *mazel tov* to you on your forthcoming wedding. I've heard so many nice things about you and we're all looking forward to meeting you!"

My heart leaped. Wedding? I thought. He said "wedding"! Is it still on? Aloud, I said, "I'm sure you didn't trouble yourself with placing this call just to congratulate me, uncle. What's going on? Is Yanku all right?" I held my breath waiting for his answer.

"Yankl? He's fine, *baruch Hashem*, and happy as a lark! He sends you his best and so do we all."

"So then, why did you call? What has happened?" I asked again in a shaky voice.

"Oh, there's nothing to worry about, but something unexpected has come up." I braced myself for the worst. "Well, it concerns my brother, your future father-in-law," Uncle Yidel went on. "I mean, it really concerns the whole family. The problem is that my brother's probation officer won't allow him to leave town. He won't be able to attend the wedding of his own son."

"What do you mean, 'probation officer'? Why should he be on probation? Was he jailed? Do I understand you right?" I heard myself asking, while my mind reverberated with the unspeakable word "convict"! "My heavens," I cried in panic, "don't tell me I am about to marry the son of a convicted felon!"

There was stunned silence on the other end of the line. "I guess your brother Shimon didn't tell you. Yankl's father was innocent, of course, as he insisted right from the start of the whole unpleasant affair. He was framed by the anti-Semites, only so they could rob him of a few dollars he received from his sister in America." Uncle Yidel sighed deeply. "The animals," he said with disgust. "It's been a nightmare, believe me. What that poor man went through, what we *all* went through!" There was a pause and his tone softened. "Please, Rivka Leah, I see that this has shocked you, but I must ask you to change the location of your wedding and get married in our town. You needn't give me your answer now. I want you to think about it and talk it over with your family. And keep in mind, there will be no ill feelings if you decline. It was all my idea. I've made another appointment for the telephone for eight o'clock tonight."

Before I could say a word, there was a click on the line and the telephone went dead. I gazed at the receiver in my hands in mute frustration. I was appalled at my rudeness and upset that I hadn't had the opportunity to apologize. I turned to Nechy and repeated every word of the conversation.

"It's absurd," she said, frowning. "I feel very bad for him, but whoever heard of such a thing? The invitations have been out for weeks now. This is really too much to ask — do they expect you to run away from your own wedding?"

I didn't stop to think for a second. "But that is *exactly* what I am going to do," I said with such determination that Nechy's mouth fell open in surprise.

"But you can't! There isn't even time to let our guests know! They'll come to an empty house!"

"Oh, Nechy," I cried, overcome with emotion, "if our parents were alive, and for one reason or another were unable to make it to this town at the last minute, I would move Heaven and earth to get married wherever they were. Even if it meant giving up the reception! Should Yankl's father miss the wedding too?"

That very night, Estie came home to the same red-carpet treatment as usual, but the children were more excited than ever as they sat waiting for her, huddled together in the darkened room, all wearing their new wedding outfits. When she entered, we switched on the light, yelling "Surprise!" and the children ran towards her, giggling and smiling and modeling their new clothes with obvious pride.

"Mama, look at me! Look at me!"

"And me! See my dress!"

"Look at my suit! My shoes!" They all tried to out-yell one another.

The thought of the great pain and disappointment I was about to cause them made me feel ill. I couldn't bear to look at my nieces and nephews. How on earth could I do this to them? I chastised myself. But it was too late now. I had already relayed my decision to Jacob's family. Surie had promised to help me break the news to Estie and I knew I could depend on her, but still my heart ached. There was simply not enough money to take everyone along. Fearing that I would break down, witnessing their disappointment, I slunk unnoticed out of the room and went to bed.

The next morning, I woke to find Estie gone. "She had a dentist appointment," Surie told me. Then, holding my face with her reassuring hands, she said, "Don't worry. I told her. It's okay."

"What was her reaction, Surie? Was she very hurt?"

"It doesn't matter. She'll get over it. By the time she comes home, the edge of her disappointment will have worn off."

I was very grateful for Surie's help and cooperation and I left the house in an easier mood to pick up my wedding gown from Gisella's. I knew it wouldn't be a pleasant task. Gisella would not be pleased with the idea of giving up the privilege of dressing me in her own masterpiece, as she called all of her creations. But I was worrying needlessly, for when I arrived at her house, all I saw was a hand-written note in the window: "Closed for vacation. Will reopen Monday morning."

Panic welled up in my chest. Monday morning would be too late — I had to leave on Sunday! I ran around the corner to her mother's house. I congratulated myself for having taken care of the balance of the bill at the last fitting, so that her mother wouldn't have any objections to giving me the gown. To my dismay, I didn't find her mother at home either. A neighbor told me that they had left together for a long weekend. "The doctor cautioned her mother to take it easy," she said. "You know, she was hospitalized last year for a heart ailment." She babbled on and on.

"But I must find Gisella! Where did she go? She couldn't have disappeared into thin air!" I tried to steady my wildly beating heart.

"Forget about finding her," the neighbor said. "Believe me, not even her assistant knows where she went."

With my panic over Gisella's disappearance mounting, I arrived home in time to overhear Estie, Nechy and Surie engaged in a bitter debate about my hasty decision. As I reached the door, I heard Estie say, "Do you think, Nechy, that I could make her change her mind?"

"Not a chance. She didn't hesitate for a minute," my sister whispered. "When I pointed out that she'd made her decision too quickly, she answered lightly, 'When the truth hits you, hesitation has no place.' I know how disappointed you are, Estie. You are so giving and selfless, like a mother who is marrying off her own daughter."

"But Estie, you'll *still* be marrying her off," Surie chimed in. "You'll be accompanying her to Ujhely, won't you? You'll *still* walk her to the *chuppah.* Is that so bad?"

I walked in and an awkward silence fell upon the room. "Estie," I cried, "Estie, Gisella's not home! She's out of town. Nobody knows where to find her!" I flung myself on Estie's shoulder, weeping, "Please forgive me! Can you ever?"

"Your dress?!" she asked, swallowing her intended reproach. "Oh, no, what will we do about your dress?" Then stroking my hair she whispered, "How could I be angry with you when you are showing such maturity and kindness toward your future in-laws? After all, *you* are really the one who is being cheated out of the wedding of her dreams. So let's put everything in proper perspective. Don't worry, I'll help you find your dress."

All Friday, Estie scoured the city for some clue to the whereabouts of my seamstress, but to no avail. On Saturday night, however, only sixteen hours before my scheduled departure, and after having given up all hope of having a wedding gown at all, a solution arrived unexpectedly. An old friend of the family offered me the gown of her newly-married daughter.

"She will meet you with the dress at the train station in Sarvar," the woman said. Needless to say, I was tremendously relieved.

With this matter settled, I now had one more enormous hurdle to cross. I shivered at the thought that I had yet to tell the children the disappointing news as soon as they arrived home from school. Sunday came, and there was no way to postpone it. I laid out the packages of gifts which I had prepared, to sweeten the news for them. There was something for everyone but Rifky; I hadn't been able to find something special enough for my favorite niece. Then my eyes fell upon the watch on my wrist, and I knew I had found the perfect gift for her. In an instant I pulled it off and wrapped it with a hastily jotted note that said:

My dear Rifky,

I know that it is not fair, but my wedding is going to be held far away. Please don't feel bad. It is because of a real last-minute emergency, and I promise to make it up to you as soon as I can. You can see that I have left you my treasured wristwatch. I cannot find the words for the love I have for you. The first chance we have, Yankl and I will invite you to Budapest and take you shopping and sightseeing. You are my most precious friend and niece. Farewell, and with much love,

Your aunt,
Rivka Leah

I had hardly finished attaching the note to the present when the door burst open. The children crowded around, wide-eyed and excited over their gifts. While they opened them eagerly, I told them in as few words as possible the reason for the gifts and my regrets. Then I quickly left the room, where even the children's festive clothing hanging from the curtain rods now seemed to look at me reproachfully. I ran to Nechy's house, where Estie would pick me up to go to the station, and spared myself the heartbreak of seeing the children's hurt and disappointment.

In mid-afternoon we arrived at the railway station and climbed into the third car of the train, as we had arranged beforehand with our friend whose daughter was bringing the gown. Long before we heard the conductor announce the approaching village of Sarvar, we stood up and waited near the open door to make sure we would not miss our friend's daughter and the priceless package. As the train neared the station, we noticed a young couple with a large brown box on the ground beside them. Now alerted by the roar of the oncoming train, the husband picked up the box and ran forward to meet us, passing the box through the open door.

We did not even have time to thank them properly, for the train quickly pulled away, taking me to meet my soon-to-be husband and family, and to begin my new life. The setting sun shone brightly over the skies of Hungary, but the clouds of war hung heavily on the horizon.

We rode from the station to the Kleins' home in a horse-drawn coach, and all along the way I was aware of people on the streets staring at us to catch a glimpse of me through the open windows.

"Look at the sensation you've created here!" Estie remarked.

"I don't blame them a bit," I said. "They all want to see the fool who changed her mind at the last minute and left all her friends and guests out in the cold. If they also knew that I haven't even tried on my wedding gown to see if it fits, they would without a doubt pronounce me hopelessly insane." My nervousness mounted over the imminent meeting with my future in-laws; the horses could not go slowly enough for me.

Soon the driver tugged on the reins and the horses obediently turned a corner and stopped at the first house on the street. It was old and large, set in a garden, and bustling with people. When they heard the carriage, they came running out to meet me, all of them exuding such genuine warmth that my fears and doubts evaporated like mist. They told me that my eldest brother, Shmuel Yitzchok, had already arrived; he had come all the way from Szerencz, and I burst into tears at the sight of him.

"I know it's late, Leichi," he said, relieving me of my hand luggage and taking me aside, " and that you must get dressed for the wedding, but let's sit down for just a few minutes and talk." Shmuel Yitzchok was a great *talmid chacham* and the pride and joy of our family. He had inherited my father's genius and at forty years of age was already known as an outstanding scholar. Now he offered me, in his usual humble manner, some brotherly advice on my wedding day. "Always stay as happy as you are today," he said, "but remember that happiness means giving — giving selflessly. As our Sages teach us: 'If you will treat your husband like a king, he will treat you like a queen.' This is the magic key to true happiness."

We spoke a few minutes more, and I appreciated my brother's sensible, loving words. We hadn't seen one another for five years, ever since the last family *simchah*. Now I treasured these precious moments and saw what a great man my brother was, and how much I had missed by not having him near.

I dressed quickly, not caring at all about my appearance. "Look at yourself in the mirror," my future mother-in-law urged me with obvious pride. "You look beautiful!"

But not only did I refuse to look in the mirror, I forbade the photographer to take any pictures of me. I wanted to remember only how I had looked at Gisella's in the gown of my fantasies.

Because of the last-minute change, the wedding feast was prepared in haste at a catering hall. It was a poor substitute for the lavishly prepared wedding I had left behind, but what really hurt was the absence of my family and friends. Just as my new father-in-law asked me to dance the customary *Mitzvah* Dance, two burly police officers burst into the house. They stared at us, at the wedding guests, at the decorations and the tables laden with food, and knew that this time their plan hadn't worked. They left without a word. Looking at my father-in-law, and seeing the joy and relief in his eyes, I finally realized how childish I had been, fretting about my gown.

The next morning at the breakfast table, I really got to meet my new family. My three little sisters-in-law crowded around me and the youngest one, Chayie, caught my attention first.

With shiny, dark curls and laughing, black eyes, Chayie had all the charm that a seven-year-old could possess. The older ones, Laya and Litzi, aged nine and eleven respectively, were blonde, blue-eyed and dimpled as little cherubs. The family called them "the three little girls."

"Now listen, young ladies," Jacob said to them. "If anybody asks you where I am, you must say 'I don't know'."

"Don't worry, Yankl. Mama told us already," Litzi assured him.

"We must go now," Laya announced, her dimples showing. "Guess what, Leichi — we're not going to school today! We're going to a 'slumber party' at Aunt Bracha's and we're taking our pajamas!" And out they flew like three little birds, never dreaming that their slumber party would last an entire week.

"You can't imagine what a treat it is for the girls to go to Aunt Bracha," Jacob said with a wink. "Aunt Bracha is the only one in our family rich enough to own a record player. Just leave it to my mother — the girls will stay there until we're safely out of the way. Mama is never satisfied with half-measures, and definitely will not depend on the girls' discretion."

That afternoon, I found myself sitting in the same horse-drawn carriage in which I had traveled from the station the day before. This time, it was to see off Shmuel Yitzchok and Estie, the only two wedding guests from my side of the family. Estie boarded the train first, lugging the familiar brown parcel containing the borrowed wedding gown. I had managed to get married just as well without Gisella's "masterpiece," it seemed. In difficult times, things get scaled down to their proper proportions.

I watched my brother board next. Suddenly, a tall, husky man came rushing across the platform and arrogantly pushed my beloved brother aside. "Hey, Jew, make way for an Aryan!" his voice boomed.

Shmuel Yitzchok looked at him in disbelief, a painful,

questioning look on his delicate face. The opening line of a long-forgotten poem came to mind: "Not all those are great, who grow tall." I saw it clearly demonstrated then, as this tall, small-minded man roughly shoved my frail, great brother. That big Aryan embodied only prejudice and self-interest, while my diminutive brother was the essence of all the values that civilized mankind could need: Torah knowledge, wisdom, humility, compassion and love. Angry tears filled my eyes. I watched the departing train for a long time, and even after it was gone from view, I stood watching the empty tracks, thinking how astute that poet had been.

What I did not know, was that this was to be the last time I would ever see my brother. Eleven months later, he — along with his wife Golda and their only daughter Rifky — was ruthlessly murdered by the Nazis in Auschwitz. With them also went my baby brother, Mayer, whom they had been raising as their own son.

For the week after the wedding we stayed with my in-laws, to celebrate *sheva brachos*. Throughout the whole week, my new husband never set foot outside the house, for fear that knowledge of his whereabouts would reach the authorities. We had no way of knowing if they were actually searching for him yet, but there was no point in taking chances. The family, despite their concern, maintained a conspiracy of silence on the subject so as not to cast a pall on the festivities, and no one even mentioned the terror we all shared: that the police would alert the draft board that Jacob was indeed in town.

I was greatly relieved when, on the seventh day, my mother-in-law presented us with two Pullman train tickets. "They're for the sleeping berths," she said. "You can hide behind locked doors for the entire trip and avoid discovery."

That night, we were all packed and ready to leave when suddenly there was an insistent knocking on the front door. Surprisingly, no one seemed alarmed. Before opening the door, my mother-in-law turned to me and said, "Rivka Leah, I don't know how to say this." Tears glittered in her eyes. "I thank you. I thank you for the gift, the gift of coming here so that Papa and I could both attend the wedding. I pray that the Almighty will repay your kindness." Then, drying her eyes, she threw the door open wide. "Come in, everyone. We're in here!"

The hall was suddenly filled with girls and married women, all flocking around me, kissing me and complimenting me, and wishing us all the happiness in the world.

"My aunts and cousins came to bring us gifts and wish us well once more," Jacob whispered. "Their wishes are heartfelt; all their husbands are in the work-camps."

"Oh," I whispered back, chills running up and down my spine, as if the work-camps were contagious. "Let's get out of here *now*. I don't want to miss our train."

Suddenly there was a sharp clap of thunder. "Let's go! Let's go," cried the women, "before it starts to pour!"

"Rain?" my mother-in-law said with relief. "What a gift from Heaven. No one will be out on the streets."

We're going home at last, I thought excitedly. I'm going with my very own husband to our very own home. "Oh, Yankl," I whispered, starry-eyed, "Yankl, I will make our home beautiful and comfortable, and we'll live there in happiness forever and ever."

5

Some boast of their chariots, others of their horses,
But we boast of the name of the Lord, our God.
Psalms 20:8

MY HEART WAS thumping with excitement as our train drew nearer and nearer to Budapest, and to our very own apartment, the dream of my orphaned childhood.

We hailed a taxi outside the station, and all I could think was that it didn't matter what sort of place Jacob had been able to find for us — I would somehow turn it into a real home. Just then the taxi stopped in front of a brand-new building.

"I'm exhausted, Yankl. Why aren't we going home first?"

His eyes lit up as he answered with a smile, "My dear Leichi, this *is* our home!"

I watched open-mouthed as the driver unloaded our luggage and lined it up neatly near the entrance. We rang the bell on the front door and a young couple emerged and greeted us warmly.

"Hello, hello! So, the newlyweds have arrived at last. I am Bogar, the superintendent," he said. "Let me help you with your luggage."

Mrs. Bogar embraced me warmly and led us to the elevator. "I hope you two will be very happy in your new home," she said again and again.

So it really is true, I thought, entranced. We really do have an apartment here. I looked at Jacob and whispered, "I'm afraid this is nothing but a dream. Are you sure I won't wake up and find that I imagined all this?"

My husband laughed and handed me a set of keys. "No, my dear. It's true. It's real. Welcome to our new home." My heart pounded as Jacob ceremoniously ushered me inside. All my weariness disappeared as I ran from room to room, inspecting every detail.

"Oh, my!" I cried. "A blue bathroom! Isn't it beautiful! Look at the kitchen! I'm so glad the window is facing the street. I'll never be lonely when you're not home, because I'll have the whole avenue to watch. I can't believe my eyes! Look! We have a tiny porch off the kitchen. Oh! I am so very happy!" I kept on babbling in my delight. I was in a state of euphoria. "Never in my wildest dreams did I imagine that I would live in such a palace!" I told Jacob, gazing all around in wonder.

"To tell you the truth, neither did I. But I'm doing well at work, thank God. You know, though, that under normal circumstances, I would have been but a penniless *bochur*, just out of yeshiva. We would be living in a tiny apartment near my family, and we'd be very happy without knowing that a house such as this even exists."

"You know that I would gladly exchange all this glitter for a plain apartment that was safe and secure," I said. "I can do without living in constant worry and turmoil." The choice, however, was not ours to make.

I looked around again at the lovely rooms. "I really feel very guilty being so happy when everyone around us is so miserable. I worry so about my brothers and relatives in the work-camps. But then, everything is dwarfed by my terrible worry for you."

A shadow passed over Jacob's face. "Remember what you told me yesterday, that only happiness will enter our home?"

Easier said than done, I thought, but I forced a smile for my new husband. "Of course, Yanku, of course."

The awkwardness of the moment was shattered by the ringing of the doorbell. A young couple stood in the doorway, the wife's pretty face radiating good-natured friendliness while her husband's bore a shy, boyish smile. They were dressed in comfortable-looking, at-home clothes and carried tiny cups of liqueur in their hands. Jacob and I glanced at each other questioningly.

My husband found his tongue first. "Ah! The welcoming committee!" he laughed.

"I'm Danny Brenner," the husband said, "and this is my wife Vera. We're your next-door neighbors, and we came to welcome you, and to congratulate you on your marriage." With that he began to sing "*l'chaim*!" and, pressing the cups of liqueur into our hands, danced into our apartment.

"Mrs. Bogar told us that our new neighbors had arrived while we were out," Vera explained. "I was so happy. I never imagined I'd be fortunate enough to have another young Jewish couple right next door."

"You must be the answer to our prayers," Danny added, "because we've felt so alone since we moved here. We left all our family and friends behind when we moved to the city."

"So did we," I said, still in a daze over our new abode. This handsome couple added immeasurably to my joy. I had the feeling that we were going to be very good friends.

Soon enough the men were talking together as though they had known each other for years and I myself warmed up to Vera. "I hope I won't turn out to be more than you bargained for," I told her. "Besides your friendship, I desperately need some help and guidance, because I am so very, very inexperienced." Vera's smile told me that she was more than willing to lend a hand.

"Come on, Vera," Danny interrupted, "let's leave these newlyweds alone for a while." They left our apartment in that bubbly way of theirs, leaving us light-headed with happiness.

"I go shopping every morning in the Lehel Square market," Vera called back. "If you like, I could call for you at eight tomorrow morning."

"Oh, yes, Vera," I replied, "and thanks!"

"What a lucky day!" I said to Jacob. "It has started out so beautifully. Oh, Yankl, I have the feeling that we will be very, very happy here!"

Together we began to prepare our first supper, which consisted of scrambled eggs and the delicious homemade bread and butter that my mother-in-law had given us, and we feasted like kings.

"I don't think," my husband said earnestly, "that there can be a couple who has had a better supper than we have."

"And I don't think," I answered, "that there is a couple who has a nicer apartment than we have," and we laughed heartily, like two people without a care in the world. "But you know, I feel so rich and happy and carefree now in our lovely apartment mostly because you are home, Yanku. If you only knew how miserable I am the minute you set foot outside! I get so worried when you're out there on the dangerous streets of Budapest. I'm terrified that they'll find out that you're evading the draft."

"I'm surprised at how quickly you've forgotten our rules, Leichi," Jacob said with a touch of annoyance. "Remember that we declared our home our own little *Gan Eden*, where nothing but happiness may enter. So please, don't worry about me."

He looked so worried himself, that I felt guilty for having spoiled *his* happiness. I assured him that I wouldn't worry anymore, knowing perfectly well that we both would. But at least we wouldn't mention it to one another. That would be the rule of the game: we would only encourage, and never burden, each other, despite our fears.

But whether we mentioned it or not, we lived in trepidation every second of our waking hours.

Vera and I left early the next morning, armed with our food ration tickets, which enabled us to buy specified quantities of food. Everyone was issued the tickets when he registered his address with the local authorities. We headed for the Lehel

Square fresh-food market, where, in a glass-enclosed pavilion, scores of farmers sold their produce. The fruit and vegetables they had brought at dawn on horse-drawn carts, while the big city still slept, was now neatly arrayed on wooden stands.

It looked as if every woman in town had come to the market and they shopped like sharp-eyed crows. At first, they stood stock-still, scanning the entire place, and then, without warning, they swooped down on one of the stands, snatching the plumpest, firmest produce while still maintaining their surveillance of every movement in the area. I realized that all around us lines had started to form.

"Let's get in this one," Vera said in a low voice. "He always has the best potatoes and he's still got some left. Potatoes are usually the first item to go. Since you have a few weeks' supply of unused ration tickets you'll be able to stock your pantry. You'll find that very convenient."

She briefly surveyed the surroundings. Suddenly she pointed to the opposite side of the market and whispered excitedly in my ear, "Look! The fish man is here, and I want us to get to him before he's spotted and everyone goes wild!" The man began to unload and people ran forward, many abandoning lines in which they had been standing for close to an hour. In no time, his line was the longest.

"You are marvelous," I whispered to Vera, following her example and keeping my voice low. Apparently, the sharp-eyed crows had sharp ears as well. "You know the merchants here so well."

"That's the name of this game," she replied. "If you don't use your head, you could spend all day going from one line to the next and still end up with empty shopping bags."

Now the fishmonger was laying out his catch on blocks of ice. I stared wide-eyed at the shiny, wriggling creatures. "I don't think I want any," I told Vera. "They scare me, and I don't know how to clean or slice them."

"Nonsense!" Vera said. "The fishmonger sees to all of that." She chose two of the biggest fish, one for each of us. In no time we had them safely in our bags, cleaned, sliced and neatly wrapped.

"Where now?" I asked later, hefting my full shopping bags. Vera seemed to have cast off her crow's eyes and had become her old self again.

"Home!" she announced, to my great relief. "I must be home for my children by two o'clock at the latest, and I want to take you to buy some dishes." I had told Vera that I didn't have any china or kitchenware yet. "We can stop off at the house to unload our groceries first. It's on our way."

Vera turned out to be a very helpful friend indeed. We returned home from the hardware store laden with essentials which I placed lovingly in my cupboard. Now I really felt like a married woman. How excited I was at the thought of cooking our first real supper!

Doing my housekeeping chores, I hopped about the apartment like a happy little bird who has discovered that her gilded cage has a dual purpose: to keep her in and keep predators out. I was overjoyed at the thought that we would always be able to stay at home for supper and I wouldn't have to worry that someone at the restaurant would ask why my husband was not in the work-camp. The thought was so comforting that I sang while I cooked.

The house was soon redolent with delightful cooking aromas, but when Jacob came home he pretended not to notice. He called to me with feigned urgency in his voice, asking whether I was ready to go out to eat, as he was starving.

I didn't catch on that he was joking. Proudly I announced that we did not have to go anywhere, and I grandly escorted him to the table set with my lovely new plates and silverware.

"Oh, Leichi! How did you know that fish was my favorite food?" he exclaimed with delight as I served him. "Where on earth did you get it?"

I told him how Vera had unveiled for me all her secrets of successful shopping, giving him all the details of my exciting morning. I chattered gayly, not caring whether Jacob was really interested or not. For once I had managed to banish the anxiety that followed me day in and day out, and we went to sleep that night in a state of euphoria.

The next day, when my husband was at work, our furniture arrived. Jacob was overjoyed when he came home at night. "Do you like the way I've arranged it?" I kept asking. "If not, we can move things around."

"No, no," he kept reassuring me. "It's exactly the way I like it." We went from room to room admiring the decor of our very first apartment. We both felt that we were the richest couple on earth.

"Leichi, Leichi! Wake up!" Jacob cried, jolting me out of a deep sleep. "Someone is ringing our bell!"

"What time is it?" I asked groggily.

"One o'clock in the morning."

Immediately, I was wide awake. I threw myself out of bed and ran to and fro in a panic. "Oh, no! They must have found us out and are coming to grab you and take you to the work-camp!" I felt my legs buckle as fear gripped me.

Jacob's face bore an intense look of concentration as he reached for his clothes. He ran around checking the windows in the bedroom and the kitchen, peering through the curtains to the street below. He seemed to be considering climbing down the fire escape.

I was standing still in the bedroom, but my mind was working feverishly. "Oh, God!" I sobbed. "Please help us! Where can he hide?" The bell sounded again, more urgently than before. My gaze fell on my husband's bed and an idea suddenly struck me. Quickly, I straightened the linens and made the bed; then I urged Jacob under it, fully clothed, shoes and all. When I covered the bed with the floor-length bedspread, he was completely hidden.

"I will say that I have no idea where you are," I whispered.

I hurried to open the door, expecting to find soldiers or police with guns drawn, but to my great surprise, standing there in the hall was my sister Tzivia. I nearly collapsed with relief. But when I looked at her more closely, my heart sank. My sister was hardly recognizable. She had always been a beautiful girl, with long blond hair and bright blue eyes. Now her cheeks were sunken, her eyes had become two pathetic, tired orbs, and her clothing was drab and lifeless.

Overwhelmed, I burst into tears. I drew her and her packages inside, murmuring to myself, "Thank God it's only you, thank God it's only you!"

She looked at me blankly, not comprehending my pleasure at seeing her in her present misery. But when she saw her new brother-in-law emerge, fully dressed, from under the made bed, she realized how her midnight arrival had affected us, and she began to apologize for the fright she had caused.

"I'm so sorry, Leichi, but I had no choice," she said. "I had to come to town to sell these two geese or else starve!" She indicated the packages at her feet.

"It's all right, Tzivia," I said, trying to reassure her. "You actually did us a very big favor. Because of you, we found this excellent hiding place. It might come in handy one day."

As I looked at my sister, I was overwhelmed with guilt. I thought of how carelessly I had spent money yesterday, completely unaware of her plight. I sat her down in the kitchen and placed a cup of hot tea in her hands, and we reminisced about happier times.

"Remember when I first visited you after you got married?" I asked her. "Remember how I got lost in your village the first time I was there?"

"Of course I remember," she said. "There you were in the middle of the street looking for our house — when the cattle came home! You were white and shrieking and surrounded by cows when I found you. You looked as if you thought the world had come to an end!"

"Yes, I think about that day sometimes," I said. "But more often I think of us at home, sitting by the brook and talking the entire afternoon."

"Yes, those were the days," Tzivia said wistfully. "Whoever thought then that these terrible troubles could happen to us?"

I interrupted her and quickly changed the subject. "I don't even know what your baby looks like," I said. "I've never seen him. People say he's the image of his father. Is he a redhead?"

She nodded. I saw her expression soften, and for a fleeting instant her face was transformed by the love she felt for her family, only to be changed again and filled with worry as she asked, "Do you think I will find a customer for my geese? I have to sell them quickly because I must be home before night. It's really too hard for our sister Surele to watch three little boys for so long. I can't tell you what a help she is to me. I don't know what I'd do without her!"

"Don't worry," I reassured her. "Yanku said that he can advance you the money and he'll sell your geese for you tomorrow. This way you can go home on the first train." It was almost two o'clock in the morning by then. My eyelids were beginning to droop despite my efforts to look alert, and I knew how tired Tzivia must be. I suggested that we call it a night, but she protested.

"When will we ever have another chance to talk to each other?" she said. "Did you hear that our brother Yoav gave up his grocery store, or rather, that he was forced to give it up?"

"What do you mean?" I asked incredulously.

"A Gentile opened up another grocery across the street from him," she explained. "Yoav's customers, if you recall, were mostly old farmers who came to town to sell their wares and then did some shopping before they returned home. These same farmers used to patronize the store when it was owned by Yoav's in-laws. Whenever I visited them I was struck by the fact that they all always seemed to be such good, old friends."

"So what happened after this new grocery store opened?" I asked, not believing that I had heard correctly.

"Most of them simply turned their backs on Yoav," she replied sadly. "The few who didn't were told by the new storeowner that Yoav 'the Jew' was shortchanging them. When that didn't work, he threatened them physically. And that was that."

"But what are Yoav and his family living on now?" I asked, thinking of my very favorite brother, who was so small and skinny that even the work-camp had refused him. "Oh, what bad times are upon us!" I cried. "How will it end?"

Tzivia didn't answer, and when I looked up I saw that she had stiffened and her face had turned a deathly white. Her eyes were glazed and she whispered, as though in a trance, "Do you remember the gypsy girl?"

I didn't know what she was talking about. Oh my God! I thought. She's lost her mind! The constant strain has driven her insane. "Tzivia, what are you saying?" I demanded, trying to jolt her out of her stupor.

"Remember the gypsy girl we met in the ice-cream parlor?" she whispered. She was visibly trembling and all at once I recalled that day clearly.

It was an unusually hot July afternoon and we had gone to the ice-cream parlor for some refreshment. We were sitting and enjoying our ice cream, a very rare and expensive treat for us, when all of a sudden, a gypsy girl appeared before us and grabbed Tzivia's hand to read her palm. Tzivia struggled to free her hand because the girl looked so frightening and because palm-reading is forbidden by the Torah, but the gypsy was stronger than Tzivia and would not release her. She began to read her "fortune."

"You will marry next spring," she intoned. "Your husband will earn his living with his two hands, doing hard physical labor." In spite of Tzivia's continued struggles to free herself, the gypsy went on. "You are going to have one, two, three, four sons." And then, without any warning, she began to wail and covered her eyes with her hands. She wailed as though the world were coming to an end. "Oh, Miss! How awful! I see a terrible, unending fire. Oh, how it burns!" And she kept on wailing as though her heart were breaking. I looked at my sister and saw that she was staring at the gypsy, frightened beyond words. I tried to comfort her but I couldn't reach her; she was in a state of shock.

"Don't tell me that you believe her!" I exclaimed. "She's crazy. Don't you realize that? You're not even sixteen yet, so of course you won't marry next spring. And you know as well as I do that when you do marry, your husband will be a student fresh out of yeshiva, not a manual laborer. Besides, Jews don't believe in palm-reading."

I began to feel genuinely frightened because Tzivia was beyond reach. In desperation, I thrust my hand out to the gypsy, certain she would predict something equally crazy for me too and thereby break the spell she had cast on my sister. "Do you see what you did to her?" I whispered furiously to the girl. " Tell me the same thing too." Little did I know then that the gypsy girl could have predicted the same "future" for another six million of our brethren and she would have been right.

I felt the girl's firm grip on my hand as she turned it palm up, and I fervently prayed that she would tell me the same future, and would wail as hysterically as she had when she predicted the all-consuming, unending fire for my sister. But to my dismay, as she began to speak, entirely different words came out and I cursed her in my heart, for I had done what I'd been taught was forbidden, for the love of my sister, and the gypsy had ruined everything.

I looked at Tzivia now, trembling just as she had on that afternoon. "Don't tell me that you still believe in that nonsense!" I cried in alarm.

"No, I...I don't," she stammered. "I never did. I don't know what made me think of it now. But what frightens me now is that she turned out to be so accurate in her predictions. I did marry that spring, and my husband does earn his living, or rather did before he was drafted, with his two hands, working hard in our print shop, operating the machines manually. And can't you see that I have three sons and I am pregnant with our fourth child? I know that we aren't supposed to believe in it, and I want to dismiss it as a freak coincidence, but you cannot deny that it's scary." She was almost whispering at this point.

"Oh, Leichi, come on!" my husband said, poking his head around the door. "How can you keep your sister up until all hours? Don't you know that she has to make the train in the morning?" He was right, of course, and there was nothing more to say, anyway. We bid each other good-night and went into our rooms.

I lay in bed, but sleep eluded me as I listened to the sound of the walls of our *Gan Eden* crumbling to the ground, letting in the heart-rending cries of my people that I so much wanted to deny. I knew in my bones that I would never again be young and carefree, and I knew that I would never be able to forget the pain and the fright in Tzivia's eyes. I felt overpoweringly guilty for the happiness and freedom I had felt just the day before, and for having spent so much money when my sister had none to feed her family. My husband tried to reassure me, telling me that now that we knew about Tzivia's situation, we could do something to help her. But no words could console me. I cried until morning. I sensed somehow that this was the last time I was ever going to see my dear sister.

And it was. She was killed with her four little boys in Auschwitz, and our baby sister, Surele, went with them into the all-consuming fire.

The next week brought a letter from my favorite brother, Yoav, who lived in Pápa, his wife's hometown, a short distance from Szombathely. Although the roadside grocery store he had inherited from his in-laws wasn't much of a business, it brought in enough to raise his family, albeit very frugally. The little they had, though, had always been considered quite enviable in their small town, and Yoav and his family had never seemed to feel their poverty in the least. His was one of those happy families that have everything but money, but as a young girl visiting them I used to pity them immensely. Oh, how unseeing our eyes are, I thought, looking at his letter.

My small, sickly-looking brother had worked himself to exhaustion at the grocery, but he faithfully arose every morning at three to go to *shul* to learn with his friends before he opened up his business. I remembered that one night when he had seemed unusually tired, I reset his alarm clock for five A.M. instead of three, without consulting him. I never forgot how upset he'd been the entire day for having missed those two hours of study, and never again had I interfered with his schedule. Now I tore open the envelope and read:

Dear Sister:

Tzivia told me how very upset you are that we lost the grocery store. You needn't worry, because now I earn my living as a bookbinder. You know that some of our father's sefarim *were in bad condition, so during my free time in the store, which I began to have a lot of, I started to rebind them. I thought that maybe our children would use them one day. Well, before I knew it, I became an expert at it. Now I'm working at restoring the* Kehillah's *library, for you know, Leichi, that no matter what happens to us, we won't let go of our sacred* sefarim. *Even though our men are taken away by force, our children — our future generation — are still studying Torah and we pray that they will be able to study its beautiful laws in the very near future together with their fathers, and, when the time comes, with their own children, in peace and in tranquility.*

We are healthy — thank God for that — but the anti-Semitism is so unbearable that my heart cries out in pain. How much our children suffer! Barely a day goes by when they aren't beaten by the self-proclaimed 'elite' Aryan brutes. But let's not lose hope, for I am sure that this nightmarish time will soon end. Try to keep up your morale. The whole family sends you and your husband our love and good wishes. May the Almighty lead us from these miserable times and let us soon talk of these days as though they were a bad dream long past.

Your brother,
Yoav

6

ONE AFTERNOON, I came home very excited, for I had just discovered a new place to buy chocolate, an almost unheard-of treat in those days. Every week, before Estie returned to Szombathely, I gave her a small packet of chocolate for my dearly beloved nieces and nephews. It had become a cherished ritual which I performed faithfully. In return, they sent me little notes assuring me that although they loved their Aunt Surie, who had replaced me, their love for me remained unchanged.

When I entered our apartment, I was surprised to see my husband, his uncles Yidel and Cheskel and my brother-in-law Herschel, engaged in a noisy and heated debate about a subject which I understood must have been of great importance to them. They were so engrossed in their conversation that they didn't even see me until I was standing right in front of them. I was frightened, for I immediately sensed from the tone of their conversation that something was wrong.

"What's wrong? What happened?" I asked them.

"If you show us what's in your shopping bag, I'll tell you," Uncle Yidel answered half-jokingly, in an attempt to lighten the charged atmosphere in the room and allay my fears.

"Oh, no. That is a strict military secret," I countered, playing along and making a show of hiding my bag in the cupboard under the sink.

"I've invited everyone for supper," my husband said. "That is, if you don't mind showing off your culinary skills." He studied me closely to see my reaction.

"I *might* consider making supper for an extra guest or two," I said firmly, "if somebody would tell me what is going on."

The men looked at one another intensely before Jacob spoke. "The restaurant is not a safe place to frequent now," Jacob said. Then everybody started talking at once, telling me what a close encounter they had with the law the day before at our local kosher cafe.

"As you know, the three of us always eat together at the restaurant," Uncle Yidel said. "It used to be the four of us before Yankl got married. Yesterday, when we arrived there, all the tables were occupied, so the waiter seated us in the tiny office behind the kitchen. We had just started to eat when there was a big commotion in the main room. The police were there, checking everyone's credentials. Nobody could escape, for they had stationed other policemen at the door, and they had the place surrounded. Luckily for us, the waiter is aware of our situation. As soon as he realized that it was a rousting, he alerted us and we ran out through the kitchen door before the police thought of blocking that exit too. Thank God it turned out that we were sitting in the back room yesterday. Who knows what would have happened to us had we been caught, since we are all officially draft evaders."

"I shudder to think of it," I said. "And who knows how many others walked in after that, unaware of the danger that awaited them there?" The thought of all those unfortunate people unwittingly placing their very lives in peril set my heart thumping.

"There's no need to worry, Leichi," Uncle Cheskel assured me. "We told a Jewish girl who was approaching the place to alert the men about the *razzia* and the word was out in no time."

The tale of their narrow escape left me weak with worry. "Please, be our guests every day," I insisted. "Don't ever go near that place again!"

I went to the kitchen to prepare supper, which consisted of boiled potatoes and soup that I'd made that morning. Luckily, there was also plenty of bread for everyone, so that by the end of the meal we all felt satisfied. However, cooking for five left our pantry almost empty, and seeing that we would need to replenish our supplies in order to continue to feed our guests, I went to ask Vera if she knew where to get food on the black market. The three men had never applied for food tickets, for the simple reason that they had never registered their presence in the city, so the black market was our only alternative.

Early the next morning, Vera and I set out to do some more shopping. To my surprise and dismay, I found myself standing in the same line for food in which I usually stood, waiting my turn for what sometimes took hours. I was afraid that Vera had forgotten that I had asked her to take me to the black market. I pulled her aside, out of earshot of the other shoppers, and whispered to her, "Please tell me where to stand. Which line is for the black market?"

She looked at me with an expression of wonder and amusement, and exclaimed, laughing, "Oh, Rivka Leah, sometimes you are so naive! I hope you weren't expecting to find a large black stand, advertising with neon lights: 'Attention black-market seekers! Here we are!' Why do you think I come back day after day to the same merchants? Because they know and trust me and they give me onions, potatoes or whatever they happen to be selling, for a price, even when I'm out of tickets. That's called the black market! Don't you remember that I said I was going to tell the farmer that you are my sister so that he would trust you, too?"

"Oh, Vera!" I said shamefacedly, thinking of how ignorant I must appear to her. "What would I do without you?"

She dismissed my words with a wave of her hand. "Now listen, silly girl. After I am done, introduce yourself to our farmer friend, Peter. Give him your ticket and tell him that you want to buy the full amount of potatoes and he will give you five kilos instead of one. Don't make the mistake of asking how much you owe him; just give him a ten-pengo bill and he will give you the change. I come here every day and do the very same thing, because we are feeding Irenna and Erno."

I had wanted to ask Vera about the two young people I had often seen in their home, but I had learned enough about life in Budapest to know that that was a question one did not ask. Now I looked expectantly at Vera, hoping she would continue on her own. Seeing my questioning look, she began to tell me their story.

"Irenna and Erno are Danny's half-brother and half-sister. You see, Danny's mother died when he was very young. Shortly after her death, he went to live with his maternal grandparents, who had begged Danny's father to let them raise him in order to ease the pain caused by the loss of their daughter.

"Danny's father later remarried. His new wife was a Jewish woman from Poland, and they went to live there, while Danny stayed with his grandparents in Hungary. Irenna and Erno are the children of this second marriage. There was another child as well — a girl..." Vera's voice trailed off. Overwhelmed with emotion, she continued with great difficulty. "That child, along with Danny's father and stepmother, were killed by border guards as they tried to flee to Hungary."

Vera paused for a moment and collected herself. "Why do you think that Irenna is forever babysitting? And why do you think that I am the one who always does the shopping and lugs home these heavy sacks of potatoes all by myself, day in and day out? It is because Irenna and Erno never leave the house, not even for an instant. Although they have false papers, they're afraid their accents will give them away as soon as they open their mouths. They can speak Hungarian, but their fears keep them indoors all the time."

Vera had calmed down and we had gotten back in line when she heard something which upset her all over again. She controlled herself with obvious difficulty until we were on our way home, and then she exploded.

"Did you hear those two girls in front of us in the line?" she said to me angrily. "There they stood, going on endlessly about how the Jews have money and can buy food on the black market. I could hardly restrain myself from screaming, 'Of course we do! We are *forced to*!'" She was speaking breathlessly and her eyes were burning with anger. She went on, unable to stop. "We are only two Jews among thousands in this city, and we are both forced to feed members of our families who are here illegally, hiding for their lives."

"I know," I replied. "My two brothers-in-law were serving in the army and they would have remained there but they were sent home — without their rifles and without their uniforms — with instructions to report to the dreaded work-camp."

I was beginning to get angry too, and I could feel the blood pounding in my head as I continued. "And our two uncles would be home supporting their families, or they would be in the army too, but they were also called. None of them has any other reason to hide from the authorities."

"It makes me see red," Vera said, "when I hear us condemned for the things they make us do. All we are really doing is buying time in the hope that we will live to see these harrowing times behind us. Oh, how I wish I could live without fear! If they only knew how my knees tremble every time I buy food illegally, and how I lie awake night after night, listening for the tiniest noise, always expecting the police to come and take away my sister-in-law and my brother-in-law, and with them, God forbid, my husband and children. It is as if we are the most deplorable criminals on the face of the earth, the greatest enemies of the human race! And what is our great transgression? Who are these fellow criminals we are harboring? Merely our own men and women, innocently condemned to death; sisters and brothers whose only crime is having been born Jewish. Just think of it: It is a national crime to be born a Jew!"

I stood there listening to Vera, hearing her words echo my thoughts. "You know, Vera," I said, "You're not the only one who listens, sleeplessly, night after night, for the police. I do the same, listening and worrying endlessly that Jacob will be found out and, God forbid, be taken away from me. And lately I have found myself struggling with a puzzling question: What does the word 'justice' really mean?"

Vera gazed at me, astonished. "Don't tell me that you, of all people, the daughter of one of our great scholars, are questioning God's laws?!"

"Oh, no! God forbid!" I answered hastily. "I'm not talking about our holy laws. I'm talking about the laws of our land, the laws that condemn us as guilty merely because we were born Jewish, no matter how law-abiding we are. And these same laws grant immunity to the Gentiles for harassing us!

"You know, a few days ago I had a terrible nightmare. I dreamt that I was sitting at the judge's bench in a packed courtroom. I was sending a convicted murderer away in handcuffs, when suddenly I saw the killer and his dead victim standing before me. Both of them were laughing, as they taunted me with the question, 'How do you know which of us is guilty, he or I? He or I?' It frightened me so much that I woke up screaming. After I awoke, I still pondered the question: 'I or my oppressor?'"

Vera answered me without a moment's hesitation. "Well, I know who is to blame," she said. "The trouble is that knowing doesn't help us any because these laws are not the result of rationality; they're the expression of man's basest instincts."

Vera spoke with such conviction that it calmed me to listen to her. Her ideas were not unique, but she was articulate and she wasn't afraid to express herself to those she trusted. I listened eagerly as she continued. "You know," she said, "it is already second nature for me to ask myself whenever I see a Jew: 'What is his secret? Is he hiding someone too? Does his heart also pound when he sees a stranger looking at him? Does he tremble with terror when one approaches his door?' Every time I see a fellow Jew, I want to scream, 'Please, brother! Do whatever is in your power to help your people! You may not have a second chance. It won't be long before your fate is sealed like that of your Polish and German brethren.' "

"What's the difference?" I asked, hopelessly. "It can't get much worse anyway."

"Let's pray that you never know just how much worse it can get," Vera answered as we entered the elevator with our packages.

We parted in the hallway and I went into our apartment. Exhausted, I sat down to rest before putting my groceries away. I could hear the delighted cries of Vera's children as they greeted their mother in the hall. Closing my eyes, I thought about how, in only a few months' time, I would also be a mother. I wondered how I could have kept my secret from Vera for so long, for I was yearning to share the news with her. Suddenly unable to wait any longer, I rose from the chair and rushed to Vera's apartment to tell her about the happy event. To my surprise, she looked at me horror-stricken.

"Don't tell me that you are going to have a baby in these miserable times!" she exclaimed, not believing that she had heard correctly. "Just last night I was discussing with Danny how lucky you are not to have kids yet. Do you have any idea how much we worry for our children's safety?!"

I was so confused and hurt by my friend's reaction that I could do nothing but stare at her, open-mouthed. Realizing how her words had offended me, Vera shook her head, smiled, and said to me tenderly, "Oh, how silly I am! Forget all of those stupid things I just said. Come, let's have lunch here and celebrate!" But I wasn't hungry anymore and, thanking Vera for her invitation, I walked back to my apartment.

As soon as I closed the door behind me, I headed straight for the bedroom and opened the top drawer of my dresser. Lovingly, I took out the little white knitted sweater with the matching hat and blanket that I had worked on during my every free minute. I arranged the sweater with the little hat above it and they lay together naturally, as if an infant were dressed in them. In my mind's eye, I saw my own baby dressed in the tiny outfit. Suddenly, I was filled with an overpowering feeling of love, and I picked up the sweater set, pressed it to my heart, and started to cry. Still clinging to the precious outfit, I fell asleep exhausted.

Hours must have passed. When I was awakened by the sound of someone unlocking the front door, I quickly thrust the baby things under the covers, for I remembered that we had invited guests for supper and I did not feel ready to announce my pregnancy just yet. Still groggy from sleep, I realized that I hadn't prepared a thing to eat.

Jacob walked into the bedroom, and before he could say a word, I cried, "Oh, Yanku, are you home already? What am I going to do? I fell asleep and I haven't even started to cook anything for dinner. What am I going to tell our guests?"

"You needn't be upset," Jacob said. "We have no guests, and I can wait. I'm not hungry at all."

"What happened?" I asked in alarm. "Why aren't your relatives coming as we agreed yesterday?"

"They felt that they didn't want to impose upon you, coming on a regular basis," Jacob replied.

I could hardly believe my ears. "But they shouldn't set foot in that restaurant again! You know what happened there." I was beginning to panic, for I knew only too well the dangers of frequenting such places.

"One cannot avoid them," Jacob answered, his expression suddenly becoming distant and cold. "It is not only the *razzias* that one has to fear. They are everywhere, checking credentials — in the street, on the trolleys, in the *shul*s. There is no police-proof place left."

"Then you must stay at home!" I pleaded, but he shrugged it off.

"Leichi, no hiding place is completely safe. All we can do is pray that God will watch over us." And with that, he sat down to work on some papers. Seeing that he did not want to pursue the matter further, I went into the kitchen to prepare dinner.

I made a modest meal for the two of us and we sat in our little kitchen and ate and talked. I had transformed our meal of potato soup and noodles into a rare delicacy by sprinkling them with ground nuts and a little sugar. But despite the warm atmosphere and the comfort of having my husband home with me again, I was still troubled, and Jacob, sensing my mood, insisted that I tell him what was upsetting me.

I began to tell him about my conversation with Vera earlier that day. He talked to me for a long time, trying to dispel my fears.

Finally, I looked up at him, smiled and said, "I'm not worried at all now. I feel so safe when you're home. When you're here I feel as though nothing bad could possibly happen." I wanted to assure him that I could be satisfied with very little, that all I really needed was bread and water and having him by my side always.

We were silent for a few minutes, lost in our own thoughts, when suddenly an idea came to me. "Yanku," I said excitedly, "I have a solution! I don't know why I didn't think of it sooner. Teach me about your business ventures and let *me* be the go-between. Please! I'll follow your instructions to the letter, we'll lose nothing, and you will be safe! Please, Yanku, let's try it..."

But as I looked at him, the words caught in my throat. His face had the same expression that had frightened me so much when I had first asked him to stay at home and not risk his life. It somehow reminded me of the way my father used to look at me when I was a child: a look of love mingled with pity. But in Jacob's eyes there was also naked, animal fear. Seeing all that, I ended the conversation, promising that I would stop worrying. It terrified me to think how much my peace of mind depended on his strength. And if my sleepless nights were called peace, what were the real dangers like?

Then Jacob stood up. "I have to give a message to Danny from a friend of his whom I ran into today. I'll be back in a minute," he said as he rushed out the door.

7

JACOB RANG the Brenners' doorbell and when the door opened, Danny and Vera asked in unison, "Where is your wife?" It was the first time they had ever had a visit from him without her. Jacob looked back to make sure that Rivka Leah hadn't followed him, and then he stepped inside, motioning to them to close the door behind him.

Jacob's words came tumbling out all at once. "Please, don't tell Rivka Leah what you know of the atrocities being committed in Hitler's occupied lands. She has a vague idea of the brutalities, but she knows nothing about the crematoria and the mass murders."

"I know," Vera said. "I realized that today. Your wife, like most of our people, is unaware of the horrible truth. It became clear to me when she commented that things couldn't get any worse, even if Hungary were occupied, God forbid. For a while I considered telling her, but when I saw how hurt she was that I couldn't share in her happiness over the news about the baby, I decided to keep quiet. It took a great effort for me to control myself, for every inch of me longed to scream: Prepare yourself! Do something now, so that when the time comes, you will be able to hide from those butchers!"

"And the time will come, Jacob, my friend," Danny added, almost in a whisper, "and sooner than we ever anticipated."

"I agree with you," said Jacob. "The clouds are gathering

over us already, and I can hear the thunder. It is only a matter of time until the lightning will strike. Even so, there's no reason to open Rivka Leah's eyes to the terrifying reality, for God knows, she worries more than enough as it is. Besides, I hope that with God's help I will be able to take care of her and our baby and shield them somehow. So let her enjoy her innocence a while longer — for as long as she can."

Jacob hesitated before he went on. "With my own wife, I can afford to keep silent. As for all those other Jews who are unaware of what is happening, I believe in presenting them with the facts and urging them to prepare. I tell them that once Hitler's armies invade, it will be too late to do anything to save themselves. But to my great disappointment," he continued, downcast, "I find that most people don't believe me. They simply write me off as paranoid."

"Irenna and Erno would be able to make people believe the truth, I've no doubt of that," Danny said. "They witnessed the horrors first-hand. Just imagine: they were forced to watch from the other side of the border, concealed in the shrubs, as their parents and sister were gunned down in cold blood. And if that wasn't bad enough, they also had to swallow their own bitter cries so that they would not be caught and share their family's fate. Yes, I am sure they wouldn't have any difficulty convincing others of the danger. But even so, their efforts would be in vain, for not everyone can to go his own way and leave his loved ones behind. Irenna told us that many people who were equipped with false Aryan I.D. cards turned back just before they reached the border, to rejoin family members who, for some reason or other, were unable to escape."

"It is true," Irenna said as she and Erno entered the room. "What these murderers have brought out in us is our unity, making some of us realize, perhaps for the first time in our lives, that there is a common bond between us. That realization impels us to cry out proudly: I am a Jew! And whatever fate awaits my brethren will be my fate too!"

"I disagree, Irenna," her brother interrupted. "Our newfound unity is more the result of apathy. We were simply degraded, shamed and hurt, and compelled to follow new regulations every day, regulations which degraded us even further. Logic didn't help us understand how we ever got into this hopeless situation, and soon we lost our reasoning power altogether. After a while we became like zombies. In our confusion, we wanted direction, and because we were unable to direct ourselves, we followed every order that was issued. The torture destroyed our souls long before our bodies were offered upon our enemies' pagan altar. We paid for their age-old sin: their burning jealousy of our beautiful way of life, which the Torah has taught us from the beginning of time. Yes, we are united now: united in apathy, in misery, in despair."

Suddenly Erno cried out as if in pain. He reached into his pocket and pulled out a gun. With his eyes fixed on it, he cried, "You are my hope of revenge for the deaths of my innocent parents and my little sister and all of the slaughtered innocents whose souls I hear crying out for revenge during these long, silent nights. Oh, it will be such a great surprise for those anti-Semites; they will be shocked to see a passive Jewish boy forcing them to answer for their crimes." His voice rose as he continued. "And I have another surprise for them: the passive Jewish boys and girls are all dead, and we who are alive will never again be lead into ghettos. We won't give our lives away cheaply anymore! Never! Never!"

Overcome with emotion, Erno sank to the floor with an expression of such unspeakable suffering on his face that it was too much for the others to bear. Jacob, Vera and Danny all had tears in their eyes, and they controlled themselves with difficulty. Erno's anguished speech served as a painful reminder to them of their own impotence against the Nazi menace.

One gun. It was almost laughable. Yet this one gun, and this one man's grief, were a symbol to them — this would never happen again. Vera motioned to Jacob to leave, and he quietly slipped out the door, leaving Erno sprawled on the floor, his head bowed in despair, with nothing but the feel of cold, hard metal to comfort him.

8

WHEN JACOB CAME BACK, he was unusually quiet, so we both just sat — I, picking at the rest of my supper, and Jacob, looking at his hands. Then the doorbell rang and we were both propelled into action. Jacob grabbed his half-finished plate of supper, his silverware, and anything else that might have indicated his presence in the house, hid them away and then slipped under the bed. I headed for our front door, engulfed in the fear and dread that I always felt whenever the sound of the bell imposed itself upon us unexpectedly. Hesitantly, I opened the door, and, to my tremendous surprise and relief, found my father-in-law standing there nervously.

"How happy I am to find you at home!" he said. "I was really afraid you had gone out. What took you so long to answer the door?"

I couldn't even answer him because I was choking with laughter as I envisioned Jacob cowering under the bed, unaware that it was his father who had come to see us. Without further explanation, I led my father-in-law to our bedroom and called to Jacob to come out of his hiding place. Watching his grown son emerge from under the bed, Jacob's father burst out laughing, too. Soon both of them started talking at once, recalling the time when, as a little boy, Jacob had hidden under the bed after his teacher had threatened to tell his father that he had misbehaved in school.

"It's interesting," Jacob said, sobering up a little, "that we tend to view childhood as such a tranquil time when in actuality it is fraught with problems, fears and joys just like any other period in a person's life."

Then, as if his last comment brought him back to our present troubles, my husband's eyes clouded over with worry. He turned to his father and asked him what brought him to Budapest.

"Well, my son, there's both good and bad in it. The good part is that I am allowed to travel at will, so at least part of the nightmare has ended. The bad part, unfortunately, is *very* bad. The anti-Semitism has become unbearable. Every day brings with it new persecutions. One day last week, without warning, the government revoked our license to manufacture and sell the children's coats we have been producing. So I decided to come to the city to try and make a living here."

"Papa! How awful that is!" Jacob exclaimed. "How will the family manage without you? Please let us offer you our hospitality. Consider our home as your own."

"I am sure, my son, that both you and your wife make this offer with sincerity, but I cannot accept. I know only too well that my being away for days at a time would put a terrible strain on Mama. The children would misbehave constantly if they knew that I would only be home on weekends. So, I decided that I would leave the house every morning at five. That way, I can return by midnight."

"But they won't even see you," Jacob argued. "What influence can you have on them in their sleep?"

"If they get too much out of hand," he replied, "they will know that Mama will tell me and that I will awaken them, if necessary, to teach them a lesson." And then as an afterthought, he added, "The boys are at an age when they need a strong hand and the presence of their father, even if only for a few hours each night."

What a good man he is, I thought, as I reflected upon the

great self-sacrifice Jacob's father was prepared to undergo for his family's welfare. I hastily averted my gaze so that he wouldn't see my eyes filling with tears. I turned toward the window and looked down on the street, and the sight of four drunken men caught my attention. Supporting one another in order to steady themselves, they were merrily singing some of the new, popular anti-Semitic songs. In their drunkenness they had forgotten most of the words, so they kept starting over, puffing out their chests with each repeated anti-Semitic line. These common drunkards, I thought with disgust, are the proud, faultless Aryans who would inherit the world.

My thoughts turned once again to my father-in-law, a devoted father and protective husband. Then I looked at the drunks again, and I began to realize something about the causes of anti-Semitism. I realized that these men must feel so jealous of a man of such quality and stature as my father-in-law, that in order to convince themselves of their own superiority, they must denigrate him and others like him, verbally and physically. I understood that only a pathetically insecure man would need to abuse and mock others in order to feel strong and superior.

But I also knew that I was oversimplifying matters. As true as it was that not all Jewish men were like my father-in-law, so was it true that not all Gentiles were as lowly and despicable as these four self-proclaimed blue-bloods. Then why the hatred? Why? To my dismay, the answer eluded me, just as it had every time I searched for an answer. Suddenly, Vera's words came to mind: "What difference does it make whether or not you understand their hatred of us? We cannot allow ourselves the luxury of contemplating their motives; it is too late for that now. Now we must use our brains to figure out some way to save our necks!"

Just then, my father-in-law's voice interrupted my train of thought. "Leichi," he asked, "would you mind going to the post office to send a telegram home so that Mama will know I arrived safely?"

I gladly obliged, and from that day on there was added excitement to our daily routine: Jacob would go to meet his father every morning and evening at an agreed-upon place. After a while, I didn't even have to ask. As soon as he returned at night, Jacob would automatically say, "My father left for home."

Our concern for my father-in-law was very real, for it was a great risk for Jewish men to be seen in public places. The police could arrest them at will, as if they were common criminals. They were taken to a special camp called the Tolonc, a destination originally reserved for "illegal aliens." From there the "illegals" were deported to the countries from which they had tried to escape.

In recent times, dark secrets had come to surround its walls. We Jews were even afraid to whisper the name of this dreaded place, the mere mention of which sent shivers through us. The only reliable information we could glean from the blood-chilling stories that circulated was this: whoever was led through its doors disappeared without a trace, as if the earth had opened its mouth and swallowed him alive.

We had also learned that the only chance of escape from the Tolonc was by contacting someone who had connections with the guards working there. For a price, these guards might consider turning a blind eye to an escapee. But this worked only if the guards were approached within a very short time after the Jew's arrival. Time was of the essence, because once a prisoner knew too much, once he became too well-acquainted with the true horrors of the place, he was never allowed to take his knowledge beyond the heavily guarded walls.

9

THE MONTHS FLEW BY. It was June when we had moved into our apartment, and the whole world had been so alive then with nature's wonders that even in the big city they were not hidden from us. Now it was January, and Budapest was cold and somber and covered with snow. Those endless days had become months so quickly — funny, I thought, when each day had been and continued to be an interminable struggle to remain calm as I waited for the moment Jacob came home every evening and I could see with my own eyes that he was safe. I thanked God for every day that He had given us more time together.

It seemed to me that just yesterday we had settled into our new home, all excited and happy, so sure in our hearts that if we wanted to we could make this apartment a miniature *Gan Eden* where nothing but happiness would reign. But almost as soon as we had proclaimed it to be our hideout from reality, from all the horrors of our time, our paradise had disappeared.

As I stood there looking out the window, I heard my mother's oft-repeated words echo in my ears: "The truly important things in life are the unblemished name you received from your parents, and the close bond of your family. These are your legacy, your heritage, and no one can rob you of these treasures. If your name remains unsullied, you will be able to pass it on to your own children, and they to theirs; if you retain the strong ties with your family and help one another, each of you will benefit and each of you will be the stronger for it."

I wondered how feeling close to my family was benefiting me when I couldn't stop worrying for an instant about their safety. But my heart told me that my mother was right, and I prayed that God would show Jacob and me a way to be of some help to both our families.

I was trying to sort out my thoughts when suddenly I felt an odd fluttering sensation inside me. I realized that I had just felt my baby moving for the first time. Until that moment, the idea of actually giving birth to a child had been nothing more than a vague, distant concept, but with that one kick the miracle of childbearing became a reality to me. I was carrying life, life which would soon be a very real little person.

The maternal instinct rose within me so powerfully that I actually cried out in anguish: "Oh, what will become of you, baby of mine? What kind of world am I bringing you into?" My heart ached as I realized that all I could offer my child as a birthright was unprovoked hatred — the stigma of being born Jewish. "My poor, innocent child!" I cried, "You will be labeled a criminal before you breathe your first breath. Like all of us, you will be condemned for the crime of having Jewish parents."

I trembled with fear as I imagined what my child's future would hold. What would be his fate? I asked myself over and over. In vain, I searched for reassurance. Then suddenly I had the answer. Of course! I thought, wondering why it hadn't occurred to me sooner. We would go to the Rebbe* and ask him to give his blessing to our innocent, unborn baby.

When Jacob came home that evening, I discussed my plan with him. He was pleased with my suggestion, and we agreed to try and see the Rebbe as soon as possible. The next morning

*Reb Sholom Lazer Halberstam of Ratzfeld, the Sanzer Rebbe's son.

we went to the Rebbe's house but we were not immediately granted an audience. For almost a day and a half we were repeatedly told to come back later. Then, at last, the door was opened for us and we went into the Rebbe's room.

Although it was already getting dark outside, the lights had not yet been turned on, and I held my breath in awe as I tried to discern the figure of the Rebbe amid the shadows in the room. Then I saw him. He was sitting at the head of the table, flanked by two men. I remained standing just inside the doorway while my husband approached the Rebbe's table. Jacob whispered something to one of the men, who in turn wrote down what he said on a slip of paper. The man handed the paper to the Rebbe, and as he looked down at the words, a heavy silence fell upon the room.

I stood there, watching the Rebbe, and I recalled a long-forgotten incident from my childhood. Years back, the Rebbe had stopped at our house to rest for a while during a lengthy journey. He and my father had sat for hours in the study, until late in the afternoon, when my father asked for me. I could still feel the excitement that I had felt then, as my mother tried to smooth my unruly black hair. Looking at me fondly, she instructed me to go to the door but not to enter until my father summoned me. Then, too, I stood at the doorway, silently watching as the Rebbe and my father sat, lost in discussion, surrounded by shelves upon shelves of *sefarim.*

When my father looked up, his blue eyes lingered on me for an instant and he beckoned to me to come in. "My little gypsy girl," he said fondly, the nickname referring to my almost pitch-black hair. (My darkness was outstanding, for I was the only dark-haired child among his fair-haired brood.)

I tiptoed into the room and then, as my mother had instructed me, I kissed the Rebbe's outstretched hand. Thinking with relief that I was through with the ordeal, I started to run toward the door. But the Rebbe called after me, "What is your name, little girl?"

I turned to face him and whispered through trembling lips,

"Rivka Leah." Just as I was wondering what to do next, he took out a coin, blessed it, and gave it to me. I grabbed it and flew from the room.

Now, as then, I stood awkwardly, halfway between Jacob and the door, not knowing what to do with myself. In the hushed silence that had fallen over the room, no one moved. The Rebbe sat staring at the paper in his hand. Then the holy sage looked up, and I felt my knees quaking as I heard him ask me the familiar question: "What is your name?"

Dazed, I heard myself respond automatically, just as I had so long ago, "Rivka Leah."

"The Rebbe did not mean your given name," said one of the men. "He wants to know your father's name."

Ashamed of my ignorance, I whispered my father's name. "Did you say that you are Avrumele's daughter?" the Rebbe asked. I could only nod, for the words were caught in my throat.

"So, you are Avrumele's daughter," the sage repeated. His voice possessed a strength that was surprising for a man of his years. "Bring her a chair," he told the men at his side. "This is the daughter of a great *gaon*." Then he turned to me and said, "Tell me what is in your heart."

I was even more frightened now than I had been as a child, although my instinctive feeling was the same: all I wanted to do was run out of the room. But I obeyed him now, as I had then, and I heard him ask again, "What is your problem, child?"

I replied in a hushed tone, for the awe of being in the presence of greatness had nearly struck me dumb. I told him of my fears for our future, and of my fears for our unborn baby.

He looked at me intently and his eyes seemed to penetrate my very soul. "What would you like me to bless you with?" he asked.

"I do not know," I answered in a whisper. "I do not know what God means to do with us and what He has written on our page in the Book of Life and Death — are we to survive these persecutions or are we to succumb to them? There is only one thing I beg of you: please, please promise me that we will not be torn away from one another, come what may. Promise me that the three of us — Jacob, our baby, and I — will all be together, and that whatever will happen to one of us will happen to us all."

"Do not worry, Avrumele's daughter," he said in a loud voice. "God will grant you your request and you will all survive together." (It was well-known that the Rebbe answered in a very loud voice those requests that he felt would be granted by Hashem.) With those words, the Rebbe indicated that our audience was over and we silently left his chambers.

As soon as we entered the hallway, Jacob turned to me, his face flushed with excitement, and said, "Do you realize what the Rebbe promised you? Do you know how lucky we are? Did you know that his sainted father, the Sanzer Rebbe, blessed his children, before he died, with the power of having their promises fulfilled?"

I could hardly contain the joy and relief that I felt as I listened to Jacob's words, and I began to grasp the true significance of the blessing the Rebbe had given us. But something Jacob had said puzzled me. "Why, then, doesn't the Rebbe wish away this curse, this anti-Semitic government of ours?"

"Because this he cannot do, so he will not promise it. That's why he doesn't promise survival for people if he knows it's not meant to happen."

[Author's Note: After the war I learned that the Rebbe's disciples had begged him to try to escape from the Nazis. They provided him with false papers and planned out his escape route thoroughly, but he refused to go. He said to them, "How can I go? I know that I could save myself, but as long as I am unable to promise the same for my people, I want to stay with them. Their fate shall be mine as well."

And that is what happened to him: together with millions of our brothers and sisters, he was murdered in Hitler's gas chambers.]

The next day, Jacob arrived home with packages in his arms. "Guess what!" he said breathlessly. "My parents are coming to visit us tomorrow. I am so excited! I haven't seen my mother in such a long time, and neither have Janku and Herschel, so I invited them for supper as well. I even invited Uncle Yidel and Uncle Cheskel, to make it a real family gathering. I hope you don't mind," he said hesitantly. He was pleased to see my pleasure at the prospect of having my in-laws over. "Here, I bought two chickens." He laid the packages on the kitchen table and began to unpack kilo after kilo of vegetables and fruits. "Do you think that there will be enough food for all of us?"

"Oh, Yanku," I said, "you are the best husband in the world! What would I do without your help? I *never* could have managed to get so much food. There's enough here to feed an army! And two whole chickens — what a luxury! I don't think the king of England will have a better supper tomorrow than we will!"

Bursting to tell Vera the exciting news, I ran straight to her apartment and found her standing at her ironing board, a tape measure around her neck. Curiously, she kept consulting the tape as she ironed folds into her linen. Alongside the ironing board was a stack of pink tissue paper which she was using to line the linen as she folded it along the precisely pre-measured creases. There were linens already arranged on her table, as neat and straight as a soldiers' lineup before inspection, and all done up with little pink ribbons.

"What on earth are you doing?" I asked, dumbfounded.

"Can't you see that I'm ironing?" she replied impatiently.

"But why are you using a tape measure and why do you need the pink tissue paper?"

Now it was her turn to be surprised. "Don't tell me that you don't stack linen in your armoire, measured and lined, just as I'm doing!"

"No, and I would never have the patience to do it either."

"Well," she said, shaking her head, "I can tell that you grew up motherless. The first thing my mother drilled into me was that the most important thing in a house is the appearance of your closets. 'That is the yardstick by which your skill as a homemaker is judged,' she always said."

Vera's comments left me unmoved. "So, I will be judged remiss in the pink-lining department," I said with a smile and a shrug. "What of it?"

But Vera became very serious. "What will your mother-in-law think of you?" she admonished. "I'm sure she'll inspect your closets."

"How could you imagine such a thing!"

"Well, this is only further proof that you had no mother to teach you how to behave during your mother-in-law's first visit," Vera concluded matter-of-factly. "But don't worry! Irenna and I will come over and reorganize your closets tonight after we put the children to sleep."

Sure enough, they came and despite my protests they redid my closets, refolding all my linens with their pink lining paper and pink satin ribbons. When they finished, they stood back and admired the new look their ministrations had given my armoire.

"Sooner or later," I said jokingly, "my mother-in-law will find out the bitter truth about me."

But Vera was entirely serious about her project and wouldn't take any chances with my happiness. She continued opening the drawers, one by one, with obvious satisfaction. Then, to my complete surprise, she bent down and looked under the bed.

"What are you doing now?" I asked.

"Mother-in-law-proofing your house," she replied earnestly. "She might look under your beds."

"You don't know her, Vera," I said. "She would never do that!" For some reason, I was beginning to feel that I had to defend that fine woman who had treated me so kindly.

"But what if she does?" Vera persisted.

"I wouldn't mind at all!"

"Sure," she said, knowingly. "Now you talk big, but you would die of shame if she were to find dust balls and soiled laundry there." And she meant every word of it. It was as if the laws of good housekeeping had been passed down to us from Mount Sinai along with the Laws of Moses.

When my mother-in-law arrived the next morning, our house was as spick-and-span as it had ever been. In Vera's words, it was "mother-in-law-proofed." This was the first time my mother-in-law had visited us and she seemed genuinely delighted with our apartment. She loved it as much as I had when I first saw it, and now she walked back and forth through the rooms admiring everything she saw.

Then we sat down and talked over a cup of coffee. She told me about home and how much the "three little girls" had wanted to come with her to visit us. I told her about shopping in the market. And so it went, until before we knew it, the morning had disappeared.

It occurred to me that if I wanted to have supper ready on time I should begin preparing it. Reading my thoughts, my mother-in-law stood up and asked me for a dish towel. My heart skipped a beat and I thought to myself, Well, this is the big moment! I asked her to help herself to whatever she needed and led her to the armoire, but to my dismay she flatly refused to open it.

Suddenly, I didn't care about showing off my closets anymore; I just felt hurt. "Please don't feel like a stranger in our house," I pleaded with her, close to tears.

"Now listen, my child," she said, looking at me lovingly. "It has nothing to do with not feeling at home in your house. The only reason that I won't look in your closet is that you are an orphan, and I don't want you to think that I am looking at your trousseau to see what you have. I want you to know that your trousseau is no concern of mine. Papa and I want you to know that we are overjoyed about our son's good fortune in having married you."

"But I have no secrets," I cried, throwing open the doors of the armoire. "Please, see for yourself."

"My!" she exclaimed in surprise. "What a housekeeper you

are! I have never seen a closet arranged so beautifully. Well, it's just one more point in your favor, my dear, and it makes me wonder what other surprises you have in store for us."

Her candor was too much for me to bear. Shamefacedly, I told her how my next-door neighbors, Vera and Irenna, had come the day before to arrange my closet. "They did it so that I would make a good impression on you, but I have to admit that I would never have the patience to do it myself." She threw her arms around me and embraced me as a mother would embrace her child.

10

I SPENT THE ENTIRE afternoon preparing supper for our guests. The food must be perfect, I thought, eager to show off my culinary skills to everyone. But when suppertime came and I saw our guests seated by the table, grim-faced and withdrawn, I knew that all my efforts at winning their approval had been in vain. No one seemed at all interested in eating. My father- and mother-in-law wanted only to hear about the welfare of the others. My uncles and brothers-in-law were interested only in hearing about their wives and children, who had all moved in with my in-laws. Jacob's mother recounted anecdote after anecdote, describing all the little things their wives and children had been doing in the months since they had left, and the four homesick husbands and fathers drank in every word.

Suddenly, my brother-in-law Janku Frankle jumped up, his face contorted with rage, his eyes glittering. "What a miserable existence this is!" he shouted, pounding his fist on the table. "All I know about my family is what others tell me. In all my married life, I have never been able to stay at home with them. For the first three years after we got married, I served in the army, counting the days until my next furlough. But the joy of returning home for those few days was always marred by the knowledge that soon my furlough would end and I would have to leave again. And now, since I've been in hiding here in

Budapest, I'm deprived of even those few fleeting moments with my family. I'm approaching thirty now, and I've never had the chance to be young and carefree!" As he uttered these last words, he stopped abruptly and, unable to go on, sank down in his chair, his face bathed in sweat.

Overwhelmed by Janku's outburst, everyone sat motionless, and a heavy stillness descended upon the room. Then Uncle Cheskel cleared his throat and we all turned toward him expectantly. As soon as I saw his face I knew that he had something very unpleasant to tell us. His eyes, which were always as blue as the June sky, were clouded now and his fair skin was unusually pale beneath his beard. He was studying his hands, avoiding our eyes, and he sighed heavily.

"Nu, tell us. What happened?" my father-in-law asked him quietly, breaking the silence.

"The police checked our papers in *shul* today," he answered.

"And?" we urged him in unison.

A peculiar half-smile appeared on his face. "Yes, my papers too, if that is what you're asking."

Everyone stared at him, horrified. We all knew that our uncle, who was forty-two years old, carried false credentials that declared him to be fifty-five, the age at which one became legally exempt from work-camp duty.

"And they let you go?" I asked.

"Why not?" Uncle Cheskel replied, pointing to his beard. "Look at this. It is completely white. I hadn't realized until today how much I have aged during the past year while I've been hiding out here."

"You should be grateful. Your white beard helped save your life today," said my father-in-law. He paused before asking the question which was in everyone's mind. "Was anybody caught?"

Uncle Cheskel nodded his head gravely.

"Who?" my father-in-law asked in a low voice.

"Alex Weis," Cheskel said hoarsely.

They all paled as if their blood had drained away that very instant. Hearing of a fellow Jew getting caught by the anti-Semites always came as a shock, even if no one knew him personally. But Alex Weis had been a neighbor of Jacob's family in Ujhely and they were well-acquainted with him and his family.

"Do you have any idea where he was taken to?"

"Yes. I followed him," Uncle Cheskel replied, shifting uncomfortably in his chair. "There is no doubt about it. He was taken to the Tolonc."

"When I hear about the Tolonc," said Uncle Yidel, who until now had been sitting silently across from his brother Cheskel, "I wonder if we wouldn't be better off coming out of hiding and enlisting in one of the work-camps."

"What could we gain by it? Haven't you heard how terrible the conditions are there?" Uncle Cheskel argued.

"Yes, I have," Uncle Yidel replied quietly, "but at least I have met people who were there and will talk about it. However, I have never met a man who came back from the Tolonc who was willing to discuss anything about the place, and that is what makes it so frightening. It seems that the worst kind of fear is fear of the unknown."

"I think," added Jacob, "that the worst kind of fear is the fear of that which you *do* know, but are powerless to change or avoid."

I looked around the table at all the grim faces and my first impulse was to leave the room so that I wouldn't have to hear any more of their disheartening conversation. It came as an enormous relief to me when the meal finally ended. I collected everyone's plates and headed for the kitchen, relieved that I had a good excuse for avoiding their company. My mother-in-law followed me into the kitchen, and we began cleaning up.

"I wish I knew the answer," she said. "Maybe the men *would* be safer in a work-camp than here where they are constantly in danger of being discovered."

"Oh, Mama, no one has all the answers," I said. "However

many people there are, that's how many opinions you'll hear." Then I remembered something. I reached into my pocket and took out a folded sheet of paper. "Please read this," I said. "It's from my little sister Esther. She's sixteen and she's living with my Aunt Brandl in Szombathely. I just received it today." I handed my mother-in-law Esther's newest poem and she read it quietly.

Yesterdays, todays, and tomorrows
Make up the span of your life.
Today is the most fragile of them all —
Be careful! Don't break it in half!
It's no use crying about the yesterdays;
Rather, try to salvage whatever you can
So as not to wrap your today in thorns
And pierce your still-living, breathing hearts.
It's no use comparing today with yesterday;
Yesterday is gone!
And you can never bring it back.
Who knows which tomorrow will be the one
That will slip out of the reach of your grasp?
So grab today while it is still yours,
And make of it the best of the best.
Stop worrying about yesterday and tomorrow —
Only today is yours! Today is your life!

She handed the poem back to me and gazed at me for a long time, her eyes lingering on my heavy body. Then, without warning, she started to cry. She checked herself hastily, left the kitchen, and returned after a short time, carrying the tablecloth we had used for the meal.

"The air is so charged with their pent-up emotions," she said, glancing in the direction of the door, "that I fear this whole place might explode."

The next moment, we heard my father-in-law's voice through the closed door. "What a shame for six Jews to sit around wasting time," we heard him say. "Yankl, bring me that *sefer* from the shelf."

I sensed that the men were apathetic, joining in just to go along with my father-in-law. But in no time their half-hearted discussion was transformed into a heated debate. Gone from their voices was the pain and despair I had heard only minutes before. Once again they were proud, free men, carrying the torch of wisdom and lighting the way with Torah.

I loved to listen to the sounds of learning; there was no music more soothing to my frazzled nerves. "I expect great things from you, Rivka Leah," my mother's voice rang out from the past, "because no other child in the world has absorbed as much Torah with her mother's milk as you have. During those endless nights when you wouldn't sleep, your father used to take you from your crib and hold you on his lap while he learned. And when the morning star appeared, the two of you were still together, with Papa deeply involved in the study of our laws."

Well, I thought wistfully, I still don't know what things my mother expected from me, as I'm surely not destined for greatness. But one thing is certain: nothing makes me feel so very secure as the sound of men learning.

My thoughts drifted back to the day of my father's funeral. He had passed away during a visit to my older brother, who lived at the other end of Hungary at the time. I closed my eyes and I saw it all clearly again. I was a frightened child clinging to her mother along with the rest of the children. There were people all around, streaming into an overcrowded courtyard. Then more people arrived, on a special half-fare train, to pay their last respects to my father, a great *tzaddik*. And then the van arrived, bearing all that remained of my father. I sobbed and covered my eyes.

The shrill wail of the air-raid siren shocked me back to the present. The next thing that I heard was my mother-in-law crying out: "My children! Oh, my God! I want to go home!" We all ran down to the shelter and huddled around the little portable radio which Jacob had brought with him.

"Mama," Jacob said, "listen to this news bulletin. It's just been reported that only Budapest is under attack. In Ujhely they haven't the faintest idea that there is any trouble here."

Eventually she became calmer, but she decided to leave Budapest on the first train in the morning, and no amount of begging or pleading could make her change her mind.

A short while later, we returned to our apartment and bid our guests good-bye. Exhausted from the events of the last few hours, we retired for the night. Unable to still my turbulent emotions, I tossed and turned in my bed for what seemed like hours. I thought I heard someone moving about in the other room and, hoping it might be my mother-in-law, I quietly tiptoed to her door.

Mama? Are you awake?" I whispered through the closed She opened it at once. "I see that you're not sleeping er," I said, feeling awkward about approaching her at this hour. "Would you like to come out to the kitchen for a cup of tea? I have so many questions I need to ask you before you leave." We slipped silently into the kitchen and I put up a kettle of water as she seated herself at the table.

"I'm sorry for disturbing you," I continued apologetically, "but since you're going home in the morning, I won't have another opportunity to talk to you."

"Oh, Leichi," she replied, "don't apologize. I'm flattered that you feel you can confide in me. What is it, my child? What would you like to ask?"

Pausing for a moment, I reflected upon the things which had been weighing on my mind lately. I had many questions about childbirth, but I was too embarrassed to ask them. Since this was my first baby, I was particularly worried that I wouldn't know when it was time to go to the hospital, so I decided that I would ask my mother-in-law about this matter first. But as I stood there, facing this woman who had brought thirteen healthy children into the world, I felt so vulnerable and ignorant that I couldn't muster the courage to speak.

She looked at me expectantly. "Don't be afraid to ask me anything, no matter how silly your question may seem to you," she encouraged me. "Remember, I was also young once and didn't know as much as I know today."

I stared at the floor in embarrassment. Finally, I blurted out, "How will I know when it's time to go to the hospital?"

"Oh, that!" she said, laughing. "I wouldn't lose any sleep over it. I promise to come and wake you when it's time to go." But then she gave me a thorough, honest answer. She was quiet for a few moments afterwards and then she said, "I've heard about your doctor. He has a very good reputation. Why didn't you ask him this question? Why did you let this bother you so needlessly?"

"I guess I don't feel that a man can really understand my feelings," I said. "He never went through childbirth and he never will. I wish I had a woman doctor."

"Don't be silly. Your doctor is trained to know all about your symptoms. You shouldn't be afraid to ask him questions about childbirth." She hesitated for a moment and then went on. "You know, I can see that you have many different and conflicting feelings these days. What you really want now is your own mother, who you think would understand you best. I know how you feel, because I was once in the same position you are in now, and I never missed my mother as much as when I was expecting my first child. Well, Rivka Leah, I know that I can never replace your own mother, but please feel free to ask me anything, and I will answer you just as I would my own daughters."

So we sat in the kitchen and she continued to answer all my questions tirelessly and patiently until I no longer felt so confused and uncertain. After a while the conversation drifted to other topics.

"Tell me about Yankl," I said.

"What shall I tell you?"

"Tell me what he was like as a baby and as a little boy."

She looked at me lovingly, and I realized that she understood my need to know. Then she told me everything, story after story, incident after incident. I was amazed that she could recall each one in such detail.

"How can you remember all these little things when you have such a large family?" I marveled.

"But how could I not?" she replied, surprised. "No matter how many children I have, I only have one of each." Then she began to laugh. "I just remembered an incident I'm sure you would enjoy hearing about. It happened about ten years ago, at Yankl's bar mitzvah. On that day Yankl felt very important. He was wearing a brand-new suit, his first suit with long pants, and he strode into our kitchen and said to me, 'Please, Mama, I would like to have potato latkes for supper, alright?' 'Fine,' I said. 'I will make them for you and you can have as many as you want.' You see, our children never get birthday presents, but at their bar or bas mitzvah, it is their privilege to ask for their favorite food, and that is what is served to the entire family that day.

"Well, suppertime came, and I kept refilling Yankl's plate with latkes and he kept asking for more. All at once, he stood up and left the room. 'Go and see if he is alright,' I told his older brother Herschel, because I was afraid he had made himself sick from eating so much.

"My guess was right. Sure enough, Herschel found him moaning and pale as a ghost, being sick all over the garden. When Yankl noticed his brother, he managed to tell him that he thought he was going to faint. Panic-stricken, Herschel dashed to the well in our garden, grabbed a bucket of water, and emptied it over Yankl's head!"

My mother-in-law's eyes now shone with laughter and her thin, pale face radiated an inner beauty I had never seen before. She paused for a moment and then continued. "And do you know what Yankl's first words were when he came to? 'My new suit! He drenched my brand-new suit!' And when I asked him if he wanted more latkes, he laughed and said, 'Yes!'"

We had such a pleasant time talking that we only realized it was morning when my father-in-law and Jacob appeared at the kitchen door and asked if they could have coffee before going to *shul.* I poured the coffee and then we all sat together for a short while.

"I want to ask you something, children," my father-in-law said, looking directly from me to Jacob. "I want you to promise me something."

"What is it, Papa?" we asked together, Jacob sounding as puzzled as I.

"That you, my son, will never go to sleep at night without first having learned some Torah and that you, Rivka Leah, will encourage him to always do so."

"But of course," I protested. "Yankl learns *every* night, without fail!"

"I'm sure of that, but as times get harder and harder, the day may come when none of us will have the strength or the patience to learn anything."

"Of course I'll learn," said my husband. "I think you can trust me to do that."

"How could we survive without learning, especially during these trying times?" I added, recalling the events of the night before. "It was amazing to see how it affected your morale last night."

"You are right," my father-in-law said. "Torah study keeps us united and gives us the courage to go on. It is the secret of our survival and must never be taken lightly — never, come what may! And this is why our most learned men and scholars are the first to succumb in the work-camps: they are no longer able to submerge themselves in the study of Torah, the source of their soul's nourishment."

Agitated, he took a handkerchief from his pocket and wiped his perspiring forehead. Then, changing the subject, he said to Jacob, "I will leave for the train directly from work this evening. Please bring some food along when you meet me." He wished his wife a safe journey, looking at her for a long time. The next minute he was gone.

Later that morning, after my mother-in-law's departure, Vera and I were heading toward the market when a little girl approached us, holding a bunch of tiny white flowers. "Buy some snowflowers," she chanted through chattering teeth. Snowflowers! Those delicate buds bloomed in the fields in the winter cold, between patches of melting snow, announcing the coming of spring. Under normal circumstances, the appearance of snowflowers would have delighted us. Ordinarily, both of us would have called the child over and bought a bouquet from her. But in our present state of misery, neither the flowers, nor the promise of spring, meant much to us.

As we passed, she waved two bouquets at us and we glanced at the tiny peddler. She was but a child dressed in rags, a red kerchief pulled low over her forehead, her brilliant black eyes pleading. Before I could reach for my purse, Vera held out the money for both bunches, but refused to accept the flowers.

"Sell them to someone else," she told the girl. "That way you'll make more money." To our amazement the child burst into tears.

"Please take them!" she implored Vera. "Don't make me stand out in the cold any longer." Vera took her flowers, and then, as the wind brought the tantalizing smell of freshly-roasted chestnuts from a vendor's stand nearby, she thrust another coin into the startled girl's palm.

"Go, dear, get yourself some hot chestnuts, and I am quite sure that the lady will even let you warm your little hands by the fire."

"You are giving me this money to buy chestnuts?" she asked, not quite believing it. "Oh, you are such a beautiful lady, and such a good one!" And with a squeal of delight, she raced to the chestnut stall. "I wish you were my mother," she called back to Vera. "I wish you were!" We watched her as she ran off, and then we turned and continued in the direction of the market.

"It seems that spring is approaching," Vera commented.

"I know," I replied, "because I'm counting the days until my baby is born." I hesitated and then went on. "Vera, I'm so confused. Sometimes I can't wait to see and hold my child, while other times I wish I was like the mother elephant who carries her young inside her for years. That way I'd be able to protect my infant from an uncertain future."

Vera didn't answer. She looked down at the snowflowers in her hand, sniffed them and, as though making an important scientific discovery, she announced, "They haven't the slightest scent."

How appropriate, I thought, for the harbinger of a spring that would be singularly lacking in fragrance.

11

JACOB DIDN'T HAVE to tell me that something terrible had happened when, a few days later, he arrived home unexpectedly in the middle of the morning. One look at his face was enough to alarm me. I started to tremble with fear. "What's wrong?" I asked him.

"It's Papa. I went to meet him at the train station and he wasn't there." For weeks now, the arrangement had gone like clockwork.

"I'm sure there's a simple explanation," I said. "Maybe he just decided to stay home today."

"No. I know what happened," he said softly. Then he stopped abruptly, as if he were afraid to bring the harsh truth out into the open.

"Not the Toloncl" I cried in terror. Jacob merely nodded. "Oh, my God! What shall we do? What shall we do?"

For a few moments, we just looked at each other, stricken. Then Jacob broke the silence. "I don't know whom to turn to," he said, overcome with despair. "The man who helped free those few Jews by bribing one of the prison guards has disappeared. Rumor has it that the guard he bribed is now hunting for *him*, in order to insure that no one discovers his own role in the escape." Jacob turned and grabbed his coat. "I can't stay here any longer. I must go out and find someone who can help me."

As soon as he left, I reached for my coat too. I took a sheet of paper and, with a trembling hand, scribbled a note to my husband.

My dear Yanku,

I am going to the Tolonc to try and free your father. I hope that, with God's help, I will succeed in releasing him. I pray that when you come home, I will already have returned with good news, and you won't be burdened with additional worry for my safety. Don't lose hope, no matter what happens! Please forgive me. I love you.

Leichi

I don't remember how I reached my destination, but soon I found myself standing before that dreaded, hateful edifice which had swallowed up so many of my brethren. Staring at the building, I felt as if my head might explode from the countless arguments repeating themselves in my mind. "Don't you know," reasoned one voice, "that the rumors about the Tolonc are true?" "The rumors don't describe even a fraction of the horrors that lurk behind its walls, because of the secrecy that surrounds this place," a second voice reminded me. "You are risking the life of your unborn baby," cautioned another. But I couldn't be stopped now and no amount of reasoning could restrain me. Mercilessly driven by some strange force, I strode to the entrance, and without the slightest hesitation, reached for the bellcord and pulled.

A scrawny boy in uniform appeared at the door. "Whom do you wish to see?" he asked politely.

"I don't know his name," I said, shivers running down my spine. "But I would like to speak to the head of the department."

"Which department?" he asked patiently.

"The department that deals with the newly-arrived Jewish men."

The boy's eyes opened wide in surprise and his prominent Adam's apple bobbled in his long neck. Then he asked me to follow him. We entered a large, beautifully furnished room with a massive oak desk at its center. He directed me to a chair and then turned and left.

Alone in the room, I looked around nervously, trying to find a clue to the character of its occupant. The walls were lined with books, and my heart pounded wildly as I read all the anti-Semitic, hatred-inciting titles on the shelves. I was frightened beyond description. Then my gaze fell upon the desk and I found myself staring directly into the eyes of Adolph Hitler. A large, framed image of him was displayed on the desk top. On impulse, I sprang to my feet thinking, I must get out of here! And then I almost laughed out loud at my reaction. What did you *expect* to find here? I berated myself. I sat down again and waited.

The door opened noiselessly to reveal a man standing in the entranceway. Immediately, I rose from my chair. The man was an imposing figure who must have been in his late forties or early fifties, and his army uniform bore various military decorations. It was obvious from his bearing that he was accustomed to giving orders. He looked at me steadily and then his eyes narrowed as if he were trying to recall an episode from the past. Then he shook his head and said, "I have never met you before."

"No, sir. We have never met before."

"Sit down," he said, "and tell me what you want."

I remained standing, afraid that if I moved, all my courage would leave me. "Sir," I blurted out, "I am a Jewish woman, and I have come here to beg you to grant me a favor."

His thick eyebrows arched in disbelief and his face darkened. "You are a Jew?" he thundered. "And you came here of your own free will? Foolish woman! Don't you know that no Jew has ever escaped from here? What do you want of me? Talk!"

"A man named David Klein was picked up by the police

today. This man is my father-in-law. Please let him go. He did no wrong."

The officer's face registered surprise, but he did not respond. Wordlessly, he pointed to the chair, indicating that he wished me to be seated. I was grateful, for the confrontation had drained all the strength from my body and I thought that at any moment my knees would buckle under me. As I sat, he began to pace the floor and my eyes anxiously followed him. After a while, he stopped, faced me and asked, "Why should I let this man go?"

"Because he is innocent! He committed no crime!" I insisted, almost shouting.

He didn't seem to be listening to my words. "Tell me," he suddenly bellowed, "what did this man do to deserve such devotion from you? Do you realize that you have placed your life and that of your unborn baby in jeopardy? I can detain you here indefinitely, if I so choose."

I could not answer. Tears were welling up in my eyes, and I struggled to control them, because the last thing I wanted was for this man to see me cry, but my efforts were in vain. The tears ran down my cheeks as I sat there helplessly, cursing my naivete.

Then, as if through a haze, I heard him saying, "I'll order my men to shave off his beard today and tomorrow he will be deported to his hometown."

"Thank you, sir," I said sincerely, a wave of relief and gratitude washing over me. "I will never forget what you did for us. And I will keep you in my prayers."

"Don't tire yourself," he said, shrugging off my thanks. "You have more than enough praying to do for yourself, so leave me out of it. Besides, I don't see how my releasing this man does you or your people any good. And remember, this is the first and only time that I will let any Jew leave here." And then he looked me straight in the eye. "Do you want to know why I am doing this? I will tell you why: because you showed me a kind of courage that would put a lot of men on the battlefield to shame. I am a soldier in body and spirit, and will be until my dying breath. I can't help but respect courage, even if it is displayed by a Jew."

He was finished speaking and it seemed I was dismissed, so I rose and headed toward the door.

"Halt!" his booming voice rang out, and I stopped in mid-stride, my heart in my throat. The first thought that ran through my mind was: He's going to keep me here in the Tolonc after all. I turned around and saw him filling out a pass. Then he called for the boy who had brought me to his office and instructed him to escort me to the place where my father-in-law was being held.

The boy led me through a labyrinth of corridors and doors guarded by armed men who swiftly locked each door behind us with large, brass keys. As we walked, my mind raced. Will he imprison me under the pretext of taking me to see my father-in-law? I wondered. I consoled myself with the knowledge that if the officer had wanted to arrest me, he possessed the authority to have done so in his office.

I could tell that we were nearing the prisoners' quarters when we approached a large, black iron door guarded by a number of uniformed soldiers. They all eyed me curiously, and then the soldier who was holding the keys took my pass and studied it carefully. Looking at me with wonder in his eyes, he thrust the pass back into my hand and said, "You had better hold onto this, because if you lose it, you won't be allowed to leave."

The iron door opened without a sound. Cold air struck my face and I saw that I was standing in an open courtyard where yet another guard checked my pass and asked me whom I wanted to see.

"Wait here," he snapped, and he sent another man to summon my father-in-law. Soon I saw him walking toward me, tall and erect, like a king, but his face was as white as a sheet and his features were distorted. He walked past me without a glance in my direction.

"Papa!" I cried. He turned and stared at me, unbelieving.

"You have ten minutes to visit. Then I will be back," said the guard.

"How did you know I was here?" he asked, incredulous. "How did you persuade them to let you in?"

"I came here to tell you the good news. Tomorrow you will be deported home."

"What did you say? How can you know this? Who arranged it?"

"Let's not waste time on that. The guard will be back in a few minutes."

"I was so frightened when the guard came for me; I expected the worst."

All at once we heard one of the guards shouting at us, "Get moving! You think you own the place?" We continued walking while we spoke, and when we paused for the briefest moment, the same man approached us. "Keep moving!" he commanded us, waving his stick menacingly.

"The beasts!" I hissed. "But who cares, Papa. You are going home."

A shadow crossed his already pained features. "I am not convinced that I am going to be sent home," he said, "so I want to give you some messages to the family. Send my love to them all. I know I don't have to say this, because of course the older children will do their best to take care of Mama and to help support the little ones, but I will feel better if you tell them to anyway."

"Please believe me!" I pleaded. "You are going to be sent home." Then, looking down at the ground, I added quickly, "Please don't be upset, but they are going to shave off your beard."

"No!" he cried out, but then he quickly checked himself and continued speaking. "If I don't see my family again, please tell Herschel that I am so very sorry that I didn't permit him to go to America when he had the opportunity. Tell him that if we live through these terrible times, the first thing I will do is apply for papers to emigrate to America." He stopped to gauge my reaction.

"Keep talking," I urged him. "Time is running out."

"Tell them I'm sorry I didn't heed my sister's advice when she wanted to send an affidavit from America for me and the family."

"Why didn't you go?" I asked.

"Because I was afraid that the glitter and the freedom of New York would lure my family away from a strict Orthodox life. But I think I have found a solution to this problem: we will move to a small town and live as we do here, without any distractions."

"He is coming for you!" I interrupted, as I saw the guard approaching us.

"Leichi, please tell my family to emigrate to America. Tell them they must not live among these anti-Semites any longer."

"You tell them tomorrow, for tomorrow you will be home!" I cried.

"Get moving!" barked the guard, and then turning to me, he ordered, "You had better get out of here as fast as you can."

The next day my father-in-law was released and by noon we received a telegram informing us that he had arrived home safely. My mother-in-law wrote us a letter:

My dear children,

Words can't describe the feeling or the scene when Papa arrived home handcuffed and escorted by armed men. I thought to myself: This is the end. The children started to scream and I felt as if I was going to faint. Then the guards unlocked Papa's handcuffs with orders that he never again be seen in Budapest. The next time, they said, he won't be so lucky. Then it dawned on me that the wire you had sent me yesterday was really true and my happiness knew no bounds. Dear Leichi, I cannot find the words to thank you for what you have done, although I shudder when I think of what might have happened to you. And I am so greatly relieved that Papa won't be traveling to the city any longer. The strain of his daily journeys was too much for him, and the tension that I felt every night while I waited for him to come home almost killed me.

Mama

P.S. Papa went to sleep. He is exhausted beyond description but he told me to let you know that his beard wasn't shaved off. He sends his thanks and love. I hope he will be able to write you tomorrow. With kisses,

At the bottom of the letter was a short note in a child's scrawl:

Dear brother and sister-in-law,

I am in the first grade and I learned how to write so I am writing to you. Papa came home and Mama says she will never let him go to Budapest again. Please come home too because I love you.

Chaya

12

IN MID-MARCH of 1944, spring came upon us without warning. One night we had gone to sleep with the city under a blanket of snow and the windows glazed with frost; the next morning there were puddles of slush all along the streets, and birds were singing in the trees.

As we set out for the market that day, Vera and I passed the landlady, Mrs. Bogar, who was vigorously polishing the windows on the ground floor of our building. "Go home," she advised us, motioning us back into the house. "Change into your spring clothes. You'll melt in those heavy woolens."

"It's hard to believe that spring is really here," said Vera as we walked on, disregarding Mrs. Bogar's advice.

"What that good woman doesn't know," I said despondently, "is that as far as we're concerned, there won't be a spring this year."

"Of course not!" Vera replied. "How can we experience spring when our hearts are frozen by the icy glares of our fellow Hungarians as we walk among them on the street?"

We turned the corner, and as if on cue, a group of teenagers bumped into us intentionally. "Make way for your Aryan betters," one of them sneered menacingly under his breath. I looked up with a start. My eyes met theirs and I began to shiver from the naked hatred that I saw in them.

Vera was shivering too, despite her heavy winter coat. "Their loathing has turned our hearts to solid blocks of ice that all the sunshine in the world could not begin to melt." Tears were running down her cheeks now. "Only human kindness can warm a frozen heart, but clearly our fellow citizens haven't got even a drop of that in them. They have shown us repeatedly that they are not the least bit interested in helping us."

We walked in silence, our bearing bowed and defeated. Abruptly, Vera stopped in the middle of the block. Gone was her hunched posture; her eyes glittered with defiance. She stood straight as a tree and, to my amazement, burst out laughing.

"Vera! What is it?"

"Did you hear him say 'your Aryan betters'? Hah! Those swine! Those self-proclaimed elite! Why, they are the lowest..." Finding no word adequate to describe how low they were in her eyes, she spat on the ground. "They are lower than that. They should have been forced to witness my little boy's behavior today — then they would understand real greatness."

"Shh, Vera, people will hear you," I pleaded, but she wouldn't lower her voice.

"You should have seen how he carried on because I stepped on an insect," she continued. "'You... you killed it!' he cried, pointing his little finger at me accusingly. 'Maybe it was a mother bug who went to the grocery store to buy milk for her children, and you killed her while her children are waiting by the window for her, waiting forever because you killed her,' he wailed. He was inconsolable, and as I disposed of the dead insect, I knew that he would not easily forget or forgive my sin: I had killed a living thing."

"Oh, Vera," I cried out with passion, "you should have beat him black and blue to teach him a lesson: to be as unfeeling as possible in the world he lives in. Maybe if we raise our children to be insensitive to everything but their own needs, they will have a better chance of survival."

"How can you be so silly?" she asked with a faraway expression on her beautiful face. "Can't you see that this has nothing to do with upbringing? It is an inborn thing, for he is still such a small child that we cannot have exerted that much influence on him yet. His reaction came from his pure soul, and I wouldn't want to change him one bit."

There is no escape route from the cordon
Shutting in all Jewish children women and men.
There does not seem to be left in the land
A single ally to the Jew.
Hope and prayer, please remain my allies.
Don't let me falter, don't let me sway,
Whisper o whisper, please whisper into my ears:
Under this dark cloud hides the sun,
The sun with its golden rays
That tomorrow might burst forth, illuminating the sky,
As long as you will cast Heavenward your eyes.
For till you can hope and till you can pray
It will always seem near the sun, the sun's rays.
Believe in miracles and reach for the stars.
Send prayers soaring to the Heavenly throne up high.
"Hashem in Thy grace please put the power into our mouths
The power which tumbled Jericho's great walls to the ground!"
Dear allies please halt! I'm still smitten with fear.
Perhaps no longer whisper, but shout into my ears:
Ultimate faith can unlock invisible doors of escape!

Book Two

13 | March 19, 1944

"OPEN UP! LET ME IN!" Vera called through the closed door. She was crying as though the world had come to an end. When I opened the door I found a woman who did not at all resemble the Vera I knew. Her face was ashen, her eyes red-rimmed and wild-looking.

"What is it, Vera?" I asked in alarm, clinging to the doorknob for support as I felt my strength ebb.

"Hitler! The Germans!" she sobbed incomprehensibly.

"What about them? Tell me!"

"They have invaded Hungary. We are under Hitler's rule. We are lost!"

I heard her last words through a haze, and then a strange blackness engulfed me. The next thing I was aware of was my husband sponging my face with a damp cloth. I was lying on the couch and I recall thinking: his eyes, his face — they look just like Vera's did. Her words came back to me, shocking me out of my stupor.

"No!" I cried. "I don't want to know about it!" I shut my eyes to block out the painful truth.

Afraid that I was becoming hysterical, my husband slapped my face, shouting, "Stop this, Leichi! Now open your eyes and drink this water!" Vaguely I heard Danny behind him, reassuring Vera, "Don't worry, she'll be alright," and then I heard the door close behind them. I jumped up, still half-dazed.

"Sit down!" Jacob ordered me, for he saw that I had no strength in my legs. He seated himself next to me and we looked desperately at one another, bewildered by the sudden turn of events.

"What shall we do? Oh, what shall we do?" I repeated over and over, as if in a trance. Suddenly an animal-like cry pierced the air and I realized with surprise that it had come from me. What will happen to us now? I thought, as a sense of panic overwhelmed me. And oh, my God, what will happen to our baby? What kind of a world are we thrusting him into?

Jacob took my face between his hands and spoke to me soothingly. "Calm yourself, Leichi. There is nothing to gain from crying. Listen to me. I have a plan that I've been working on secretly. Never, not even for one moment, did I lull myself into believing what so many of our brothers believed: that Hitler would leave Hungary out of his bloody crusade. I knew it had to happen — it was only a matter of time. So I have made preparations for us to hide out."

"Hide out? And where will I give birth to our baby? In a cave?"

"Please hear me out," he begged, but it was useless, for I was no one to reason with at that moment.

"Oh, my God!" I wailed. "How can we survive in a jungle, surrounded by wild beasts?"

"By following its laws," Jacob said.

"Then you don't have to spell it out for me. I know the law of the jungle: the strong devours the weak. And where does that leave us, but in the jaws of our anti-Semitic predators?"

"You are right. I admit their strength over us. We are their prey, but we mustn't overlook the fact that there are two sides to every coin. Let's turn the coin. Let's try to imagine what the weak, unprotected animal would do in our position." I didn't reply, so Jacob continued. "Does the weaker animal simply give in, and willingly offer itself to the stronger one? What do you think?" I still didn't answer, so he continued. "No! He does not. Instead, he uses all his powers to pit himself against the strong. But because he is physically weaker than his enemy, he must employ cunning. By outwitting him, by evading him, and most importantly, by hiding from him, he can still have some hope of survival." Then Jacob took my trembling hands between his strong, steady ones and asked me gently, "Leichi, do you grasp what I am trying to tell you?"

I looked at him blankly. Seeing that I still did not understand him, he released my hands and walked to the armoire. He returned with a large manilla envelope that I had never seen before.

"Open it up, please," he said, handing it to me.

As I fumbled with the envelope, it opened and its contents fell onto the floor. I looked down and saw a government document from which my own picture stared back at me. I looked at him questioningly. He bent down to pick up the papers and then, thrusting one of them into my hand, said, "Read it: Kovacs, Zsuzsi, *née* Shipoc, Zsuzsi. This will be your alias. Here is mine." He pulled out a second document which bore the name Iztvan Kovacs. As I stood there in a state of semi-shock, he produced still another document, but this one was only partially filled out.

"This will be our baby's, whose name we don't know yet, of course. With God's help, after you give birth, we will go into hiding. This is the only course we can follow, for we are too weak to fight them."

"Oh, Yanku," I said, comprehending at last, "now I see what you have been trying to tell me." And as I spoke, a flicker of hope was kindled in my heart. We must never lose our capacity for hope and prayer, I chastised myself, for those are two priceless gifts that God has given us and they can never be taken away from us. God only knows how many times they have been put to the test in our pain-filled history. But they have always emerged with us, sometimes battered but never destroyed.

I gathered strength from the knowledge that all was not

lost. "We will follow the example of our parents and theirs before them on this difficult, bloody road. We will use all our strength, courage and cunning in order to survive. And above all, we must never give up — never! It won't be as hard as it looks to us now," I continued, "because nothing is as hard as deciding which course to follow in times of trouble. Only the first step is difficult, for with the second step one is no longer alone. God walks with those who put their faith in Him," I said, quoting my mother.

A knock on the door interrupted my speech. It was Danny. "Vera sent me to find out how you're feeling, and to tell you how very sorry she is for upsetting you. She feels she should restrain her emotions more when she is in your company, and spare you unnecessary anxiety, because of your condition."

"It isn't Vera who upset me," I replied. "It's the times we are living in."

"Then please come over and tell her so, because she won't stop berating herself."

"Poor girl," Jacob commented. "She is reacting just like most of us do in times of great stress. She blames herself in order to avoid the real issue, which is too frightening to face."

"But now is not the time to indulge in such behavior," Danny said. "We have to make plans for the future and every lost minute may count. Vera is a sensible girl. Let's try to talk to her and bring her out of the state she's in."

We found Vera lying on the couch, her forehead swathed in cold compresses. While Irenna attempted without success to keep the children quiet in the next room, I tried to comfort Vera. But she was inconsolable. "Please forgive me," she sobbed. "I should have known better. I was so frightened when I saw you pass out."

"Stop this right now, Vera," I said sternly, hoping that my tone of voice would make her come to her senses. "I'm fine now. Besides, how can you blame yourself? You're not responsible for the Nazis' invasion and nothing can change the fact that they are here. Don't forget that we are all in this together."

"Rivka Leah is right," Danny agreed. "Please try and be

sensible about this, dear." He extended his hands to help her off the couch. "Let's go next door and discuss what to do now. At least let's try to begin planning."

Then Irenna called out, "Vera, can I let the kids come in?" Before she had a chance to answer, Vera's children rushed into the room, straight into their mother's arms. They kissed and hugged her, laughing and singing: "Hurray! Mama isn't sick anymore!" Their joy and excitement proved too much for Vera to bear and she stood up and hastily left with Jacob, Danny and me.

When she reached our apartment, she broke down completely. "Those Nazi brutes!" she cried. "How can they hurt our innocent Jewish children?" She covered her eyes and wept. "To murder them in gas chambers, when those little lambs know only to love and to trust." Then she pulled herself up straight, a gesture that was so characteristic of Vera when her emotions overwhelmed her. She was still groping for words which wouldn't come. A moment later, she dried her eyes and said with determination: "But they will never get them. Oh, no — not *my* children!"

Then Erno entered our apartment. We could see that he was agitated.

"This is the second time that my sister and I have been forced to live through a Nazi invasion," he said. "First they came to our home in Poland, and now they are here." He sank into a chair, exhaustion and tension making him look older than his nineteen years.

Irenna came in quietly behind him, gently ushering the children in with her. She immediately picked up where Erno had left off. "To think of all that we went through to get here — and it was all for nothing, absolutely nothing!" she exclaimed. "Most of the Hungarian Jews have at least had the blessing of being unaware of what is in store for them, but we know. Soon, we'll be ordered to wear the yellow star, and after that will come the ghetto, and from there, it is only a short way to the gas chambers."

Gas chambers? I said to myself. First Vera and now Irenna

had referred to them. Ignore it, a voice inside me said. But curiosity got the better of me. "What do you mean by gas chambers?" I asked. The room became silent and I noticed with alarm that everyone was avoiding my gaze.

"You mean that *you* don't know about it, either?" Irenna asked, astonished. "What do you think happened to the Jews of Europe? Do you really believe the Nazis took them all to Germany? Do you really think the Germans need additional mouths to feed? Of course not. As a matter of fact, if the Germans weren't stealing food from the mouths of the people whose lands they've occupied, they wouldn't be able to feed their civilian population, let alone their enormous army."

Irenna's thin, pale face was flushed with excitement, and her almond-shaped, dark brown eyes flashed fire. She continued, her thin body tensing with each word she uttered. "I told you about the ghetto, didn't I?" I merely nodded, for I was frozen with fear and couldn't speak. "First, we'll be forced to wear a yellow star and live in specially assigned houses. Then we will be packed into cattle cars that will take us to Germany, where the young and healthy will be imprisoned in slave-labor camps and the old, the infirm and the children will be killed with poison gas in gas chambers and their bodies incinerated in crematoria."

"Don't say any more!" I cried, covering my ears. "I don't want to hear this!"

Jacob, taking one look at me, made a desperate attempt to change the subject. "How is it that you are a Hungarian citizen, Danny, while your brother and sister are Polish?" he asked.

"We don't have the same mother," Danny answered. "I was born here in Hungary. I lost my mother when I was a little boy. Not long afterwards, my father married a Polish woman and moved there with her. My grandparents, whose only child had been my mother, begged my father to leave me with them temporarily until they could recover a little from their grief. But I never did go to live in Poland; I grew up in my grandparents' home in Budapest. I spent every summer with my father and his new wife and my new brother and sister. They lived in a little village..." His face lit up for a moment with happiness as he remembered his younger, more carefree years. But it clouded over the next instant as he asked, "Where are those happy days now?"

"Our parents are dead, murdered by the Nazis!" Irenna cried out, tears glistening in her eyes. "They killed them, they shot them right there in front of us..."

"Let me try to explain," Vera interrupted, to spare Irenna the pain of continuing. "Danny and I were married in June of 1939, the same year that Hitler occupied Poland. Two years later, Danny's parents managed to find someone who was willing, for a price, to help them escape to Hungary with their children. We received a message to wait for them in a little border town near the place where they would be dropped off. I can't describe our excitement. We bought a house in Ercsi and put the deed in my in-laws' names; everything was ready and waiting for them.

"We set out to meet them on the prearranged night. We sat in our car and waited at the border. After a short while, Erno and Irenna made their way toward us in the pitch-black darkness of night. Moments later, we saw movement in the bushes ahead of us and as we strained our eyes, we made out the form of my father-in-law coming toward us. 'Here they are!' I whispered under my breath. 'Yes, I see them coming,' Danny whispered, and he stepped on the gas, ready to flee with them. That's when the shots rang out." With these last words, Danny covered his eyes and Erno and Irenna began sobbing loudly. "There was nothing for us to do but grab the children and escape as quickly as we could, and leave the others dead on the ground," Vera concluded softly. Then changing the subject abruptly, she asked Jacob and me, "Do you remember the day you moved here and Danny and I came to greet you in your new home?"

"How could we ever forget it?" I said. "It was the nicest thing that could have happened to us: to find such caring, warm neighbors when I was so afraid of the strange place we were moving to. I'll never forget the kindness you showed us in befriending us so quickly."

To my surprise, Vera burst out laughing. I was hurt by her reaction and looked at her, puzzled.

"By now you surely must have figured out the reason behind our friendliness," she explained. "You will never really know how difficult it was for us to extend ourselves to perfect strangers as we did, but with these two 'illegals' living in our house," she said, pointing to Irenna and Erno, "we couldn't take any chances. We had to find out if we could trust you. To our good fortune, not only did we discover that you wouldn't harm us, but we found in you two wonderful friends."

"I think I speak for both of us when I say how grateful I am for all your help, Vera," I said. "I can't even begin to imagine what I would have done without you."

We were interrupted by the sound of weeping. Irenna was in tears. "For almost two years we have been hiding here from the Nazis, and now that they've invaded Hungary, it is as if we are right back where we started," she cried. "For all our trouble, we have accomplished absolutely nothing!"

"Your coming here has not been in vain!" Danny protested fiercely. "Thanks to Vera, who thought of the plan, the little farmhouse in Ercsi that we bought shortly before you escaped has become a refuge for Vera's parents, who are living there under our dear deceased parents' names. They have built up a very reputable image as devout Catholics and are accepted in that tightly-knit Catholic town. And my mother-in-law has made sure that all her neighbors know about her darling children and grandchildren who live in the besieged city of Budapest. She tells everyone that all she wants is for them to come home to Papa and Mama in their small town of relative safety. And that is what we are planning to do, just as soon as I can get away."

"You see, Leichi, we all own forged Aryan documents," explained Vera. "A man called Feri prepared false papers for all of us. It was right in our apartment that we introduced Jacob to him and it was Danny who christened you Zsuzsi Kovacs. All these preparations were being made while you were still living in your dreamworld."

Suddenly, I felt left out and hurt. I confronted my husband indignantly. "Why did you have to do all these things behind my back?"

"Because I felt that it would be much healthier for you and our baby if I spared you the horrible facts for as long as possible."

"I think it's time for us to go," Vera said. She and Danny took little Tomas and Monika in their arms. Both children bore a striking resemblance to their mother. Their daughter was too young to realize it, but she was very lucky, for Vera was a most beautiful woman. In a few moments, they were gone and we turned in for the night.

The next morning I pleaded with my husband not to go to *shul.* "Please stay home with me!" I cried. "Please don't put yourself in danger once again!"

Jacob looked at me with surprise. "How can you ask me to stay away from *shul* when I've never needed God more than I do now?" he asked.

"God hears us no matter where we pray," I insisted stubbornly.

"That's true," he said, gazing at me steadily, "but I also have another reason for wanting to go. Unfortunately, our Jewish brothers can't hear me if I'm not there, and I must communicate with them, too. I must alert them." And with those words, he left and I knew there was no stopping him. He wasn't going for himself; he was going for his people, and all thought of personal safety was lost on him. Although I was worried, I couldn't help but feel a great sense of pride and admiration for that brave man who was my husband.

14 | March 22, 1944

IT MUST BE THE GESTAPO, I thought when I heard the doorbell ringing, my imagination running wild. Hesitantly, I opened the door, only to find my brother and sister-in-law standing in front of me. "Shimon! Estie!" I exclaimed, still not believing that it was really they. Quickly, I guided them inside. "What are you doing here in Budapest? And what happened to you, Shimon?" I cried out as I noticed Shimon dragging his leg behind him.

"Like all the other Jewish patients, I was evicted from the military hospital, with strict orders to go straight to the station and take the first train home," Shimon answered. "But we came to see you first so that I could meet your husband."

"But why were you in the hospital to begin with? And what happened to your leg?" I asked.

"I had an accident. A heavy machine fell on my leg in the work-camp."

"It's a miracle he's alive at all," my sister-in-law added.

For a while no one spoke. We stood there staring at each other for a few moments, and then Jacob entered the room and broke the silence. "*Shalom aleichem.* I am happy to meet you," he said, extending his hand to Shimon.

"*Aleichem shalom,*" my brother replied. An awkward silence

followed. Then Estie started to rummage about in her pocketbook. She took out an envelope and handed it to me.

"Rifky made me promise that I wouldn't forget to give this to you," she said.

Seeing the familiar handwriting of my beloved niece was more than I could bear, and I realized how terribly I missed them all. "Please don't leave!" I cried. "Stay with us!"

"How can you ask such a thing of us?" my sister-in-law retorted sharply. "All we can think of now is how much we want to be with our children."

There was an edge in her voice that I had never heard before, and it frightened and confused me. Still, time was running out, so I tried to mollify her and continued calmly, "Estie, don't worry. We fill find somebody to bring the children here, to Budapest."

"And I will help you obtain forged Aryan papers," Jacob continued, "and an apartment where you can try and hide out from the Nazis until the war is over."

"Why should we hide?" Shimon exclaimed."We are not criminals!"

Jacob was astonished by Shimon's words. "Do you mean to tell me you don't know what fate awaits us under Hitler's rule?" he asked.

"I am aware of Hitler's anti-Semitic doctrines, but no matter how much he hates us," my brother explained matter-of-factly, "it is already so bad for us here in Hungary that I don't believe it could get much worse. And we all know that this is Hitler's last desperate attempt to stand his ground. It won't be long now before he loses the war. We can certainly hold out until then."

"Please listen to me!" Jacob shouted. "You don't understand!" He grabbed hold of Shimon's shoulders, as if by sheer force he could make him believe his words. "Hitler is planning to annihilate us all."

"Yes, it's true!" I exclaimed. "Soon we will be ordered to pin a yellow star on our chests. After that, it won't be long before we will be shipped to Germany, where our young and able will be thrown into slave-labor camps while the elderly and the children will be burned alive in Hitler's furnaces!" Unable to go on, I just looked at Shimon and Estie pleadingly.

My heart sank when I heard Shimon say, "Let's go, Estie. They are mad."

"I know that life won't be easy under the Germans," Estie said, "but lately it hasn't been so good under the Magyars either. And right now the only thing that matters" — she looked directly at Shimon through tear-filled eyes — "is that you come home with me to our children. Whatever happens, we'll be better off together than apart." She spoke to him as though we weren't there. And it did seem as if our presence, like our words, no longer mattered to either one of them.

Still, Jacob made one final attempt to convince them of the truth. "I see that, just like most of our people, you have no idea what is going on. But listen and believe me: unfortunately every single word we have said is true. Every one of the few Polish Jews who were lucky enough to escape from Poland and who now live in Budapest under false identities has warned us about the badges, the ghettos and the camps. They have constantly urged us to prepare to hide in the event of a German occupation."

"Then all of your informants must be paranoid," Shimon insisted stubbornly. "And so are you two. How can you believe that this could happen in the twentieth century? Use your heads! Do you believe that, even if Hitler were capable of destroying us, the world would stand by and let it happen?" He turned to Estie and repeated harshly, "Let's go!" and he quickly led Estie through the door. Before they entered the elevator in the hall, my brother rasped through clenched teeth, "You both need help!"

No sooner had the elevator door shut than I grabbed my overcoat and ran down the stairs to catch up with them. I met them at the corner of our street. We walked in silence; there was nothing left to say. But as the train station came into view, the finality of the moment struck me and I broke down. "Please listen to us!" I cried. "It is suicide for you to go back there!"

"Leichi, we are going home and you can't stop us!" Shimon shouted.

"Alright," I said, letting out a deep sigh of resignation. "But remember, our offer still stands should you change your minds. Just send us a postcard asking me to 'send back the purse which you accidentally left here' — we'll understand and try to get new identification papers for you and your family as quickly as possible."

The station was packed, mostly with Jews from out of town who had been in Budapest on the day the Germans occupied Hungary, and had now been ordered to immediately return to their hometowns. There was almost no place to stand, let alone sit. All around were anxious men and women who stared vacantly at the passing crowds, each locked in his own misery.

Then the train whistle blew as thick black smoke billowed up from the smokestack. Suddenly the stony-faced people came to life, pushing their way through the crowds and heading toward the train. I became separated from Shimon and Estie and I didn't see them board the train, but as it slowly started to move, I spotted them waving vigorously from one of the windows. In that instant, I remembered the dream and wondered if Estie remembered it, too, for she had dreamt it. But what difference would it make whether she remembered it or not? It was too late now, I thought, feeling as though my heart would burst from pain. I turned and slowly made my way home.

When I reached our apartment I found my husband nervously pacing the floor. He turned to me and, with barely concealed anger, said, "Now you can see for yourself what I mean when I complain that most of our people don't believe us. I must arrange a meeting with Feri as soon as possible."

Then he looked at me closely and asked, "Are you alright, Leichi?"

"No, and how can I be," I sobbed, "when Shimon and Estie have gone and sealed their own fates? Do you know that years ago Estie had a terrifying dream about today's visit? I realized the connection only after they had boarded the train, an instant too late to do anything."

"Don't be silly," Jacob chided me gently. "You know that we don't involve ourselves with interpreting dreams."

"Oh, Yanku, you don't understand! It isn't that I am trying to figure out the meaning of the dream. It's as clear as could be: my mother returned from her grave to warn and advise us. But neither Estie nor I remembered in time, and now it is too late!"

"My poor Leichi! You are trembling like a leaf," Jacob said with concern. "Please, have a drink and calm yourself." He hurried to bring me a glass of water from the kitchen. "We won't talk about it now. Just try to forget it."

"But I *must* talk about this dream and I want you to hear it," I protested.

Jacob sat down beside me. "I am listening," he said softly.

"It happened around two years before I met you," I began, "and I had no inkling then that I would be getting married. Estie dreamed this dream repeatedly. At the time it scared her very much and yet, when it could have guided them to safety, it slipped her mind.

"My mother came to her in the dream. Estie saw her disembarking from a large bus wearing her *tachrichim*. 'Mama!' she exclaimed, and ran to her and kissed her hands. 'The anti-Semitism is so unbearable!' she cried. 'Please, Mama, pray for us all!' And Mama replied, 'My child, neither I nor anyone else can help you. This is a decree from God.' Then she walked back to the bus, but as she mounted the stairs she looked back and said hurriedly, 'Only one person in the world can help you: Leichi, when she is married and living in Budapest.' The next moment she was gone.

"I didn't know what to make of it then, but now the circumstances shed a new light on Estie's dream. Now I know for certain that I will never see my brother and his wife again!" I buried my face in my hands, my tears flowing without end.

[And sure enough, after the war we learned that, of all my brothers and sisters, only those who hid with us during the war survived. Of my three sisters and four brothers who were taken to the camps, not one survived.]

Vera and Danny visited us after supper but I was in no mood to entertain. I sat alone in the bedroom, asking myself over and over, "How could I have convinced them to stay?" I cried into my pillow a hundred times: "I should have locked them in the house by force!" Finally, fatigue overpowered me and I fell into a fitful sleep.

15 | March 23, 1944

THE SUN CAME IN strong and bright through the window, casting a lively pattern on the wall opposite my bed. "Spring is here and each day brings us closer to your birth," I whispered to my baby contentedly, and then I laughed out loud with happiness. I was only half-awake and my thoughts were still in dreamland. Then I glanced at the clock on our night table. "Oh, my God," I exclaimed, flying from the bed in a panic. "Where is Jacob? He should have been home from *shul* hours ago!" Rushing into the kitchen, I found a note on the table:

Sleepyhead! I've been home since eight o'clock. When I found you sleeping so soundly, I didn't want to wake you, so I went to Danny's. Call for me.

Yankl

Moments later, Jacob walked through the door. "How on earth can you sleep so well?" he asked, incredulous.

"Oh, Yanku," I answered with a sigh, "I wish that I could hibernate like the bears do and sleep through this whole nightmare."

Jacob fixed his gaze on me. "Well, I don't think it would work," he said, "because if we want to be alive when this war is over, we have a lot to plan for and even more to do." He looked at his wristwatch. "I made an appointment with Feri for two o'clock this afternoon. I want him to prepare false papers for our families."

"Can I go with you?"

"Of course, if you like. But before we go to see him, we must decide upon aliases for everyone."

"What difference does it make what names go on the papers, as long as they sound Hungarian?" I asked impatiently.

"You're right," Jacob replied. "It doesn't matter. It's just that preparing documents for one person entails providing the names of his parents, his grandparents and *their* places of birth and current residences. It is extremely time-consuming to invent so many names and I don't want to burden Feri with this task when he's so busy."

"Oh, now I understand. Everybody requires several documents, not just one. Each person needs a birth certificate, his parents' birth certificates and citizenship papers, too. Do you realize how many names and towns we will have to make up? This could take hours! Let's get to work right away."

We sat at the kitchen table with pen and paper and proceeded to compose our list of false names. After a stormy debate, we finally agreed upon the name Csaba Fahey for my father-in-law, which we thought had a nice Hungarian ring to it. Then we bickered over my mother-in-law's maiden name, until we eventually decided to call her Ethal Toth. Joska was the name I suggested for one of Jacob's brothers.

"No!" Jacob snapped. "That reminds me of Yosef from the Torah. I think Oscar is a much better name."

"Wonderful," I retorted. "And have you ever met an Oscar who wasn't Jewish?" And so it went with each new name until we were both satisfied with the choice. By the time we finally came up with all the names to take to Feri, we were hardly on speaking terms!

We arrived at Feri's house promptly at two o'clock, and a wraithlike young girl opened the door for us. "Your names, please?" she asked.

"Jacob and Rivka Leah Klein."

"Feri is expecting you," she said softly, and she disappeared behind one of two identical oak doors, leaving us standing in the high-ceilinged entrance hall.

"Is she Feri's wife?" I asked in a whisper.

Jacob nodded. "I heard they were all stunned when he announced one fine day that he was about to get married. Apparently, he had always tried to talk his friends out of getting married, saying it was irresponsible to marry in such unsteady times. 'Why should you have to worry about a wife if you get caught?' he would say. Or, 'You are taking on a millstone, a dead weight on your neck.' But when he announced his intentions and his friends threw his words back at him, he simply looked at them innocently and exclaimed: 'You don't understand. I fell in love with her.' I'm sure she's a nice girl, but no one can figure out what on earth Feri sees in her."

Suddenly, the big double doors at the end of the hallway swung open, flooding the narrow hall with light. There in the doorway stood Feri's wife.

"Come inside," she said, smiling, and as she smiled her face was infused with unbelievable beauty. I watched, fascinated, as the light picked up a thousand little particles from her golden-brown eyes, eyes that sparkled with laughter.

"So, you are Iztvan and Zsuzsi Kovacs?" she said breathlessly. "I am Aliza, Feri's wife, and I am very happy to meet you. Please, come inside and sit down. I'll be with you in a moment," she said, and left us again.

We found ourselves in a spacious, sunlit room, elegantly furnished with large comfortable chairs upholstered in subdued browns and beiges. The floor was covered with a wine-colored oriental carpet, woven with designs of all shapes and colors.

"I have never seen a more beautiful room," I whispered as I looked around me, and then my gaze fell upon a painting on the wall. "I wonder who painted that," I said.

"Why, what a question!" Jacob exclaimed. "Feri painted it, of course. Didn't I tell you that he is Feri Hoffman, the famous artist? His studio is in there," he said, pointing to the doo opposite us. "But he spends most of his time nowadays in secret room in the basement, hidden from the outside world Danny and a few of his friends helped to build it and get i ready."

Jacob's description of this man piqued my curiosity. "All o this sounds so mysterious," I said. "Now I'm really anxious t meet him."

The door opened once more and Feri emerged, lookin like a construction worker in his baggy gray overalls and ca He was talking with a young couple, bidding them good-by

"I see you've been working," Jacob said after introducin me to him.

"Yes, I am quite busy these days," Feri replied. Then h turned to the couple. "Janos and Olga Fanyas, I'd like you t meet Iztvan and Zsuzsi Kovacs, two of our most recent 'co verts' to the Aryan race," he said with a smile. For a fe minutes, we carried on an animated conversation with th couple, for we felt an immediate kinship with these peopl whose plight was so similar to ours. Then, wishing them su cess in their efforts, we bade them farewell.

Feri quickly ushered us into his studio. There were nume ous half-finished canvases scattered around the room togeth with easels, paintbrushes and tubes of paint, and Aliza's almo life-sized portrait looked down at us from a large easel. seemed as though he had just stepped away from the canva Jacob handed him the sheet of paper we had prepared with a the names.

Feri grimaced as he scanned the list. "You don't expect m to do all this right now, do you?"

"Please," Jacob begged him, "do as many as you can no while we wait. We'll come back for the rest tomorrow."

"Tomorrow," Feri repeated, still studying the names an addresses and shaking his head. "I can't promise, but I'll tr and I'll let you know when they are ready, through Danny. see him every day anyway." Then he handed the list back t

Jacob. "You have so many names here that I don't even know where to begin. Please mark the ones you want me to prepare first."

"I can't!" Jacob cried, his face turning white. "These are my parents, my brothers, my sisters! How can I choose who should be rescued first?"

"I think it's fair to say that your parents should be last," Feri reasoned, "because I know how parents are: they will never consider coming to Budapest and leaving even one of their children behind. Besides, your parents and your three little sisters could wear peasant clothing and come to Budapest passing as country folk who have come to sell their goods here. They wouldn't even be noticed by the police. Your father is past the age where he'd have to serve in the army and if they move up here quickly enough, before it becomes mandatory to move into the ghetto, the risk will be minimal." He spoke as if he had long experience in these matters. "On the other hand, your brothers must have some documents attesting to the fact that they are on assignment for the government." By this time he was half talking to himself, but then he looked up at us and said firmly, "Your brothers will definitely be stopped by the authorities to have their documents checked."

"Try to do as many documents as possible today," Jacob urged him, "because I'll have an opportunity to send them home tomorrow, with Ignatz Gelb."

"Is he strong enough to travel on the train already?" asked Feri.

"Strong or not, he is being discharged from the hospital tomorrow, and he will be put on the train by hospital personnel."

"Then how will you manage to give him the papers?"

"Rivka Leah will deliver them. She goes to visit him every day in the hospital and brings him food. So it's unlikely that anyone will suspect her."

Feri glanced at me briefly and then back at Jacob. It was clear from his expression that he was skeptical about my chances for success. "Don't worry," I assured him, "I'll manage. Just have them ready, please!"

"Then let me take your list of names with me to my 'labor room' and I'll try to give birth to a few new Aryans," Feri said with determination as he took the sheet of paper from Jacob's hand. He went into his bedroom where a secret passageway led down to his hidden studio.

Moments later Aliza appeared, carrying a tray of buttered bread and a pitcher of freshly brewed black coffee.

"How did you guess that we were starving?" I asked as she offered me the tray. Biting into the warm, soft bread, I exclaimed gratefully, "This is delicious! How did you know that fresh bread and butter is my favorite food?"

"I'm glad," Aliza replied. "I baked it today. Feri also loves fresh bread and butter. He even prefers it to the costliest roast. Which is fortunate," she added with a smile, "because we haven't seen meat in the longest time."

"Tell me," I inquired, recalling her husband's attire, "is Feri also a construction worker?"

Shadows darkened Aliza's sensitive features. "Construction worker? With those hands? Why, that would be a crime, especially when he can use his God-given talents to help save lives!" Aliza replied hotly.

"Don't be insulted," Jacob said soothingly. "Rivka Leah was simply puzzled by his clothing. You see, she has no idea about the character of this section of the city."

Mollified, Aliza went on to explain. "In this neighborhood, you see, most men dress that way. So Feri wears the same kind of clothes in the hope that if he ever has to escape from the authorities, he could easily slip away unnoticed."

"If that should ever happen," I cautioned, "make sure that he hides his hands in his pockets. They might give him away."

"You have a good point," Aliza said thoughtfully, "and I will mention it to him right away. But I hope to God that he will never have to carry out his escape plan."

We passed an hour or two in conversation with Aliza until

Feri entered the room. Immediately, we all rose, as if on cue.

"How many?" we asked excitedly.

"Five," he said.

"Oh, Feri, how can we ever thank you?" I blurted out, overcome by emotion.

"Please don't thank me for it," said Feri quietly, his eyelids heavy from fatigue. "The only thanks I wish for will come after the war, if it turns out that my papers actually helped save Jewish lives. Right now, the time for talking is past. I hope to live to see good results." All at once, his tiredness seemed to disappear. He clasped his hands in front of him and his dark eyes shone with a mysterious fire. "May the Lord please bless His servant's handiwork," he murmured. Aliza stood next to him, not moving, and her pale skin made her look like a statue carved from ivory. But as I looked at her closely, I realized that her lips were also moving in silent prayer.

The next day I hid the incriminating documents under my clothing and set out to visit old Mr. Gelb in the hospital. I decided to walk, rather than use public transportation, because the streetcars were often the target of police searches and I feared that if a policeman so much as looked at me, I would immediately give myself away.

I walked along Dob and Kiray Utcas, the area most densely populated by Jews. This was the first time since Hitler's occupation that I had come to the area, and I was astonished to see the drastic changes that had already taken place there. The streets were filled with small groups of frightened people. A few looked defiant, and they spoke with anger in their voices, but most of them appeared haggard, almost lifeless, as they listened passively to the others speaking. From their bearing alone one could tell that they had been stunned into complete resignation. Trembling, I turned my head away; I didn't want to see their misery. But wherever I turned, there were only worse things to see. I noticed a few young mothers surrounded by small children who were tugging at their skirts for attention. The mothers didn't seem to notice the children at all; they were preoccupied with their own suffering.

The children, those beautiful, once well-cared-for Jewish children, were now dirty and unkempt, and it hadn't taken them long to realize that they were no longer restrained by the old rules. They were wild and running free, leaning out of high windows and over the low railings of the long balconies. My God, I thought, these mothers are worrying about their children's future when they are in mortal danger right now! I stared at the ground as I walked on, and I was relieved when I finally reached the hospital, away from the horrid street scene. Remembering the dread I used to feel upon entering a hospital, I reminded myself that everything is relative.

I stepped into the large, sun-filled ward. There was a row of six beds on either side of the room. At any other time I would have stopped to chat briefly with each of the patients in the room, but today I was filled with despair; I didn't want to see anymore suffering. Deliberately avoiding the gazes of the others, I headed straight for Mr. Gelb.

"Hello, Mr. Gelb. Today I brought you some chicken soup," I told the old man as I helped him sit up and placed the container of steaming broth on the little table next to his bed. "You're going home today?"

"Yes," he moaned, "but I'm still in terrible pain."

"Don't worry. Your wife will take such good care of you that you'll recover in no time." Then I bent down and whispered, "After lunch, pull your curtain closed. I have the papers and I want to pack them in your suitcase."

"Is there one for my Nachum, too?" he asked.

"Yes, there is one for your son."

His face lit up. Just then a nurse came over to his bed and said, "Hello, Grandpa. Do you need help packing?"

"You are the kindest nurse I have ever met, but thank you, I need no help." He pointed to me. "She promised to help me pack. But right now, I am very tired and I would like to nap for a while. Can you please draw my curtain?"

As soon as the nurse left, I went to Mr. Gelb's locker,

removed his belongings and carried them to the bed, making sure the curtains were closed behind me. I picked up the old, worn suitcase which lay on the floor and began the work of packing. I started with the two pairs of flannel pajamas which Molly Gelb, the old man's wife of forty-nine years, had sent with him in the hope that they would keep him warm and comfortable. I folded them neatly, hiding the incriminating documents inside the folds. Then I placed these between two shirts and topped them with his underwear. Last I folded his socks, which were lovingly darned with an array of different-colored threads. I put them into the suitcase and quickly closed it.

"My *tallis* bag!" Mr. Gelb whispered. "You forgot to pack it. It's by the foot of the bed. I keep it there because I don't want them to touch it."

I picked it up. The purple velvet was now old and faded and the golden thread which Molly had used for the embroidery was now blackened and torn.

Had she been as happy to embroider her fiancé's *tallis* bag so long ago as I was only last year? I wondered. Was she as proud and happy as I was? And will we live to be as old as they are and will my husband's *tallis* bag be as worn from long use as this one is? I asked myself these questions, thinking of Jacob's dark blue *tallis* bag with his name embroidered in shimmering gold letters. You are wasting valuable time! I berated myself, shuddering. Hastily, I bent over and whispered in Mr. Gelb's ear, "There are five complete sets of documents packed in your pajamas. One is for your son, Nachum, as I promised. Please take it and the four other sets which, as you know, we are sending for my husband's family. Please let them know right away that you have them because they don't know that we have sent anything with you. And please convey our wish that they come to Budapest on the first returning train."

The old man closed his eyes.

"Can you hear me?" I asked gently.

He opened one eye and smiled at me. "Go on, please."

"You must keep this in the strictest confidence. No one besides your family and ours should have any knowledge of what we've done. That could spoil our entire plan."

"I understand. Now if you'll excuse me, I think I'll have a rest. I am very tired."

As I was leaving the hospital, I saw a streetcar stop on the opposite side of the road. I started to run towards it. "Don't hurry," called the conductor, with true Hungarian courtesy. "I'll wait for you."

When I got on, I was disappointed to see that the streetcar was packed with passengers. My legs were still unsteady from my criminal activities and I was longing to sit down. Rivka Leah Klein, passing along forged documents! I chided myself. You'd better get used to it, said another voice within me. You will have to live a lie from now on, Zsuzsi Kovacs.

Someone tapped me on my shoulder and I looked up with a start. It was a policeman. My heart began to pound. He must have seen the guilty look on my face, I thought to myself with dread.

"Hungarian sister," he said, gallantly offering me his place, "please be seated." I sat down with a great sigh of relief. It hadn't even occurred to him that I was a Jew.

At home I found Jacob, Danny, and a man whom Vera and I called "Mr. Antique" engrossed in conversation in the hallway. We had given him this nickname because everything about him was reminiscent of the previous century. He wore old-fashioned clothes and used archaic expressions, but what was most distinctive was his courtly manner. He would bow whenever he met a woman, reserving special flowery phrases for the fairer sex. He seemed to have stepped out of an earlier, gentler era.

An expression of relief crossed Jacob's face when he saw me, but he made no comment. The men continued speaking in subdued tones and I was certain something terrible must have happened, because the chivalrous Mr. Antique failed to greet me. I opened our door and invited everyone in, but

Danny and Mr. Antique declined. I looked at Jacob questioningly as we went inside.

"The yellow star," he said softly, staring at the floor. "We have to start wearing it from the thirtieth of the month. That's Thursday, only six short days from now."

"Oh, no!" I wailed. "We may have to move into the ghetto before I have my baby!" I could not believe the Germans were proceeding with such dizzying speed.

"No!" he asserted, his voice ringing with determination. "I will never walk into a ghetto of my own free will and on my own two feet. Nor will I let you or our baby go there either, at least not before we have exhausted all possible alternatives."

"I don't want to think about it," I said emphatically. "It's too frightening." My mind worked quickly. "Yanku, why don't we just forget about everything and grab these four days for ourselves? Do you remember telling me about the way many people reacted in Germany when Hitler rose to power? You said that they were so shocked that they couldn't cope with reality, and they built a dreamworld around themselves, a castle from where they could view the world through rose-colored glasses." I looked away, fighting back my tears. "Oh, Yanku! I never thought that I would feel like they did. But it seems I can't face the devastating reality, either."

"Stop it!" shouted Jacob, gripping me firmly by the shoulders and forcing me to look at him. "Don't you remember the way you reacted when I first told you about those people? Don't you remember what you said? I do: 'The most deplorable and dangerous of all lies is the lie we tell ourselves.'" With that, he thrust his hand into his jacket pocket and pulled out the yellow stars. He pressed them into my palms.

As the hateful items touched my skin, a burning sensation raced through my entire being. I looked at the stars with loathing. "Yanku!" I cried out. "I feel as the branded slave of centuries ago must have felt, when the red-hot iron burned into his exposed flesh." In that moment, I felt a genuine kinship with all those who had been forced to endure cruelties from the beginning of time, because that innocent-looking yellow star conveyed the same message as the brand. It proclaimed loud and clear our helplessness and our humiliation, stripping us of all human dignity and reminding us that we were no longer our own masters, that we were slaves!

"What you've said is true," Jacob pointed out calmly, "but there is one difference which can give us courage. Unlike the branded slave, we can discard our badges of shame without leaving any trace of them."

"That can't be as easy to do as it sounds," I countered.

"It's not, but it's a starting point," he replied.

That afternoon, Vera and I decided to go on a shopping spree. Our plan was to hoard as much food as possible and thus delay having to go out wearing the demeaning yellow star. But food was so scarce at that time that we returned home with only a meager surplus. Consequently, on March thirty-first, only one day after it became mandatory to pin the yellow star on our clothes, I was forced to leave the house in search of food.

I ventured out early on that Friday morning, hoping that I wouldn't meet a soul to witness my shame. But when I did meet the first Aryan, my reaction surprised me. I straightened myself automatically. Gone was the feeling of shame. My whole being wanted to cry out for the entire world to hear, "*You* are the one who should feel ashamed. It is the mark of *your* cruelty that I am wearing on my chest."

Then I came across a boy and a girl who made a big show of looking at my blouse where the yellow star was pinned. "Yes, I am a Jew," I called out to them, "and I am proud of it!"

When I returned home, Jacob was waiting for me in the foyer. He didn't ask how I had felt wearing the star, but reassured me quietly that it would never again be as difficult to wear as it had been today.

I was sitting in our kitchen reading a letter as I waited for

Jacob to return from *shul* later that morning, when Danny and Vera knocked at our door. They both looked haggard.

"We've had an argument that we can't settle," said Danny heatedly, "so we decided to seek your advice."

"I'm not so smart," I protested, but my words didn't discourage Danny, who continued impatiently. "I want Vera to go home to her parents with our children and my sister and brother."

"And where will *you* go?" I asked.

"He wants to stay here in Budapest," Vera said, "and I've told him a hundred times already, but if he wants to hear it again, I will say it again: I won't go!" Her lips were firmly set, and I recognized in that now-familiar expression a determination that was a force to be reckoned with. Moments passed as I searched for a way to resolve the impasse. "What made you change your plans so suddenly?" I asked.

"Oh, we had such a terrible night," Vera lamented. "Irenna had nightmares the whole night long. It must be the yellow star. It seems to have opened up old wounds for her. It was heartbreaking to listen to her cries. I kept on waking her throughout the night but it didn't help." She paused thoughtfully. "I think that the solitude, being locked up in our apartment like a prisoner, is depressing her too. She is on the verge of a breakdown and she needs a little freedom and fresh air, so we decided to give her a new identity. She will pose as a German nanny for the children. I pray that it helps."

"Rivka Leah," Danny interrupted, "please help Vera see that she has no right to put everyone's life in danger just because I'm not able to leave Budapest just yet." His words were met with total silence. "Am I right or wrong?" he demanded. "Will you please say something?"

"I wish you hadn't put me on the spot," I began haltingly, "because no one can question that you are right." I chose my words carefully. "But I must also admit that your position stands up much better in theory than in practice. You can't expect me to be so hypocritical as to advise my very best friend to do what I wouldn't do myself. I could never leave Jacob — never!"

"Poor fellow," Danny retorted with mock pity. "He got stuck with the same type of wife that I did, the type that Feri describes as 'a millstone around a man's neck.'"

"Then tell me," I asked angrily, "why did he get married in these terrible times? Explain *that* to me, if you can."

"Because," Danny answered quietly, "it is women like Vera and you who supply us with the courage and the will to go on."

Just then I heard the sound of the mailman opening our mailbox outside. I opened the door and, recognizing my mother-in-law's handwriting on one of the envelopes, I quickly snatched the letter from the mailman's hands. In the apartment, I tore the envelope open impatiently, anxious to hear who would be coming to Budapest with the identification papers we had sent with Mr. Gelb.

But there was no mention of their having received the papers, much less about who was coming to the city. I read and re-read the letter, disappointment and dread welling up within me like a vile-tasting poison.

"I see that you have gotten bad news," Danny said, pulling up a chair. "Sit down, please. You look as if you might faint."

Then Jacob walked in with his *tallis* bag under his arm. "Ah, we have early visitors," he called from the foyer. But as soon as he stepped into the kitchen, he knew something was amiss.

"I'm sorry," I stammered, handing him his mother's letter.

My dear children,

I wish to God that I could tell you about some happy occurrence, but unfortunately, things have taken a turn for the worse. Last night was bedlam. There was a knock on our door and two SS men came and took Papa away in the dark of night. They wouldn't tell us why they had come for him or where they were taking him. They just looked right through me, as if I didn't exist. But when morning finally came and I went to try to find out where he might be, I learned that there were ten more such knocks on the doors of various members of our Kehillah *last night. We are all bewildered and have no idea what to do. Here is a list of the names of those who were taken away. Perhaps you know somebody with connections.*

Love,
Mama

Jacob handed Danny the letter without saying a word. Danny read it quickly. "I don't know these people, but my guess is that they are the leaders of the community."

Jacob didn't answer. He began pacing back and forth like a caged animal. We all knew there was nothing he could do, but none of us said a thing. We just stood there and watched him, suffering with him, and praying.

16 | April 10, 1944

THE DAY BEGAN in true April fashion: one minute it was raining heavily and the next minute it was all sunshine.

"Come now, make up your mind," I said to the sky as I stood by the large window facing the street. "Will it rain or shine today?"

Suddenly, a black limousine, the unmistakable symbol of the Nazi Secret Police, pulled up to the curb next to our house. Trembling with fear, I watched as two officers emerged.

"Jacob, hurry!" I screamed, pushing him into our bedroom. "Hide under the bed. They are coming for you! No! Don't go near the window — they may notice you," and I virtually shoved my startled husband under the bed. I held my breath and waited anxiously for the knock at our door or the Brenners'.

Several minutes passed without a sound. "Look out the window," Jacob ordered impatiently from behind the dust-ruffles.

Nervously, I parted the curtains and peered outside. "Now I see their car parked in front of the house next to ours," I whispered.

Jacob was out of hiding in an instant. He came to my side by the window and the next moment exclaimed, "Look!" We watched as the front door of the adjacent building burst open and one of the German officers stepped out. He strode to the limousine and held the door open. I started to tremble again when I saw a robust-looking, middle-aged couple emerge from the building, accompanied by an armed officer who swiftly steered them toward the car and followed them into the back seat. Then, with a squeal of tires on the damp road, the limousine was gone.

"They grow bolder by the day," Jacob murmured, his face pale. "They came for my father under the cover of darkness, and now, just a few days later, they're arresting people in broad daylight, for everyone to see."

"Then let's go out!" I cried, pulling him toward the door. "Let's run out right now so that if they come to arrest us too, we won't be here!" And we dashed down the steps, stopping only for a second to alert the Brenners to the danger. No one answered. Apparently, they had also seen what happened and decided not to open their door.

We ran outside and raced down the street, holding on to each other like two frightened children. On the corner we bumped into one of my husband's former classmates from Ujhely. "What are you doing outside on a day like this?" he asked. "Don't you know there are policemen all over, rounding people up? Just a minute ago I was almost caught but luckily, at the last moment I realized what was going on and I escaped in the nick of time." And with that, he quickly left us.

"Not in the house, not on the street," I cried in dismay. "Oh, Jacob, where shall we go?" All of a sudden, a sharp pain pierced my body. I cried out with the agony of it, grabbing hold of a lamppost for support.

"Leichi, don't panic," said my husband, who was as panic-stricken as I was. "Do you think that you can manage for a little while longer? Dr. Rona's office is just around the corner."

Slowly, we made our way to the doctor's office. When at last we arrived, I staggered to the nurse's desk and asked if I could see the doctor. "You have no appointment today," she answered curtly. Helplessly I sank into the nearest unoccupied chair while Jacob explained, his voice full of indignation, "She is not well. Can't you see she's in pain?"

The nurse eyed me carefully. "Come on, then," she said. "You'll be next," and she ushered me into one of the examining rooms.

"You have started labor," Dr. Rona said after checking me thoroughly. "It is often brought on by shock."

"But I'm not due for another month!" The doctor looked at me blankly, and I began to feel desperate. "What can I do, doctor?"

"You have two options," he said, staring at the floor. "One is to do nothing and let nature take its course. Maybe that would be best for all concerned. The alternative is to try bed rest along with daily injections to inhibit the contractions. It may help."

Jacob was brought into the examining room and the doctor explained the situation to him. My choice was clear. I looked up into my husband's encouraging eyes and rolled up my sleeve. "Please try your best to save our baby," I said to Dr. Rona as he prepared me for my first injection.

The needle pierced my flesh and I heard Dr. Rona say, "I'll see you tomorrow at your house, after office hours, to give you your second injection. If you decide between now and then that you don't want anymore medication, just let me know."

By the time we left the doctor's office the street was quiet, with no SS in sight. We walked home in silent despair. The moment we entered our apartment, I opened up my purse and took out the tiny white pill which Dr. Rona had said would help relax me. A few minutes after I swallowed it, I felt my eyelids getting heavy, and soon I was oblivious to the world.

The next morning Vera came to see me. She tried to be cheerful and encouraging, but her words sounded unnatural and both of us knew it. After some awkward conversation, she finally excused herself.

When she returned, she had a book in her hand. "Look, dear," she said with feigned cheerfulness, "I bought you the latest best-seller. It's written by a new American author. I loved it and I know you will, too."

"Yes, I'm sure I will," I replied in the same affected manner as I placed the book on the night table.

Then Vera turned to me and I saw that tears were streaming down her cheeks. Falteringly, she asked me, "Rivka Leah, are you sure you have the right to fight for the life of this child within you? After all, what kind of security can you offer it?"

"Vera, would you leave your children uncared for, if they were sick now, so they would die of neglect, just because you can't offer them security?"

Vera didn't answer and she left the room in tears, but I overheard her telling Jacob before she went home, "I'm happy that Rivka Leah feels this way about the baby, but I'm even more impressed by her remarkable strength and faith."

Later that afternoon the doorbell rang. I put on my dressing gown hastily, wondering who it could be. It was Dr. Rona, and when he saw me up, his face turned red. He was livid. "What are you doing out of bed?" he shouted. "I've come all the way to your house to give you your injection because you are supposed to be lying flat on your back, and here I find you parading all over the house!"

"Please, let me explain."

"There is nothing to explain," he yelled, following me into our bedroom and colliding with Jacob who had just crawled out from under the bed. "What is going on here?" he bellowed. They both lost their balance and the next moment the two men were sitting on the floor, roaring with laughter.

Dr. Rona was the first to come back to himself. His dignity restored, he announced in a very authoritarian voice: "Mrs. Klein, you *must* stay in bed even though the first crucial twenty-four hours have passed without incident."

After giving me the second injection, the doctor gathered his instruments and picked up his bag. "I'll see you tomorrow, same time," he said as he was leaving. And he did come faithfully for five consecutive days. On the fifth day he told me that I needed no further bed rest and that I could start walking around indoors. He said that after two more days of recuperating in the house, I would be free to go out.

When I finally did leave the house, to go shopping with Vera, I was surprised to see how much less food there was for sale in the market than there had been just the week before and I said as much to Vera. She looked around cautiously but said nothing. As we approached our house, she went through the same motions: she stopped and looked around carefully and resumed walking without a word.

"I never noticed this habit of yours before," I remarked. "You keep looking around as though you think we're being followed. Is everything alright?"

"Yes, everything's fine but I have something to tell you and I don't want anyone else to hear."

"In that case," I said, "unload your packages and then come over. But hurry! I'm anxious to hear what it is."

When she came into our apartment a few minutes later, she looked around the room in her new suspicious fashion. "Even the walls have ears," she said softly, motioning me to follow her to the middle of the room.

"Tonight is the night," she whispered.

"Oh, Vera! I wish all of you the greatest *hatzlachah*." I paused for a moment. "But what made you decide so suddenly?"

Fear was clearly reflected in Vera's honey-colored eyes. "The Nazis are so experienced already," she said, "that they are able to execute their evil plans with great efficiency. Hitler has occupied our country for less than a month now and he is already preparing the ghettos in the provinces. The Nazis have learned their vile skills well, at the expense of our unfortunate Jewish brothers in the occupied countries. At least those poor Jews are all dead now, put out of their misery. I am afraid that we will envy them in the days to come..."

Then she stopped abruptly. I didn't say a word; I could only stare at her as she raised her hands like the *Kohanim* do when they bless the congregation. Angry words poured forth from her lips. She sounded almost delirious. "Germans, I curse you, each and every one of you who helped bring this government into power, and I curse the rest of you who could have prevented it but didn't. God, please let them learn firsthand how it feels to suffer what they have made us endure!" she wailed. "Oh, what a heavy burden it is to know what awaits our people and to be powerless to help them. And how guilty I feel for separating myself from the fate of the rest of the Jews. I keep begging their forgiveness, but I owe it to my children to save them. Oh, God!"

I stood there watching her, mesmerized. "Vera," I said softly, "I know what you are trying to say. I, too, grapple with the same question: Do I have the right to hide out because I know what's in store, because I have a husband, God bless him, who is capable of arranging an escape plan for us? I ask myself this question countless times, night after night. And then I remember the words of my old school principal. He said, 'It is written: He who saves but one Jewish life is considered as if he has saved the entire world.' Since we are all condemned to death, why not save those whom we love most, ourselves and our closest family?" I stopped and looked at her quietly, waiting for some reaction. I could see she was beginning to calm down.

"You have put my problem in a new perspective," she said at last, dabbing her eyes with a handkerchief. "I can look at it now from a different angle. Thank you, Leichi."

"Vera," I asked, "how will we know that you've arrived safely?"

She still had that faraway look. "Oh, I'm sure we will keep in contact with Feri," she replied. "Believe it or not, that's one of the reasons I came here: to tell you that we must keep in touch with each other and keep each other up to date by passing information through Feri. Please, let's not disappoint one another!"

Then it was time to say our final good-bye. "Stay well, Leichi!" Vera began.

But I couldn't bear the thought of parting with this dear friend of mine, so I responded somewhat harshly, "Oh, stop it, Vera. I hate good-byes, and besides, who knows? Maybe for some reason your trip will be postponed until tomorrow."

"No, we must leave tonight. You see how cloudy it is? According to the forecast, it will be cloudy tonight as well. That means that the sky will be completely black. We will have the darkness we need to cover our movements."

It was exactly eight o'clock that evening when the Brenners stepped out the front door of our building. Immediately, they were swallowed up by the pitch blackness of the night. Jacob and I stood for a long while at the window, gazing into the darkness. I saw vividly, though only in my mind's eye, Vera pushing their sleeping son in his carriage and Danny carrying their groggy daughter on his shoulder. With them walked Irenna and Erno, taking their first breaths of fresh air in two years, under open skies. We looked after them in silence, a silence broken only by the sound of my sobbing as I prayed fervently for their safe arrival.

17

THE BRENNERS made their way along the row of acacia trees which lined the road leading to the train station. The night air was mild and redolent with the scent of the trees' blossoms. Their fragrance bewitched Irenna and she walked behind the others as if in a trance, absorbed in her own private world.

Elation welled up inside her. She was light-headed, and her wildly pounding heart was filled with song. When did the world become so unbelievably beautiful? she asked herself in wonder, and the answer came to her readily: It must have happened without my knowledge, while I was confined like a prisoner in my brother's house.

Now all the painful memories came back to her, memories of those nightmarish times when, bereaved and terrified, she had first set foot on Hungarian soil. Now she was fifteen years old, and tonight was the first time in two years that she had stepped outside. What a long, dreadful two years it has been, she thought to herself. And how many times did I feel like giving up and turning myself in when the walls of their home seemed to be closing in on me. But every miserable moment was worth living through, just to experience this magic spring night! And some strange, unexplainable, never-before-felt yearning and joy engulfed her, playing havoc with her heart and speaking to her of new springs to come, filled with freedom and life. Yes, of life and of love! Love, she thought. How strange! I feel as though I'm in love with the whole world tonight, she concluded and laughed aloud in the soundless night.

"Psst," Erno hissed urgently. "Are you crazy? What is there to laugh about? Better keep quiet. We're almost there."

After they had walked for quite a while, they heard the rumbling sound of a departing train, and they knew that they were finally in the vicinity of the Keleti station.

"We're here," Vera said quietly. "Let's stop and organize ourselves. Erno and Irenna, go and seat yourselves in the first car of the train. Danny, the children and I will sit in the last car. Now, let me describe my parents' house to you again..."

"Oh, no, not again!" Erno interrupted. "If you think I can listen to that description yet another time, you're mistaken."

"Alright, then tell me how you are going to find the house if, for one reason or another, we lose each other in the dark?"

Erno was in no mood for logic at this point. "If you say one more thing, I'll scream," he said through clenched teeth. "Come on, Irenna, let's go." He grabbed his sister by the arm and walked well ahead of the Brenners.

"He is such a bundle of nerves," Vera said with a groan.

"He'll be alright," Danny assured her as they entered the Keleti Pályaudvar, the larger of the city's two train stations. Under normal circumstances, the huge building was bathed in bright light, but now it was hidden under a blanket of almost complete darkness, broken occasionally by a dim lightbulb. Despite the gloom, it was swarming with people and alive with their loud chatter.

"What a crime it is to cloak this magnificent work of architecture in darkness," Vera remarked.

But Danny made no reply. He was busy watching Erno and Irenna as they made their way through the crowd toward the first car. As they disappeared inside, he turned to Vera. "Let's go," he said, and they quickly headed for the last car of the train.

The train started moving the moment they reached their seats and there was nothing to do but hope that everything would turn out for the best. "Soon," they reassured each other, "soon this ordeal will be behind us."

Vera's beauty always drew stares, but now her two golden-haired children upstaged her. In no time, the Brenners were surrounded by fellow passengers who not only admired the little ones but also asked far too many questions. In order to get rid of them quickly, Vera started yawning and Danny, following her lead, went a step further. He smiled sheepishly and closed his eyes.

In the first car Erno and Irenna sat down next to the door and they too feigned sleep so as to be left alone. After a while, Erno opened one eye to observe their surroundings. He was pleased to see that the seat opposite Irenna was vacant and the one across from him was occupied by an elderly woman who was deeply engrossed in prayer, her fingers busily telling the beads of her old rosary. In the row behind them sat a young couple who had eyes only for each other.

Unknown to Erno, this serene-looking couple were none other than Janos and Olga Fanyas, whom Rivka Leah and Jacob had met at Feri Hoffman's house. "They look harmless," he whispered to Irenna. As the conductor checked their tickets without a comment or a second glance, he breathed a sigh of relief.

"Another twenty minutes," he said quietly to his sister, unaware that she was not the least bit nervous about the journey, that in fact she had never been more relaxed in her life. Now she and her daydreams were inseparable, uniting the young girl with the woman inside who had been hidden from her until this very minute. And this new woman spoke to her of feelings she had never known before.

"Ten more minutes," Erno informed her jubilantly. Irenna opened her eyes, smiled at him, and quickly closed them again so as not to lose the thread of her daydream. She was so absorbed in her own world that she didn't even blink as the door of their compartment flew open and a hulking police officer, accompanied by the conductor, appeared in the doorway.

"*Razzia*!" the officer boomed at the top of his lungs. "Ladies and gentlemen, make your documents available for inspection!" People started to rummage through their purses and pockets and the dark car came alive with the sound of rustling papers. Erno felt as though the train itself was trembling in fear along with him as he watched the officer check one passenger after another.

Suddenly the policeman's voice echoed through the hushed car: "Where were you born?"

"Can't you see for yourself?" came the answer in a coarse, drunken voice. "It's all written down there."

Laughter rang through the darkened compartment as the policeman shone his flashlight in the drunken man's red face.

"Of course I can read it, brother," he said, "but I enjoy listening to your heavy Vasmegyei accent." He laughed loudly at his own joke, more for the benefit of his captive audience than for the drunkard, who had dropped off into a deep sleep and was already snoring.

The word "accent" ran like an electric current through Janos' troubled soul. All he could think of was his and his wife's pronounced Polish accents. He sprang to his feet as though bitten by a viper and as his mind worked feverishly, he realized that the train was slowing down. His mounting anxiety interfered with his ability to think, and it seemed as if from every corner he could hear the threatening words: "Your accent, your accent!"

Through a haze, he saw that everyone's back was turned to him as they watched the *razzia* in progress. I've got to escape, he told himself. To fall into the hands of the police at this point — after all we've been through — never! Then he noticed that the train had come to a complete halt. Without a moment's hesitation, he grabbed his unsuspecting wife's hand and with one tremendous stride, he was at the door of the train. He yanked it open with all his might and leaped down the steps toward the tracks, pulling the stunned girl along with him.

They were running so fast that neither one of them noticed the oncoming train. They heard the ear-splitting roar just as they were crossing the tracks. Frantic, they tried to turn back but the train's headlights blinded them and the huge, iron monster roared toward them at full speed.

The express jolted to a halt and panic-stricken passengers started to spill out from both trains, running in all directions and shouting, "An accident! An accident!" The wind carried the sorrowful message across the open fields: "An accident! An accident!"

"Oh, God," Vera whispered. "I hope Irenna and Erno have the good sense to leave the scene of the accident before the police arrive to investigate!" At the first sign of panic, she and Danny had disembarked with their sleeping children in their arms, abandoning the carriage and all their belongings and fleeing the site under cover of darkness.

They were far away when they heard the message over the police bullhorn: "No one is to leave the train until further notice. Everyone must remain on the train. This is an order from the police!" They stopped behind a house for a moment to catch their breath, and then resumed their flight at the same speed, not stopping again until they reached their destination.

18

THE SIREN'S WAIL shattered the quiet of the night and we immediately ran downstairs to the bomb shelter. For several minutes confusion reigned as everyone crowded into the small room. "The Brenners are missing!" someone cried out, "Where are they?"

"They must have slept through the alert!" said our neighbor, Rosa.

"Then we must go and wake them," another neighbor suggested. "Yes, yes, we must bring them down here with their children."

Just as I was beginning to wonder if I should say something, Mr. Bogar, the superintendent, announced in a loud voice, "There is no reason to worry. Last night the Brenners left with their children to visit her parents in the provinces."

Suddenly the shelter reverberated with the rumble of planes flying overhead.

"Listen!" someone cried out. "They're flying so low! And more are coming! Those blasted bombers!" Just then the night was pierced by a high-pitched whine and a shell exploded with a roar. The earth beneath our feet shook and plaster rained down upon us.

Instantly, the shelter was transformed into bedlam. People were running in all directions, half-crazed with fear. As I sat there petrified, Mr. Antique turned to me and said calmly, "Tell me, why should a Jew be afraid of a bombing? We won't survive this war anyway, so wouldn't it be a mercy if this house were to explode, and we would be killed us instantly, rather than suffering a much more agonizing death at the hands of our German tormentors? As for me, I would much prefer to go under with our enemies, to pull the building down with me, just as Samson did. Oh, if only the Lord would grant me that pleasure!"

Just as he finished speaking, another bomb exploded right outside the small, barred window of the shelter, its impact shaking the room violently. People started screaming again, but Mr. Antique stood perfectly still, his face radiant. "Nyugati station! Nyugati station!" he repeated jubilantly, while the others sat there, frozen with fright. "This must be the answer to my prayers," he said to me in a low voice. "I hope the Allies level both the city's train stations, the Nyugati and the Keleti, so that not a single train will be able to arrive or leave or even pass through. I want all transportation systems in the country destroyed, paralyzed. More, more! Send more bombs before those accursed trains carry us to Hitler's gas chambers and our deaths!"

Silent tears glistened in Mr. Antique's dark, close-set eyes. "One could call me a traitor for praying for the destruction of my homeland," he said quietly so that only I might hear. Then he held up his left hand which was atrophied and lifeless. "Here, can you see? It is paralyzed. I still carry a pellet here from the Great War. But then it was an honor to fight for my homeland, and I was ready to give my life for her."

Slowly it grew quiet outside and soon, to our great relief, we heard the all-clear siren signaling the end of the attack. Everyone was anxious to see what the city looked like in the aftermath of the bombing, and people started to push and shove each other impatiently, as if this were the first major air raid we had experienced. Jacob and I were the last to emerge.

I was afraid to look, but all eyes were riveted to the scene outside and everybody's excited cries convinced me that it would be best for me to go straight upstairs without viewing the destruction. I headed toward the stairs.

Then I heard Janko, a poet who lived directly above us on the fourth floor. "Lord, how great is Your might," he exclaimed, "that even as You try to destroy us, to punish us, You do it surrounded by beauty!"

"Come, Leichi. Let's go see," Jacob insisted, pulling me out to the street against my will.

"It's breathtaking!" I cried as I gaped at the burning city with its golden-red flames leaping up against the blackened sky. "But how much suffering this has caused! My God!" I hid my face in my palms.

At once, I heard someone yell from behind me, "Don't do that! You mustn't touch your face when you are startled!" I turned around to see one of our neighbors eyeing me with concern. "A friend of my father's cousin was born with the image of a mouse on his face, because when his mother was pregnant with him, she touched her face after having been startled by a mouse."

"Oh, that's just an old wives' tale," my husband exclaimed in exasperation. "We don't believe in that sort of thing. Leichi, I think it's time to go home." He quickly guided me toward the stairs, as if to protect me from anymore of our neighbor's "helpful" advice.

When we reached our apartment, Jacob sat me down on the living-room couch and collapsed in his armchair. "I really don't believe in such superstitions," I assured him. [But until my baby was born and I saw that no burning city was etched on her little face, I continued to worry.]

Suddenly there was a sound in the hall and my husband sprang up from his chair. "Shh. Do you hear? Who could be coming here at two o'clock in the morning?" Within seconds, Jacob was in his usual hiding place under the bed. I tiptoed over to the foyer and listened carefully, my ear pressed against the door. I heard footsteps heading for the Brenners' apartment. Then I heard the scratch of a match being struck, as though someone were trying to read the doorplate.

I ran to the bed. "Yanku," I whispered breathlessly, "it must be the police coming to search the Brenners' house. Oh, God in Heaven, they've been found out!"

"Don't mention a word about Irenna and Erno," Jacob cautioned me, "and keep to the story that you have no idea where the Brenners went."

The footfalls were growing fainter with each passing moment. "He's going away," I said with a sigh of relief. We heard the elevator door slam shut.

"Peek out to the hall and see if it's safe," Jacob said.

My legs shaking, I tiptoed out into the foyer. Something rustled under my feet and I bent down to examine it. There, on the floor, lay an envelope. It had obviously been pushed under the door by our visitor. I opened the door a crack and peered into the dark hall. It was empty. Whoever had brought the letter was gone.

I went back inside and Jacob and I eagerly opened the envelope. It was meant for us after all. It was a letter from Jacob's mother:

My darling children,

I want to share this good news with you. Today we learned from reliable sources that Papa is alive, thank God. He is imprisoned in the Tolonc with the rest of the missing men from our Kehillah.

Can you imagine my being happy that Papa is back in the Tolonc? But you see, everything is relative. Remember the anguish we felt when he was taken there a few months ago? It seems like a hundred years ago now. All that matters today is that he is alive. And while there is life, there is hope, and hope is what keeps us going!

The reason I am sending this letter through a courier is to inform you that two of the documents you sent have found their way to our door, and I am very grateful for your having sent them. Now that I know that Papa is alive and in Budapest, I long with all my heart to be there and to bring the rest of the family, even though I know that I won't be able to see him. But even the remotest possibility that I might, gives me the will to try to hide out with the false papers.

Please try to send the other documents right away, because it is rumored that we will have to move into the ghetto soon. Aunt Rachel has asked me to move in with her and Uncle Shia because their house falls within the boundaries of the ghetto, but I have qualms about the practicality of our living there. How could they cope with my lively brood in their childless, quiet house? But naturally, the children are all excited. You know how much they adore Uncle Shia and Aunt Rachel. And because of that, I might just consider it, if and when I will be able to state my preferences. But it would still be best if we could escape. Do you have any idea where we could live in the city?

Please write as soon as you can.

Love and kisses from Mama

P.S. The children all send hugs and kisses to both of you.

Jacob read and re-read the letter, his brow furrowed with concern. At last he spoke. "We must do everything in our power to try and free Papa."

"Yes, and I wish it were morning already so we could go to Feri's to get new papers for Mama. Time is of the essence."

We both slept fitfully in the few remaining hours of the night. Jacob woke up early, and went to *shul* for *shacharis.* When he returned, he was in a grim mood. "There isn't a thing we can do for Papa," he said sadly, as he sat down by the kitchen table.

"Don't be such a pessimist," I replied. "We haven't even tried. Why give up so soon?"

"Because hundreds of people have tried already and they have all failed. Do you think that we are the only ones? Hundreds of men have been picked up throughout the country and thrown in the Toloncz for no reason at all. They're unreachable!"

"Come on, then! Let's not waste any more time. We have to see Feri immediately and persuade him to work quickly. At least we can help your mother in that respect."

Jacob agreed. "Alright, let's go." He reached for his hat and headed towards the front door, but then he stopped. "Oh, no! First we have to choose new names. What if someone is using the old ones? We can't have two people hiding out with the same identification. And let's face it, whoever stole those papers intends to use them. The fact that they gave back two of them indicates only that their consciences must have bothered them."

"But how could anyone do such a thing?"

"Well," Jacob commented pensively, "I really can't blame them. The will to survive is the only drive which, combined with the fear of death, would compel almost anyone to do the same thing."

We came up with new names as quickly as we could and went directly to Feri's. Aliza answered the door. One look at her and we knew that something was wrong. Her eyes were red-rimmed and she was unusually pale. As soon as she saw us, she burst out crying. Then, hastily wiping away her tears, she ushered us into the living room and hurried out, slamming the door behind her.

Jacob and I looked at each other in alarm. "We should have asked her what was wrong," Jacob said. He, too, was troubled by Aliza's behavior.

"I was tempted to, but I dismissed it, thinking it must have been something personal between her and Feri. Would you like it if I told everyone of our quarrels?" I spoke teasingly, just to get him to smile.

Feri threw open the door of his studio and we sprang to our feet, startled by his appearance. His hair was unkempt and his normally bright, dark eyes were dull and bloodshot.

"Feri!" Jacob cried. But Feri was unable to speak. He simply handed us the newspaper he held in his hand. There, on the front page, the words screamed at us:

POLICE ARE INVESTIGATING THE INCIDENT OF TWO YOUTHS, JANOS AND OLGA FANYAS, WHO COMMITTED SUICIDE BY LEAPING IN FRONT OF THE BUDAPEST-MISKOLC EXPRESS.

Immediately, I recognized the aliases, and a feeling of dread engulfed me. "No, it's got to be a mistake," I cried. "It can't be true. It can't!"

We all sat down in stunned silence, shattered by the news of the tragedy. A haggard-looking, middle-aged man came to see Feri. He stopped in the doorway and eyed us with distrust.

"Don't worry," Feri said. "They're alright. You can talk." Feri turned to us and said, "Jacob and Rivka Leah Klein, this is Morris Katz. Mr. Katz is in charge of claiming the young couple's bodies for a proper Jewish burial. They will be buried under their Jewish names, of course — Baruch and Yenty Kohn."

"Poor things," Aliza sighed. She turned to Mr. Katz. "I hope you'll succeed in bringing them back here. If they had to die under Christian names, at least let them go to their eternal rest with a Jewish burial and Jewish names."

"What really happened?" Jacob finally asked.

"There was a *razzia* on the train shortly before it pulled into the station," Mr. Katz explained. "Apparently they panicked... he panicked. Witnesses have testified that it was Baruch who pulled Yenty along. He wanted to elude the police. How was he to know about the oncoming express?" he concluded grimly.

After a brief conversation with Feri in private, Mr. Katz turned to go. When he left, we remembered our reason for having come. "I received word from my mother," Jacob began. "My father has been taken to the Toloncz. She wants to come to Budapest with the family and hide out, but not all of the false papers you prepared reached her. That's why we've come — we need you to replace the lost documents."

"*Ribbono shel Olam!*" Feri exploded. "I can't work anymore and I won't work anymore!" He pounded on the living-room table with such force that it broke, sending pieces of wood flying all over the room.

"Feri, at least give me my sister's papers," I pleaded. "You promised me you'd have them ready by today."

"Don't ask anything more of me!" he bellowed. "It won't help. God wants us all dead and so it will be." But when he saw the pained expression on my face he softened. "Alright," he grumbled. "A promise is a promise. But this will be my last document." And with that, he disappeared into his studio.

Later, when Feri emerged with my sister's papers, Aliza turned to him and said, "Look at Rivka Leah. This is how I want you to remember the effects of your work: the joy, the hope that you gave to so many."

I looked into Aliza's eyes, silently pleading with her, while my husband implored, "Please, try to convince Feri to prepare these papers for my family."

Just then, I saw the golden sparkle light up in her eyes. "She'll help us," I whispered to Jacob excitedly.

But it soon became apparent that the sparkle in Aliza's eyes had nothing to do with our request. In fact, she had forgotten our presence altogether. All she knew was that her Feri was suffering, and nothing else mattered. She took Feri's face between her hands, as a mother would a child, and spoke to him soothingly: "I want you to come down with me into your workroom and I want you to destroy every last piece of evidence. It is about time you gave some thought to our lives, too. I want us to get out of here before the police catch up with us." Then she stepped back and looked into his eyes. Her words rang out. "And I want you to remember the hope that you gave to people. I want you to remember the happiness your papers gave Rivka Leah just minutes ago. I want you to be proud of yourself, at least half as proud as I am of you, because do you know what I think of you? I think you are a saint! Countless times, with each new document, you put your life in jeopardy. Yes, my dear husband, you are a saint."

The whole scene looked so unnatural, so mystical, almost as if we were witnessing a performance from an ancient Greek tragedy. There they stood, tall and erect, their complexions pale and smooth as though carved from marble. As I looked at them more closely, I saw Aliza's lips moving in silent prayer. We watched them, mesmerized, and then Aliza broke the silence. "Come, Feri," she said. "Let's go to work."

"No!" Jacob cried desperately. "Please prepare my mother's papers first."

They looked at us with surprise. "What more can I do for you?" Feri asked, dazed.

"Please," Aliza insisted. "You must leave us alone now."

"We'll be back in the morning," Jacob said. He thrust the envelope into Feri's hands. "Please, please, make up these documents. I'll help you destroy all the evidence tomorrow." Absentmindedly, Feri took the envelope out of Jacob's hands.

"I'm certain he'll prepare the papers — after he calms down," I assured Jacob on our way home. "I couldn't have concentrated today either."

But when we rang their bell the next morning, there was no answer, nor the next day, nor the day after that. Then Jacob came home with the news that Feri had disappeared. He'd moved on to a new address under a false name.

19 | April 24, 1944

Sátoraljaujhely

My dear children,

I don't know how it is in the city, but every day we get new orders via large posters pasted on the walls and small notices tacked up all over town. So each day, first thing in the morning, I go out with your sister Minda to read the newest "decree." But today, as we approached the spot, I knew instinctively that the news must be devastating. You should have seen the crowd and the appearance of our friends. I felt like running back into the house, but of course I didn't. "It can't be that bad," Minda whispered to me. "Look, it's only a small notice." But I knew how deeply those small notices could wound — like the order about the yellow star. In my innocence, I told Minda to take heart, that at least we know we have already hit rock-bottom with the Nazis. After all, what worse could they think up for us? But today — today they spat venom on us:

> NOTICE TO THE JEWISH POPULATION!
> ON THE DAY OF APRIL 27 THE GHETTO WILL BE READIED FOR OCCUPATION IN THE VICINITY OF MUNKACSY AND ARPAD UTCA. EVERY JEW IS THEREFORE ORDERED TO MOVE AT THE APPOINTED TIME, ACCORDING TO THE REGULATIONS OF HIS NEIGHBORHOOD. FAILURE TO COMPLY WITH THE ABOVE LAW WILL HAVE GRAVE CONSEQUENCES!

Now, listen to the rules and regulations:

EACH FAMILY MUST OCCUPY ONE ROOM, SHARING FACILITIES WITH ALL.

(Can you imagine how many of us will be crammed into each apartment? I shudder to think of it!)

MAXIMUM BAGGAGE: ONE KNAPSACK PER PERSON, THE WEIGHT OF WHICH SHALL NOT EXCEED ITS BEARER'S ABILITY TO CARRY IT.

I stood there, gazing at the notice, thinking it was all a bad dream. But then the reality of the situation struck me as I looked around and saw all of the members of our Kehillah, *our neighbors and cousins, along with many others I have never seen before, all wringing their hands nervously, asking one another, "What next?"*

Jacob, I have a terrible sense of foreboding. I am truly afraid!

The three little girls greeted us at the door. "Is it true?" they asked with happy anticipation. A friend had told them we were to move to a new apartment where only Jews were allowed to live. I nodded. "Yay!" they cried. "There won't be any Christian children to throw stones at us," and they sang with joy as they started to take their belongings from the drawers for me to pack, chatting excitedly and making plans to play ball games outdoors again, fearlessly, among their own. They worked like little elves. The tables and beds were soon cluttered with all their clothing and toys. I didn't say a word — why spoil their fun? There will be plenty of time for that when they open their knapsacks and find out how I trimmed the load.

I couldn't go on reading anymore. My tears blinded me. All at once, a feeling of exhaustion overcame me and, leaving the letter on the dining-room table, I went to lie down on my bed. As I lay there, I pictured my three little sisters-in-law as they had looked when I first arrived at their house as a bride. Eleven-year-old Litzi, the oldest of the three, was standing in the corner, tall and graceful as a growing tree. She greeted me shyly, while Laya, the official beauty of the family, blond-haired, blue-eyed and dimpled, peered at me boldly from beneath her golden tresses. Then, apparently satisfied with my appearance, she leaped over to me and gave me a big hug and kiss, telling me with all of her nine years of experience how pretty I was and how much she loved me, and loudly urging her little sister Chayie to welcome me, too.

How happy I was then, I thought wistfully. And how did all these troubles befall us in only ten short months? And why hadn't I and most of us seen these problems earlier? Then I envisioned Jacob pointing his finger at me accusingly and saying, "People see whatever they want to see." But how long will people continue living in a dreamworld? I asked myself, and I supplied the answer right away: They'll know the vile truth soon enough. Hitler will make sure that we all come face-to-face with our bitter destiny. Only then, it will be too late.

A peculiar sound coming from the next room brought me out of my reverie. I quickly went to investigate. There I found Jacob sitting in a chair and staring at his mother's letter, trying unsuccessfully to swallow his sobs. "I am cursed to know so much!" he moaned and he laid his head on the table and cried so hard that I thought his heart would break.

20 | May 1, 1944

THE QUESTION OF HOW we could save our family continued to plague us. We were overwhelmed with panic and guilt, not only over our failure to locate Feri, but also because, since we had not been able to find a reliable courier to deliver the documents he'd prepared for my sister Esther, even these were serving no purpose. They still lay hidden under the lining-paper in my dresser drawer.

Finally, Jacob came home from *shul* one morning with good news. "I have just the right person to deliver the documents to Esther!" he said excitedly.

"But Yanku," I explained, "it is forbidden for a Jew to travel outside the city."

"Don't worry. This one is a genuine Aryan."

I was dumbfounded. "You mean to say you met an Aryan in *shul* this morning?"

"No, of course not. But I did meet Arye Friedmann in *shul*, and he told me about this woman. I left in the middle of *davening* to speak to her and she is willing to undertake the trip."

"Who is she?"

"Her name is Zsofi Teleki. She lives in the building where Mr. Stern used to have his office."

I had heard of this woman and of how much she had done for our people. "Why didn't I think of her before?" I chastised myself.

Now it was Jacob's turn to be surprised. "You never told me that you knew her," he said.

"I don't know her personally, but I heard a lot about her from my sister-in-law Estie. In fact, I used to pack the slaughtered goose that Estie would bring her every Sunday to compensate her for the use of a corner of her apartment. Mrs. Teleki let her store the goods there that she received from Mr. Stern, and it was there that Estie's customers would pick them up." I reached for my overcoat. "I'm taking the papers to her right now."

"You needn't," Jacob replied. "She will be free to go only after the fifth of May. She is responsible for collecting the rent from the other tenants in the building at the beginning of the month."

"Oh," I said, disappointed. "By the way, how much did you offer her for her assistance?"

"At first she refused to discuss payment. She was adamant about doing it just to help. Nevertheless, in the end we agreed upon a handsome sum, to be given in two payments: half when she leaves, and the rest when she returns with your sister."

I carefully hid the incriminating documents under the folds of my maternity blouse and set out for Mrs. Teleki's house. Before ringing the doorbell, I touched the front of my dress to make sure the documents were still there. The rustling papers reassured me and I smiled to myself, satisfied that at last I was able to do something constructive.

A small woman with wispy, mousy-brown hair appeared at the door. She was wearing a spotlessly clean, stiffly starched housedress and she looked pleasantly welcoming.

"I am Mrs. Heller," I said, introducing myself and extending my hand. As a precaution, I had decided to use my grandmother's name rather than my own. She took my hand and shook it for a long time. "Come inside," she said, full of smiles as she offered me a chair. I sat down and looked around. The living room was immaculate, almost too neat and clean, as though unlived-in. I felt chilly and uncomfortable.

"When do you think you can leave, Mrs. Teleki?" I asked, trying to hide my anxiety.

"I am free to leave whenever you want me to."

"The sooner the better," I said. "Who knows when the ghetto will be sealed? By then it will be too late."

"I will leave on tonight's express, then," she stated decisively.

"Wonderful!" I cried. "Oh, how will I ever be able to thank you for what you are doing?" Nervously, I extracted the money which I had hidden under my blouse. But before I could take out the documents, a horrible feeling came over me. My hand stopped in mid-air as I looked up into the ice-blue eyes of an entirely different Mrs. Teleki. In that moment, those chilly eyes reminded me of a frozen lake in a long-forgotten incident from my childhood. It was a clear day in midwinter, and I had gone to view the frozen lake near our home after it had swallowed two little neighbor boys. They had gone out on the ice, trusting it to bear their weight, without first checking its strength. The hole through which they had disappeared had frozen over once again and the treacherous lake was the same ice-blue color as Zsofi Teleki's eyes.

Before I had the chance to reconsider, Mrs. Teleki grabbed the money from my rigid hand and with an ear-piercing, bone-chilling laugh she pointed to the door. "Get out — before I change my mind and call the Gestapo!"

I staggered out to the vast foyer. It was deserted, and each tile echoed with Mrs. Teleki's derisive laughter .

I dragged my tired, trembling body to a corner of the hallway near the entrance and leaned against the wall next to the great front door. There I gave vent to my misery. I don't know how long I had been crying when I became aware of a man's reflection in the glass door. He was watching me closely.

The Gestapo, I thought. So, she called them after all.

The man must have realized that I had noticed him because he started to walk toward me. "Come," I said aloud. "Come finish your dirty job. It is better than this guilt, this helplessness. Just do it quickly for I am a coward and dread pain."

The man's eyebrows arched in surprise. "Who are you and what are you talking about?" he asked.

"You Nazi," I hissed with contempt.

"Stop name-calling and tell me what this is all about."

"She betrayed me!"

"*Who* did?" he asked, still puzzled.

"She promised to bring my sister from the ghetto and then she called the Gestapo."

"I am not the Gestapo," he said, "but if you have reason to expect them, let's go quickly!" His gaze lingered on my yellow star, then he tapped my hand lightly. "Now move!" Half-dazed, I started toward the door. Then he inclined his head toward me and asked urgently, "Who are you? Where do you live?"

Without thinking, I replied: "Rivka Leah Klein. I live at 1014 Vacy Utca." And I fled from the building as fast as I could.

As I hurried home, it occurred to me that by confiding in this stranger, I had put our very lives in danger. My mother's words came back to me, only too late: "A word spoken and a stone thrown are both out of control."

Jacob was waiting for me at the door. "What took you so long?" he cried. "I've been nearly out of my mind with worry!" Then he controlled himself. "But it doesn't matter now. You are home, thank God."

His concern was too much for me. My face contorted with unshed tears. I've betrayed you, my dear, I cried silently, guilt-ridden and terrified.

"What's wrong?" he asked, frightened by my expression.

"Everything. Everything is wrong. Mrs. Teleki tricked us. She grabbed the money and threw me out of her house."

"Oh, no," he exclaimed, pounding the table in impotent

rage. Then a new realization dawned on him, and his tone of voice changed. "How fortunate that you gave her a false address and your grandmother's name. At least she can't send the Gestapo after us! Oh, how did I ever let you undertake this trip? How? *Ribbono shel Olam!*"

Oh, if only you knew what I have really done, I thought to myself.

"Don't worry. We'll find someone else to bring Esther here," Jacob reassured me, assuming it was fear for my sister's safety that was troubling me. "The only thing that counts is that you are safe. We are together. You are home. Try to cheer up!"

The whole day long, Jacob tried to lift my spirits with words of comfort and encouragement. But his kind words made me feel all the more guilty. I wanted to shout at him, "Please don't be so good to me. I don't deserve it!" But my lips were sealed, no matter how difficult it was to hold back the truth from him. Instead I concentrated on listening for suspicious sounds outside. The day seemed endless, yet I dreaded the night even more. I feared the infamous Nazi tactic: the midnight knock on the door.

That night, the minute my husband fell asleep, I got dressed, so that I would be ready if they came for me. I lay in bed, paralyzed with fear, hardly daring to breathe. After what seemed like hours, I heard footsteps in the hall. "Jacob! Jacob, fast!"

"What is frightening you so?" he asked, still half-asleep.

"Somebody is coming! Quick, hide under the bed!"

There was a knock at the door. I bent down and whispered to my stunned husband, "Promise me that you will not move, no matter what happens. Do you understand?"

"What has gotten into you? Go open the door."

"No! Not until I have your promise."

"The knocking is getting louder."

"Promise," I whispered, my heart racing like a locomotive.

"I promise! Now answer the door!"

I opened the door and there stood the stranger, the man I

had seen in Mrs. Teleki's lobby. I felt the blood drain from my body. I'm going to faint, I thought. But if I do, Jacob will come out. I mustn't faint. I won't. "Please don't be frightened," the stranger said. "I come as a friend. I am sorry to have come here so late, but there was no other way." Then he added, as if it were a minor matter of no great significance, "I've come to offer my assistance in bringing your sister out of the ghetto."

"What did you say? I don't think I heard you right."

"I've come to offer my help in bringing your sister out of the ghetto," he repeated in the same, steady, calm voice.

"But why? Why should you do this for a perfect stranger?" I asked, shaking like a leaf.

"I don't know myself. I guess it broke my heart to hear you crying for your sister. To tell you the truth," he said with a touch of wonder in his voice, "I kept fighting the urge to come. I fought myself the whole day not to get involved. But this evening when I tried to get to sleep I couldn't close my eyes. I could not shut out your sobbing."

I just stood there staring at him, saying nothing, simply studying the man. His voice has the ring of truth, I thought. He has a clean, honest face. If he is trustworthy, then this is a miracle, and he is an angel sent from Heaven. I felt the suspicions and doubts evaporating from my heart. Oh, if only I could talk this over with Jacob.

"Tell me," the man asked gently, "was it Mrs. Teleki, the superintendent of the house, who reneged on her promise to bring your sister out?"

At once, all my hopes vanished. Liar! Double-crosser! Nazi murderer, I wanted to scream. I was half out of my mind with rage. How could I be so foolish as to trust a stranger again? "So, you are from the police after all!" I cried.

"No! No!" he said quickly. "I didn't mean to frighten you at all. I only asked because I thought that if you knew Mrs. Teleki, then you might also know my wife, Magda Bitter. She worked for Mr. Stern. It must have been Zsofi Teleki," he continued, more to himself than to me. "How my wife hated that woman. She hated her with a passion. Magda told me that she would do favors for Jews for a price and then curse them behind their backs." Then he looked at me again and his thoughts returned to the present. "Excuse me for not introducing myself. I am Karoly Bitter. You are shivering," he said, eyeing me with concern.

"Excuse me. Please come in and have a seat. I'll just get a sweater."

"Please do," the stranger said kindly.

I ran into the bedroom and closed the door. "Jacob, do you know a woman called Magda Bitter?"

"Who is here?"

"First answer me — do you know her or not?"

"You are acting so strangely tonight."

"Please, quickly, answer me!"

"Yes, I know her."

"Is she an anti-Semite?"

"First tell me who is here," Jacob insisted.

"Her husband, Karoly Bitter. He has offered to go to Szombathely to get Esther."

"Oh, why didn't I think of him before?" he cried, rolling out from under the bed. "It is no secret that Madga and her family are anti-Nazi." He ran into the living room in his pajamas, and I quickly followed him.

"Mr. Bitter, this is my husband, Jacob Klein," I said excitedly. The stranger's eyes lit up.

"Congratulations," he said happily. "You cheated the Nazis out of one more victim. Now let's join forces and do it again."

The two men shook hands vigorously. "Rivka Leah," Jacob said, "please put on the kettle. We could use some tea."

When I came back into the room with tea, the men were already deep in discussion. I placed the tray on the table and stepped back to absorb the scene. Everything about it seemed so unreal that I pinched my arm with all my might to make sure that I wasn't dreaming. I cried out in pain and both men jumped up at once. "I pinched myself to make sure that this is really happening," I explained to them. Mr. Bitter smiled again, his face aglow with kindness. Just then, it occurred to me what had made me blurt out my secret to him that morning. It was his sensitive face, his open, direct gaze and his unmistakable kindness. His face was an open book of good nature. "Mr. Bitter," I said, "you are a godsend."

We all began to discuss the details and arrangements for Karoly's trip. "Leichi," my husband asked, "how can we convince your family that Karoly can be trusted?"

"As frightened as they must be, that will pose quite a problem," Karoly agreed. Suddenly his face lit up. "Rivka Leah," he asked, "is there any saying or code word among your family that they would recognize?"

"When they say, 'I met Gitta,' " Jacob volunteered, "it means, 'Be quiet, someone is eavesdropping.' "

An expression of relief crossed Karoly's face. "Fine. Tell me more."

I took the tablecloth off the table and began to fold it neatly. "Here, take this. Esther embroidered it for us as a wedding present."

"Perfect," Karoly said. "She'll surely recognize it and it will dispel any doubts they may have about me." He glanced at his wristwatch. "Oh, my!" he exclaimed. "I must be running right now or I'll miss the train." He closed his suitcase and walked hastily to the door.

"Wait!" I called out.

"Sorry, there is no time. I must be on my way." He slammed the door and was gone.

"Jacob, please run after him!" I cried, chills running up and down my spine. "Don't let him go! What do we know about this man?" My voice rose as I became more and more frantic. "Who is this stranger we've trusted with my sister? My God, who is he?"

Jacob did his best to try and calm me but I refused to listen. "You're the one who told me," I ranted on, "that it's written that as long as a man is unknown we must consider him equally likely to be a demon or a saint."

"It's true," he replied, "that's what *Chazal* say. They mean that in our daily affairs we should be equally fair to all." Handing me my *siddur*, he said, "This is true in normal times. However, in these extraordinary times when we are gambling for such high stakes, we have to take every chance we find, and then we still have to pray for mercy."

21

IT WAS WELL PAST midnight when the train pulled into the station at Szombathely. As he disembarked, Karoly realized just how uneasy he felt about arriving in this unfamiliar place in the dark of the night. Although he had no idea which way to go, he didn't dare ask directions for fear of calling attention to himself. He knew that in the eyes of the law he was a criminal, and consequently, he tried his best to avoid being noticed.

He began walking in the direction he thought most likely, according to the Kleins' hasty instructions. He stopped at the first blacked-out lamppost and lit a cigarette, thinking that he might find a street sign there. In the flickering light of the match he made out the words "Szel Kalman Utca" painted on a small blue plaque. Good, he thought. Now just by counting the blocks I will be able to find my way.

He walked through alleyways and down winding streets, until he came to the synagogue in the courtyard of which Esty Einhorn lived with her aunt Brandl. He was jubilant at having located the building without anyone's assistance. Recalling Rivka Leah's description, he noticed that there were three entrances to the courtyard: one on Thokoly Imre Utca and two on Brenner Janos Utca. The second of those two led straight to Brandl's front door. But to his dismay, Karoly discovered that all three entrances were locked and there wasn't a living soul in sight.

It began to drizzle. How shall I handle this, Karoly pondered, without attracting attention to myself? The drizzle quickly turned into a downpour. Soon he was drenched and shivering. A baby's cries pierced the quiet of the night, followed by another, and then, yet another and another. Infants wailed, older children screamed and mothers tried in vain to pacify their frightened tykes. I will never get in, he realized, unless I do something drastic. Then Rivka Leah's words came back to him: "This is the last chance we have to free my sister. The ghetto will be sealed tomorrow night. Karoly, you've miraculously come to help us at the very last minute."

Without further consideration, he scooped up a handful of pebbles and tossed them at the nearest window. There was no response. "Poor things," he murmured to himself. "How I must be frightening them. They must think that a gang of anti-Semitic youths has come to attack them. But what else can I do to make myself known?" He saw a window open slightly. Someone had heard him!

"Please open the door," Karoly whispered. "I've come to see somebody. I am a friend."

"Who do you want to see?"the shadow in the window asked suspiciously.

"Esty Einhorn."

"Wait." Soon he heard movement behind the locked entrance and then a small, frightened voice asked, "What do you want of her?"

"I have a message for her from her sister and her sister's husband."

"What are their names?"

"Jacob and Rivka Leah Klein." He heard the click of a lock, and then the entrance gate swung open. "Come in fast!" the woman hissed. As soon as he was inside the courtyard, she said in hushed tones, "I am Nechy Leitner, Esty's sister. Please wait here until Esty and I wake my aunt. They share their bedroom with six strangers and I don't want them all to know that you are here."

With that, she disappeared from sight. A minute later she reappeared, carrying an umbrella which she quickly handed to him. "I beg your forgiveness for not inviting you indoors right away, but the front room is full of sleeping children and if they were to wake up while I was in the back room with my aunt and find themselves alone with a stranger, it would frighten them no end. You'd be surprised," she added with a sigh. "As young as they are, they understand so much."

It occurred to Karoly that she was making excuses. She herself doesn't trust me, he thought, and as God is my witness, I don't blame her. He shivered in his wet clothes. Standing in the blackness, he listened to the sounds of the ghetto, where human beings were thrown together and heaped up like parcels of goods. "The throbbing of the ghetto," he muttered, as feelings of shame and anger overwhelmed him. The noise! The crying and moaning, the coughing and screaming — it all merged into one dreadful din which chilled his soul. And the stench, he thought with disgust. If Dante were alive today, this is surely how he would describe hell. And to think that this Gehenna was made by men for their own brothers. God in Heaven, please forgive our sins!

Karoly was startled out of his thoughts when someone tapped on his shoulder. It was Nechy. "Come in, please," she said quietly. He entered the apartment and saw an elderly woman in a long, old-fashioned, black dress standing next to a beautiful young girl. From under her thick, black brows, the girl's emerald-green eyes scrutinized him. He could see the fear shining in them.

"My aunt Brandl and my sister Esty," Nechy said softly.

"Karoly, Karoly Bitter." The women acknowledged him with a nod. Karoly looked around the crowded little room. He noticed two small boys sleeping side by side on a mattress on the floor. There was an awkward silence. He realized that they were all waiting for him to speak. Karoly cleared his throat. "I am a friend of Jacob and Rivka Leah. They asked me to take Esty out of the ghetto." Then he handed Esty a letter. "They sent this for you."

"Aunt Brandl, you read it please," Esty said, quickly handing it to the older woman.

"I can't," Aunt Brandl protested. "I left my glasses in the other room." She passed the letter to Nechy, who read it over several times. Then the three women retired to a corner and began to discuss what to do. They spoke in Yiddish, which Karoly didn't understand, so he was left to his own thoughts again. Let them talk, let it sink in, he said to himself, as he watched them out of the corner of his eye. After a minute or so, he took the tablecloth out of his valise and held it up high for them to see. "I brought this as proof that your sister sent me," he explained. "Rivka Leah told me that Esty made this as a wedding present for her. And Jacob told me the meaning of 'I saw Gitta.'" Laughter filled the room. He had finally broken the ice.

Nechy headed for the back room. "Come on," she said, glancing over her shoulder at Esty. "I'll help you pack."

"No! I'm not going."

"What do you mean?" Nechy asked, astonished.

"I won't go!" Esty repeated, her eyes filling with tears. "How can I leave Aunt Brandl when all of her sons are away at work-camp? I'm the only one she has now, and besides," she added, throwing her head back defiantly, "what is good enough for you and Aunt Brandl is good enough for me, too." Then she fell on the old woman's shoulder and started to cry bitterly.

Aunt Brandl stroked Esty's hair and held her close. "Please don't ask me what you should do," she whispered. "I can't tell you." But a moment later she was able to say with determination, "Go, my lamb. Go try your luck."

"I think," Karoly said, "that your sister needs you very badly now. She is expecting her baby any day."

"She is alone, without any help," Nechy urged. "You can't

let her down." Without waiting for Esty's reply, she began to remove her little sister's belongings from the closet.

"Here," Karoly offered. "Put those things in my valise. That's why I brought it." Then he turned to Esty. "Here are your new identification papers," he said, as he handed her the documents. "Memorize your Hungarian name, and the names of your forebears, too," he instructed her.

"Anna Shipoc," she murmured, still bewildered, as she read the name on the papers. Before she had a chance to think about what was happening to her, Karoly motioned to her, and they slipped out into the darkness.

As Nechy locked the courtyard gate behind them, Karoly said, "Remember, Esty, if anything happens, we don't know each other! It won't help you and it would incriminate me unnecessarily. I have a wife whom I love and a darling daughter of six months whom I adore. So I'll walk behind you and I won't sit near you in the train compartment either."

"Just please tell me which streetcar to take to find their apartment," she breathed faintly, "in case we get separated."

That night was one of the longest and most harrowing ever for both travelers. But when Karoly and Esty finally arrived at the Kleins' house, the joy that everyone felt at their reunion made up for all the tension and misery of the night before. "Oh, Karoly, you did it! You did it!"

They were all seated at the kitchen table about to drink some coffee when Jacob exclaimed, "Oh, Karoly! What a disgrace! We've all forgotten how your wife must be worrying about you! Please call her."

"There's no need to call," Karoly said. "She knows nothing of my trip last night."

"Why not?" they asked in unison.

"My wife Magda and our darling little Macika are staying with my parents outside the city. I see them only on weekends. I have to admit that I hate this arrangement and so does my Magda, but we have no alternative. You see, we haven't lived in our own apartment during the entire two years of our marriage. Until last year we lived with Magda's parents. Then a succession of misfortunes occurred. Magda's father died suddenly and her mother moved in with her eldest daughter on the outskirts of town, leaving her rented apartment to us. But the landlady appropriated the apartment for her daughter, whose husband was fighting at the front. Legally, we hadn't a chance. The court awarded the apartment to her and out we went. And since you live in Budapest, I don't have to tell you how difficult it is to find an apartment here."

"I'm so sorry to hear this," Jacob said. "I only wish that our apartment were bigger so that we could accommodate you and your family."

"I wish so too," Karoly replied. "I miss them terribly and I can't see any way out of this predicament." He stopped speaking and gazed into space, looking sad and defeated.

"You know," Rivka Leah said, "I would never have imagined that you, a genuine Aryan, had *any* problems." Karoly looked surprised and hurt by her comment. "What I mean to say," she continued, "is that when sickness or any other calamity strikes someone, he becomes so preoccupied with his own problems that he imagines that those who are spared that particular curse live like fairy-tale princes, 'happily ever after.'"

"Rivka Leah, war touches everyone," Jacob remarked, "Jew and Aryan alike."

22

STANDING INSIDE the courtyard, Nechy prayed for the safety of her sister: "May God bless you and watch over you; may the light of His Face shine toward you; and may He send you Peace." She began reciting *Tehillim* as she walked toward the house, and she asked herself over and over, "Was I right to make Esty leave against her wishes? Was I?"

Her thoughts were interrupted by the sound of her brother Chaim's voice. "Nechy!" he called anxiously from the doorway. "Where have you been? Avromi was crying for you. Don't worry, he went back to sleep, but when I couldn't find you, I was concerned."

"Shh, even the walls have ears. Let's go into the kitchen and I'll tell you what happened." Once inside, Nechy told Chaim the story of Karoly's visit.

He was quiet for a while. "Nechy," he began, "you must calm down and try to go back to sleep. I'll stay up and recite *Tehillim*. All we can do now is pray."

Chaim paced the floor of the tiny room, quietly reciting one psalm after another. After a while he noticed Nechy sitting up in bed, her eyes wide open. "Chaim, listen," she whispered. "I want to talk to you." They walked to a far corner of the room and stood by the window. "Do you remember," she asked him, "how upset Shimon was when he told us about the things Jacob predicted would happen to us?"

"Yes," Chaim replied, recalling their brother's angry reaction to Jacob's warnings.

She stood very still with her back to her two sleeping little boys. She can't face them, Chaim thought, because everything Jacob predicted has come to pass.

The tension in the air was palpable. "They are burning our people alive!" she cried out. Chaim didn't answer, and Nechy fell silent. Moments passed, and then she continued. "Chaim," she said in a voice so soft that he had to strain his ears to hear her, "for you there may be a chance."

"What do you mean?"

"You must enlist in work-camp."

"How can you possibly suggest this to me, when you know full well the situation there? And why should I volunteer when boys in my age group haven't even been called yet?"

"I know, but don't you see? Most Aryan men are in the army, and there is still a lot of work that needs to be done behind the lines. Jewish men are valuable. As long as there is a need for laborers, our men won't be turned away." Nechy looked down and studied her work-worn hands. Then she went on. "Look around you, Chaim. Who do you see here in the ghetto?"

"To tell you the truth, I never really thought about it."

"All right, then I'll tell you." Her voice began to quaver. "The old and the very young, the women, the infirm, and the little children..." The last word stuck in her throat. She couldn't bring herself to talk about the children.

They stood at the window looking out into the dark, rainy night, debating the soundness of Nechy's proposal. A sliver of moonlight shone into the room, illuminating Nechy's face and emphasizing its wanness. I never realized before how terrible she looks, Chaim thought. What a curse it is to know everything. But even if Shimon hadn't told her what Jacob had said, she would surely have figured things out for herself. For everyone knows that of all us Einhorns, Nechy is the most clever.

Then in the moonlight Chaim noticed the fear clearly reflected in his sister's eyes. "What is it?" he asked in alarm.

"I talked so freely without making you promise that you won't repeat what I said."

"Don't worry. I promise."

"You must understand," she insisted. "It would only add to the suffering."

"It's alright. I understand completely."

The next morning, Chaim hurried to *shul* to join the five other teenaged boys he learned with regularly. They met at six A.M. every day and they had become inseparable. When he arrived, his friends were all seated and ready to begin learning. Majs was the first to see him. "Chaim!" he exclaimed. "What's wrong? You look like you've just seen a ghost!"

Chaim casually dismissed his friend's comment. "It's just a bad headache." Then, after making sure that nobody else was listening, he whispered breathlessly, "I have an idea I have to tell all of you about, but it's too private a matter to discuss here. It's an emergency, a matter of life and death. Let's meet tonight at midnight in the basement of the school building and we'll talk. Will you come?" Wide-eyed, they all nodded their agreement. "But remember — not a word to anyone!"

The *shul*, which once was packed to capacity, was now almost empty. Gone were the scholars, the *talmidim*. No one came, save some adolescent boys and a few old men who mostly sat and stared into nothingness with only their memories to comfort them. Nevertheless, they came every morning, just as they had done since they were bar mitzvah, to learn Torah before starting their workday. And when they gathered together to pray, pray they did because their hearts were heavy with pain and their minds dark with worry.

By nightfall, the courtyard of the *shul* was always dark and silent. The occupants of the ghetto locked themselves in their houses, never daring to set foot outside for even a moment. For them, darkness meant danger. There was always danger in the ghetto, but the darkness brought out the SS youth. They came with stones and pebbles to taunt and maim their poor victims, who were vulnerable and totally defenseless.

On this particular night, however, doors opened and shadow-like figures quickly made their way to a certain basement. All six of them arrived on time. Five of the boys waited impatiently for their friend to reveal the reason for their meeting.

Minutes passed. Then Chaim stood up and faced the others. "My sister Esty has escaped from the ghetto," he began, "with the help of an Aryan friend of my brother-in-law's. She should be in Budapest already, where she hopes to hide out under a false identity with Rivka Leah and Jacob. Last night, I had a long talk with my sister Nechy. I won't repeat our discussion word for word, but what it basically comes down to is that she's urging me to run away too, because, in her words," he paused briefly before continuing," 'we will all go from the ghetto into Hitler's ovens to be burned alive.' I'm asking you to join me in my escape."

"What?" Majs whispered angrily. "My mother, my sisters and brothers? Murdered? Why, your sister and all who believe her must be mad!"

"Let's leave our families out of it!" Chaim cried. "I believe everything Nechy said, and whoever doubts it, is free to leave." A heavy silence followed. "If you want to think about it," he went on, "go ahead. I can wait."

"No," they answered immediately. "We're all with you. Please talk."

"Well, I don't know where or how to begin. That's why I called you here — to discuss an escape plan. We have to find a way!"

Shmuel was the first to speak. "I have an idea," he whispered. "Who says we have to escape from the ghetto? We can hide right here in our own town."

"Fine," Nochem replied angrily. "And we'll parade in the

streets where everybody knows us and tell the authorities that we just didn't feel like staying in the ghetto!"

"No, no! Let me talk," Shmuel insisted. "What I mean is that we can use this very basement as a bunker." A long, heavy silence followed his words and all five boys stared at him in wonder.

"I see!" Majs exclaimed. "Oh, Shmuel, what a brilliant idea! And I know just where we can hide. Now follow me. Come, let's join hands so that none of us gets lost in the dark."

"Where are we going?" Nochem asked.

"Just follow me," Majs replied abruptly. He led them as they slowly made their way in the darkness. The air was charged with suspense. Finally Majs stopped. "I hope it's not locked," he murmured to himself. He felt the wall with his hands. "Here we are!"

"Where?"

"You've all been here before. In elementary school, we used to run to this room during recess time to ask Mr. Fisher for pieces of matzah. In other words," he said triumphantly, "we're in the matzah bakery! Here, this is the oven," he added, tapping on it lightly.

"How did you ever find this place in the dark?" Chaim asked, impressed.

"Oh, I could have found it even in my sleep," he chuckled. "Now don't laugh, but as a kid I used to lie awake nights worrying about this oven. I used to imagine that this was the same oven where the wicked witches of the fairy tales would drag little children and bake them for their supper. And I used to think that the white wall behind the matzah oven concealed the place where the witches lived. How it used to frighten me! I would never dare to go near it as a child. But one year I unwittingly went into the room behind that wall, and I was most surprised to find that there weren't any witches perched on broomsticks. There were just boxes of matzos stacked on shelves which lined the walls."

His words were met with fierce denial. "We never saw a

door," they all insisted, not believing a word of his childish story.

"All right, then let me tell you how it happened and you can decide for yourselves. I was nine years old and things were very bad in our house financially. Pesach was approaching, and the high cost of matzah and wine put an added strain on my father, who had saved pennies, with my mother's help, in order to buy food for *Yom Tov.* His motto was: Nobody has to know what's going on in our house. It was because of his pride that I learned about the existence of the hidden room.

"We went to pick up the matzah only a few days before Pesach. I remember Papa telling Mr. Fisher how busy he was and how he had almost no time to come for the matzah. Despite his cheerful tone, I could hear the fear in his voice as he inquired, looking around the bakery, 'Are you all sold out?'

"'Would I ever forget about you?' Mr. Fisher said jovially, as he patted my father on the back. 'Come, I'll show you.'

"My father followed him and I tagged along, staring in fascination at the large key ring which was attached to Mr. Fisher's belt and which jangled with each step he took. I watched with wonder as he sorted through the various shapes and sizes of keys until he finally found the one he wanted. Then he pushed away the row of white bakers' uniforms hanging on the wall, and opened a door behind them.

"It wasn't until we were already in the room 'where the witches lived' that I realized where we were. Mr. Fisher pointed to the top of a shelf where we could see our own name marked on one of the neatly wrapped packages of matzah. 'I never knew that there was another room back here,' my father exclaimed. Mr. Fisher smiled. 'This is where we store the unclaimed matzos until they're picked up.' My father looked at him questioningly. 'It prevents a lot of arguments with people who decide at the last minute that they want to buy more,' he explained. 'I can tell them that there isn't any more, as they can see, and I can keep the reserved packages back here where they will be out of sight. With that, Majs finished his story.

The reaction of the boys was immediate excitement. "And you know what I suggest?" Majs said jubilantly. "Since the secret room is right behind the matzah oven, we can seal off the hidden door altogether, and break the wall of the oven to make a tunnel. I can just see it: we'll have a secret tunnel leading to our bunker!"

Hushed excitement followed his words. The boys applauded and shook each others' hands. "What a brainstorm! What a lucky find!" they congratulated Majs.

"And we can dig a tunnel from our room to the *mikveh* across the alley!" Nochem suggested.

"Do we all agree that it is 'our room?'" Majs asked. "Are we all in this together?"

"Yes, yes! Of course!" they all replied.

"Fine. Then let's go home while it's still dark and no one can see us."

"Just one more thing," Nochem said. "We *must* dig that tunnel. If we can reach the bathhouse, that will solve our water and lavatory problem."

"Before we leave," Boruch, the youngest of them all, suggested, "we must pledge secrecy."

"Yes," Majs agreed. "Later we will need our parents' help, but until then no one is allowed to talk before getting permission from us all."

The boys promised not to breathe a word of their plan to anyone. Then Shmuel spoke. "Let's be here first thing tomorrow morning with hammers and chisels to see if our tunnel theory holds up in practice." They all agreed. "And one more thing. Let's keep our eyes open for spare blankets and any other supplies that we might need while we're hiding out."

With that, the six boys stepped out into the schoolyard and were immediately swallowed up by the darkness.

All except Chaim arrived home unnoticed. When he entered the house, he saw Nechy sitting by the window, waiting for him to return.

"Nechy, why are you awake?" Chaim asked. Then it

occurred to him that she already understood why he had been out so late. "You know, don't you?"

"It's alright," she answered. "I just couldn't sleep. Did you decide upon anything?"

"Nechy, I..." Chaim began haltingly. "I'm embarrassed to answer you like this, but we all pledged secrecy. I have to ask permission from the group to talk to you even though you initiated the whole thing. Will you please forgive me? Tomorrow, when I come home from *shul*, I'll tell you everything. Now please go to sleep."

Chaim could tell by Nechy's expression that she was very pleased with his decision. "I am happy to see how sensibly you are conducting yourselves, and whatever you've decided, I must congratulate you. Chaim, do you realize that tonight you took the first step? Do you understand what that means?" Nechy said, carried away with enthusiasm.

"Only the first step is hard," Chaim replied, repeating an oft-quoted phrase from his childhood, "because that one you have to take alone. But with the second step, your strength is boundless because God walks with the one who puts his faith in Him. Papa and Mama always used to tell us that." Nechy nodded, and they both turned to go to sleep for what was left of the night.

23

I DIDN'T NEED my mother-in-law to tell me when it was time to go to the hospital, as I had feared I would. I knew on my own after all.

At five forty-five A.M., on May 13, 1944, I was admitted to City Hospital in Budapest. After a short wait, a young girl motioned to me to follow her into an adjacent room. Soon a tall, henna-haired nurse entered the room.

"This is Dr. Rona's patient," the young girl explained to her and quickly left.

My heart froze as I studied the nurse's expression. "Yanku," I whispered, "look at her face! It's so cold and unfeeling!"

"It only appears that way because the color of her hair makes her complexion seem so sallow. Don't anticipate trouble where there is none," he said, trying to calm me.

But when the woman stood in front of us, she looked at us with such open contempt that Jacob himself was frightened.

"Can I go in with my wife?" he asked nervously.

The nurse laughed, her face a mask of ice. "Only you," she ordered, pointing to me menacingly. Reluctantly, I followed her. My worst fears had been re[illegible]d: just when I so much needed a kind soul near me, I [illegible]n into the hands of a bitter anti-Semite.

It was late afternoon, after almost a full day of labor, and the cruel woman had left me to suffer alone for most of that time. When she returned I finally mustered the strength and courage to ask if my doctor would be arriving soon.

"Your doctor!" she sneered. "I never called him." Her face was distorted with hatred. She pressed an instrument to my stomach and held it there for several moments as she listened for signs of life within. "We have a complication," she said, a malicious smile spreading across her face. "I don't hear your baby's heartbeat any longer. It's as good as dead and so are you! And I don't intend to call your doctor until I'm sure that it's too late to save either one of you. Ha, Jew! You thought you'd have a picnic here, didn't you? Well, you might as well enjoy your rest in bed, because it will be your last!" And laughing at her own vile words, she strode out, leaving me all alone again.

The pain was excruciating and constant, but I was beyond feeling or caring any longer. The nurse's words reverberated in my head: "Your baby is as good as dead and so are you!" My thoughts were racing. I must alert my doctor. I must! If only I could talk to my husband. But I was lying in a bed with high siderails.

I felt trapped and uttery helpless. Then I noticed that the nurse had neglected to pull the bars all the way up on one side of my bed. An idea began to form in my mind, and the realization that I was fighting for my baby's life as well as my own gave me the strength to act.

I ignored the unbearable pain. Quickly! I urged myself. Before she comes back! Somehow I climbed off the bed and hurried into the hall, holding my short gown tightly to my body with one hand and biting the other so as not to cry out in pain. I headed straight for the staircase. My husband was standing at the foot of the steps, praying from his *siddur*. Startled by the footfalls, he looked up. Immediately, I put my finger to my lips. He understood, quickly kicked off his shoes so as not to make any noise and then bounded up the stairs without a sound.

"Call my doctor!" I urged hysterically. "The nurse won't call him and he has no idea that I'm here, and she says that our baby and I are in mortal danger."

Jacob didn't need to hear more; he made a beeline for the phone while I bolted for my bed. A few minutes later, he peeked into the entrance to my room and as our eyes met, he nodded reassuringly. He held up his two hands, indicating that my doctor would be arriving in ten minutes; then he disappeared from sight just before the nurse came in through a side door.

She listened again to the baby's heartbeat. "We're getting there," she said smugly. I looked at the large clock opposite my bed. It was six-fifty P.M.

In less than ten minutes I heard the sound of running feet in the hall. Dr. Rona burst through the door, his face flushed and his chest heaving. Startled by his sudden appearance, the nurse stood at attention. "I was just going to call you, Doctor," she said, flustered. "It seems that we're running into some difficulties."

Dr. Rona hastily put on his white coat. The door opened again and a heavyset man carrying a black physician's bag walked in. "Thank you for coming," Dr. Rona said to him as he quickly scrubbed his hands at the sink. Then he turned to me. "This is our pediatrician. He's the best there is, so relax, my dear. We'll take good care of you."

Again, the door opened and a third doctor entered. It was the anesthesiologist. He was at my bedside in an instant, setting up equipment. "I'm going to put you to sleep," he explained soothingly. "I will put this mask over your face. When I do, just inhale and start counting."

Then, amidst the commotion, I heard Dr. Rona cry out jubilantly, "Mrs. Klein! Can you hear me? I found your baby's heartbeat!" I relaxed and inhaled the ether deeply.

When I next opened my eyes, I saw Dr. Rona holding the most beautiful baby I had ever seen. Her tiny face was red, her hair was black and nearly shoulder-length, and her eyes were wide open. She was looking directly at me. "She recognizes me!" I cried. "Oh, doctor, is this my baby?"

"Yes, of course," he replied, his face glowing with pleasure. "This is your baby daughter. She is beautiful and perfectly healthy," he declared as he gently placed my little girl in my outstretched arms.

My heart filled with a joy I never knew existed. The room became bright and I felt as if I were floating to the heavens on a cloud. But then my head started throbbing, and I imagined that I heard a thousand voices shouting from the street below: "Heil Hitler." It brought me back to the harsh realities of our times, and yet the love and the joy I felt continued unabated.

My unsuspecting daughter lay snuggled in my arms, resting calmly and securely, and I murmured gratefully to her, "Thank you for being born a girl and for not putting any obstacles in the way of our plans for hiding out." (I knew that if the baby had been a boy, we could never claim he was a Gentile, for his body would bear the irrevocable mark of a Jew.)

24

May 14, 1944. Hours after my daughter's birth, I was transferred to the maternity ward, where I share a large, airy room with three other first-time mothers. All of them, I was happy to learn, are Jewish. Little bassinets stand next to our beds and in them lie the most beautiful babies in the world. Of course, it isn't hard to determine which one is really the prettiest; you just have to ask one of the experts: the mothers. I am very relieved to have my baby by my side all the time. Not trusting the hospital staff, I don't want her out of my sight.

May 15, 1944. All day long, my roommates chattered on about the usual problems of adjusting to motherhood, but I didn't participate in those discussions. Nothing interests me. I just lie for hours with my baby in my arms, facing the wall. I feel as though my heart is breaking. Will we be able to shield her from the evil plotted against her?

May 16, 1944. I begged Dr. Rona to release us, for I live in constant dread of the nurses. The treatment I received in the labor room left me with great doubts about our safety in the hospital. I worry constantly: what if that horrid nurse tries to take revenge on us for foiling her plans? Dr. Rona did his best to allay my fears, but he refused to make an exception in my case. He feels that it is in our best interest to stay the ten-day minimum in the hospital. So the days drag on endlessly, with nothing to do but worry and fret. In contrast, two of my roommates, Olga and Elena, actually appear to be enjoying their stay. Today it seemed that the whole city turned out to visit them.

Early in the afternoon, Jacob came to visit. He was unusually pale. "She is gorgeous," he exclaimed, gazing at our daughter with pride, but his face was haggard and fear was visible in his usually laughing eyes. "Look at this," he said, trying to be cheerful as he showed me our baby's new, forged birth certificate.

"Little Zsuzsi," I whispered. "Who filled it in?" But before he had time to answer, I confronted him: "You shouldn't be coming here and risking being arrested on the street by the SS." I urged him to leave right away and not visit me again while I was in the hospital. Reluctantly, he rose from his chair. "Please," I begged him, "take care of yourself. You owe it to our daughter." As he was walking out the door, I called after him, "This time, don't forget to send a newspaper with Esty when she comes to visit me, and remember to stay indoors. Don't take any chances with your safety."

Esty came to visit me this evening, and we sat and talked, mostly about the baby. A short while later, my roommate Olga received a surprise visit from her husband. "I have a furlough for the night," he breathed excitedly, marveling at the tiny blue bundle in his arms.

Just then, I remembered the newspaper that I had asked Jacob to send with Esty. "May I see today's newspaper?" I asked her.

"Oh, I must have forgotten it," Esty answered in a low voice, looking the other way.

"Here, read this, Rivka Leah," Olga said, handing me the newspaper her husband had brought her.

"Thanks," I replied. "I'll read it after my sister leaves."

"It's alright. I really must be going now anyway," Esty said hastily, and she stood up abruptly and left.

I was puzzled by her strange behavior, but as soon as I saw the headlines, I understood. In large print, the headlines screamed at me, announcing the depopulation of the Jews from one of the most densely Jewish-populated cities. Starting tonight, the Jews were to be deported for three consecutive days, after which most heavily Jewish-populated cities would be *Judenrein*.

So that's it, I thought, still staring at the paper. This is why Jacob and Esty have continually "forgotten" to bring me a newspaper. They wanted to shield me from this nightmare. Anger rose in my heart. The last thing I want is to be pampered. I was overwhelmed with sorrow, but it was still better to cry and suffer with my tortured brethren, to share their pain, to lament their innocently shed blood and charred bodies than to live in ignorance. "Oh, my Lord, have mercy upon us!" I cried helplessly.

By then everyone had read the paper and the room was in chaos. Agitated voices echoed all around me; some penetrated my consciousness while others seemed to wash over me, incomprehensible. I became aware that everyone was speculating on the likelihood of a deportation from Budapest, and they were discussing who would be deported and who would take care of their infants in their absence. Then I recalled that the Nazis were spreading the word that middle-aged parents would be in charge of the very young and of the very old, while every able-bodied young man and woman would work to support them. Anger flooded through me again. They believe the Nazis' lies! I thought. They have no idea whatsoever!

"Please," I cried out, "don't believe them! They will kill us in Germany. That's why they are deporting us in the first place. Please, if they set up a ghetto here in Budapest, try to hide, try to get false identification papers. Save your lives! Don't go into the ghetto if there is any way you can avoid it! Please! Heed my advice!"

My words were met with outrage. "No!" Evelin, the girl in the bed next to me, shouted indignantly. "I would never lower myself to do such a shameful thing. Why, you are suggesting that I remove myself from the fate of my people. Never! Whatever fate befalls them I accept on myself gladly."

Olga was also incensed. Her shock was boundless. "Of all the people I know," she declared, "you are the last person I would have expected to make such a statement. Now I can see that we have nothing in common after all."

Her comments puzzled me. "Why, what do you mean?" I asked her.

"Here you are, the only observant Jew among us. That you should want to separate yourself from our people in their darkest hours, just when the rest of us are beginning to appreciate our common bond — well, that is beyond my understanding."

Elena, a Jewish girl who had converted and married an Aryan, was furious, too. "Even I, who never considered myself a Jew, let alone a religious one, now have an insatiable longing to come back to my people, to share in their misfortunes. I now identify with them in their hour of darkness. I want to yell, 'I am also a Jew! I am with you!' "

"So why don't you do it?" I challenged her in anger.

"Because...because of my son," she answered, blushing with shame.

"But don't you realize that, by the laws of the Nazis, you are considered a Jew anyway?"

"Yes," she said, weeping. "But my father-in-law has taken me under his protection, and he is a very influential man."

"Fools!" I shouted at them. "Hopeless fools! Why is it so noble to suffer, to make yourselves martyrs for nothing? If it were a choice between giving up your life or bowing to an idol, that would be different, for the Torah *obligates* a Jew to give up his life in such a situation. But to throw your lives away just because some vicious anti-Semite has decided he wants to kill you, is madness. And you should know that according to Torah law, one is obligated to preserve and to fight for one's life, and never, never give it up freely."

Then I faced Elena. "You had ample time to identify with the Jewish people when times were good, and yet you turned away from them. Well, that is beyond *my* understanding." Suddenly a thought occurred to me. "Lord in Heaven," I cried out as though bitten by a viper, "is this the reason You are letting us suffer so much? To remind us that we are Jews? To make us remember where we belong and to bring us back to You? It seems that we forget You when we are happy and return to You only when we're in pain, just like animals that edge closer to each other in times of danger." Then I turned to my roommates. "You should have shown your solidarity with our people when times were good," I exclaimed angrily. "The real depth of kinship and friendship is measured by one's ability to rejoice in another's happiness. Sharing sorrow and offering loyalty only when times are bad has value, but it mustn't be used as a yardstick for love or true loyalty."

"You have a point," Evelin said, hardly above a whisper. "You know, my grandparents were very religious people. Oh, how my grandfather used to beg me not to turn my back on their customs. And my dear grandmother was always trying to bring me to her house on Friday evenings so that I could see her light the Sabbath candles, hoping to influence me to follow her in her religious ways."

"I understand," I said. I looked at her with sympathy then, for tears were rolling down her cheeks unchecked. "But what your grandparents could not accomplish with love, with begging and with tears, Hitler has accomplished with a whip."

25

May 17, 1944. Elena went home today. She was very excited. "My dress fits me, it really does!" she bubbled, delighted that she was able to wear her flowered summer frock. "It's my husband's favorite," she explained, smiling brightly. "Soon, he will come to pick me up." But instead of her husband, her mother-in-law came for her. The moment she arrived the two women moved to a corner of the room and began a heated discussion. Minutes passed, and then I heard Elena say, "Alright, Mama. It's alright with me."

"Then stay here while I check you out at the nurse's desk," her mother-in-law told her.

Elena approached my bed. "It is really bad," she said in a low voice. "Next week they're setting up a ghetto in our town. The baby and I will be hiding out at the home of one of my husband's relatives. My husband is there now, waiting for us. My mother-in-law came here in his place because she feels that it is not advisable for us to be seen together in public."

A few minutes later, Elena's mother-in-law returned to our room. "Elena dear," she said, "the car is ready and waiting." Elena followed her meekly, staring at the floor.

May 18, 1944. Dr. Rona and Esty met in the hall and walked into my room together. After holding my baby for a minute or so, he placed her in my sister's arms. Esty's face lit up. "Little Faygele," she crooned happily over and over again. Jacob had named our baby in *shul* just this morning. She was named after our mother.

"Think of it," Esty exclaimed as she pressed the precious little pink bundle to her, "if not for Karoly, I would have missed this moment." She was radiant. I offered a silent prayer of thanks to God that Esty had found herself with this little daughter of mine. Since her arrival in Budapest, she hadn't stopped berating herself for yielding to Nechy and Karoly and leaving our aunt when she felt that Brandl needed her most.

May 19, 1944. Talk, talk, talk! Olga and Evelin don't stop, not for a minute. Their chatter doesn't bother me so much any more since the two women have finally learned to respect my wish for privacy. But tonight, after the last visitor left our room, I heard Evelin call me. "Rivka Leah," she whispered. "I think you were right the other day." I simply stared at her, having no idea what she was referring to. "I mean," she stammered, "what you said about the herd of frightened animals. It reminds me of an experience I had as a child. Let me tell you about it.

"My grandparents," she began, "lived in the country. I am a city girl, born right here in this hospital, but I would visit them from time to time. Needless to say, I was not well-acquainted with daily life on a farm. Well, one day during one of those visits, I was walking down a narrow road leading to my grandparents' house, when I heard an unfamiliar sound behind me. I turned around and saw a large herd of cattle coming home from the pasture. I can never describe the terror I felt when I saw hundreds of cows walking toward me. At first I just stood there, frozen with fear. Then I noticed a sturdy tree off to the side of the road, and I quickly climbed it and got myself out of the way of the moving disaster.

"Soon, I caught my breath and watched in awe as the

bodies of the cattle shimmered in the setting sun. I looked around and noticed that the gates to each farm were left ajar. As the herd continued walking I was amazed to see that each cow walked without hesitation into the yard of its owner. 'They are so smart,' I marveled. 'They know their addresses, they really do.'

"Suddenly, a boy about my age, barefoot and dressed in old work pants, ran out of one of the houses, pursued by his angry mother, who ran after him scolding and swearing loudly. Poor boy! He almost managed to escape her wrath, but the herd of cattle got in his way. The woman caught up with him and kept smacking him until her anger died down.

"In his frustration, the boy picked up a handful of pebbles and began to throw them right into the middle of the herd.

"My heart skipped a beat with fright. I imagined that the startled animals would run around wildly, carrying the tree and me with them. But, to my complete surprise, just the opposite happened. The herd stopped without warning as the first stone landed. It stopped with such suddenness that the whole earth seemed to tremble. And with each subsequent stone, the cattle moved closer and closer together as though they were trying to give comfort to one another and declare unity against their enemy.

"Now I understand the parallel between the herd and us Jews."

May 20, 1944. My Uncle Yidel and my brothers-in-law came to see the baby today. I was both shocked and hurt to see what a change has come over them in the past few days. Pain and despair were in their eyes as they viewed my innocent little darling. I shuddered at the thought of the risks they had taken to make this visit. "Please," I begged them, "go home and stay put. You know how dangerous it is for Jewish men to be out on the streets of Budapest."

"Who cares?" Uncle Yidel replied sadly. "We have all lost

our families. There is nothing left for us to live for anymore." Slowly, he rose from his chair to leave. The others followed suit.

I realized that my words meant little to them, but nevertheless I felt obligated to warn them. "But you might be stopped to have your papers checked," I continued. "And then your fates would be sealed, since you are all evading the draft."

"Not anymore," Unde Yidel replied flatly. "We have all registered."

I could hardly believe my ears. "You can't!" I cried. "You must never set foot in the work-camps!" But my protests were lost on them. Before I had a chance to say more, they turned to go. Heads bowed, they murmured their good-byes. In a moment they were gone.

This afternoon Esty came to visit. "Zsuzsi!" she called out, her green eyes shining.

Startled, I looked up. "What are you so excited about?" I asked. I haven't seen her in such good spirits since she joined us in the city.

She sat down on my bed. "I have something very important to tell you," she whispered excitedly. "Karoly came by this morning to let us know that he found an apartment — a big apartment."

"I am happy for him," I replied. "He deserves it."

"You don't understand," she gushed. "He found a *big* apartment." She was hardly able to contain her joy. "He already signed the lease, and he made us the co-leasers of the flat."

I looked at her, still uncomprehending. "What does this mean?" I asked.

"It means one thing, silly. Can't you see for yourself? He is willing to hide us in his family's new place. He and his wife are giving us the opportunity to live there with them under our aliases, as pure-blooded Aryans!"

"Oh, thank God!" I exclaimed, and we both started to weep. "When did Karoly decide to help us hide out?" I asked her, dabbing at my eyes with a handkerchief.

"Apparently he and Jacob have been secretly planning this since he brought me to your house."

"Is he aware of the risks to his own safety?"

"I think he is," Esty answered. "I have heard Jacob outlining the dangers to Karoly in gruesome detail, over and over again, but all he does is smile as though he considers it unimportant. He is so fearless and confident. He keeps saying: 'I couldn't live with myself if I didn't try to help you. I feel that I must help you, because you did no wrong. You are innocent. God in Heaven, this is all so shameful!' "

May 21, 1944. I spent the whole day praying. Pangs of conscience assaulted me mercilessly. What if Karoly is found out and punished, perhaps killed for his selfless act? I removed a photograph from my night table. Karoly had sent it to me through Esty. It was a picture of his wife holding their baby daughter. For several moments I stared at the young woman who smiled at me from the picture. She is so beautiful and so very young — a teenager with a baby in her arms. I put the picture back on the table and closed my eyes. What will happen to her and to her baby if we are caught? I asked myself. Do we have the right to put them in this position? All day long, these questions plagued me, but now I thank God for sending us this noble man. If anything should happen to us, I vow that no one will ever find out the truth about Karoly and his family. Until the end, we will maintain that as far as he knew, we had rented the apartment solely for economic reasons.

May 22, 1944. Esty breezed into my room. "I can't stay long," she whispered. "We are moving our things to the new apartment today. Thanks to your husband, all is running like clockwork. You should see how efficiently he's taken care of everything. Zsuzsi, do you realize how fortunate we are? On the first of June, all Jewish men who, for one reason or another, are still at liberty must report to government headquarters. By that time, the ghetto will be ready."

She stopped speaking for a moment. "Aren't we lucky to have an apartment to move into?" she asked, her voice now barely audible.

I looked up at her. Two large teardrops were forming in her sea-green eyes. They quickly ran down her cheeks and fell onto my pillow. Hastily she turned to go. "I'll come early tomorrow morning to take you home," she called back. I didn't reply, for I was mesmerized by the twin tearstains on my pillow which grew larger and larger before my eyes.

May 23, 1944. The day of our release arrived. Esty came early, as she had promised, and I was already packed and dressed and waiting for her.

Dr. Rona entered the room a few minutes later, during his morning rounds. "Lucky little girl," he said, smiling at my baby. "Yes, a very lucky little girl to be alive. Well, your nurse will have to answer for her crime, even though her plot failed. I will track her down if I am still around after the war," he promised.

"Dr. Rona," I said urgently.

"What is it, Rivka Leah?"

"Dr. Rona..." I began again.

"Come now, I can see that something is bothering you. Tell me what is on your mind."

"Doctor..." I whispered for the third time.

He put his notebook on the night table and sat down. "I don't believe," he said gently, "that after all we've been through here you're still embarrassed in front of me."

I took a deep breath. "Soon...very soon, we are going to...hide out with false documents," I stammered. "Before last week, I had never even held an infant, let alone cared for one." I looked down at the floor. "I am completely unequipped for this task," I said quietly, ashamed at my ignorance. "How will I know, for instance, when she is crying from hunger and when she is crying because she is ill? Please, give me some advice. You are the only one I can trust right now."

"Well, I am not a pediatrician," he answered haltingly,

trying to suppress his shock at my revelation of our secret plans.

"I spoke to Dr. Farkas, the pediatrician," I said quickly, "and he told me to call for an appointment. He wants to see the baby every four weeks. But I can't tell *him* why I won't be able to make any appointments."

"Alright. What do you want to know?" he asked tenderly, now calm and collected once more.

"I want to know everything. I want to do right by my daughter. I love her so very much and I am so scared!"

"Use your common sense, my dear," he advised me. "That's all there is to it. I firmly believe that God gives all mothers — human and beast alike — the instinct to bring up their young. Did you ever wonder how a cat knows when to feed her kittens, or a dog her puppies? Do you credit yourself with as much intellect as they have?"

"Oh, it's so simple for them," I argued. "They don't have clocks to follow or books to read or doctors to listen to. For example, Dr. Farkas told me to feed our daughter every four hours. But what if she is hungry before then?"

"Well, then, let me talk to you as a father, not as a doctor. I will give you the same advice I gave my wife. We never let our children go hungry if they cried, even two hours after a feeding. My wife always offered them food, as we both felt that it is cruel to let little ones cry helplessly for food when they are hungry. And another thing: let her know how much you love her in every way you can."

Seeing my helpless expression, he took the baby from my arms. "Look at her," he said. "Did you ever stop to think what a frightening experience birth must be to the human infant?" One minute everything is dark, quiet and effortless; the next minute not only are the surroundings unfamiliar but she actually has to work to sustain her life — to breathe, to suckle. For the first time, she has to adjust to cold, heat and above all, the blinding light."

Then he put the baby on the bed. "This is how you do it,"

he said, bending until his face was level with the baby's. He lay his own face on her tiny pink face and body. "They like to feel human warmth." Then he stood upright. "This will do at times," he said, covering my baby's face gently with his sensitive hands. "Just let her feel that you are near, whether she is awake or not. In other words, don't be afraid to love her to pieces. That is what she wants and needs. Aside from this, I can only repeat my previous advice: that you must believe that mother knows best. With this newly-gained confidence in your abilities, you will!" He lifted my baby from the bed and handed her to me. "Rivka Leah, I want to wish you all the luck in the world." And with that, he left.

Esty pulled at my sleeve. "Let's go," she said impatiently. "I have lots of work to do in our new house. I'm anxious to unpack and put the house in order before you arrive with Jacob and Faygele."

"Yes, fine," I murmured, pressing my daughter close to me as we walked out of my room. With the yellow star pinned to my chest, I left the hospital, carrying my baby in my arms.

Beads of perspiration formed on my face, and yet I shivered with cold as I stepped out into that beautiful, sunlit spring day in 1944.

26

JACOB GREETED US at the Brenners' front door. "We have moved all our belongings to the new apartment already," he said, "so I borrowed Danny's apartment for the day."

"I'm sure they wouldn't mind," my sister said matter-of-factly. Then her face suddenly clouded over with worry. "Please come as soon as you can, though," she urged us. "We will count the seconds until your arrival at our new home."

"Don't worry," Jacob told her. "But if for some reason we haven't shown up by, say, ten o'clock tomorrow evening, do not, under any circumstances, come back to this apartment to inquire after us. We'll leave a message with the Bogars; understand?"

Esty covered her ears with her hands. "Stop this nonsense. Please stop! Nothing will happen; with God's help, everything will be just fine." She reached for her handbag. "I must go now so I can start unpacking. I'll see you soon," and she walked out the door.

"We'll be there tomorrow," I called after her.

The next morning, our excited cries filled Vera's house as we prepared to give Faygele her very first bath. Jacob filled the little pink tub with water and placed it on the kitchen table while I spread out the bath towel and brought the baby powder and baby oil.

"I wish we had a baby hairbrush," I lamented. "How will I take care of all of this?" I ran my fingers through her unusually long, dark hair.

"Leichi," Jacob exclaimed as he looked at our baby, "her hair is turning blond!" I checked and sure enough, the new growth at the roots was light. "She is taking on the color of the 'master race' to match her new identity," Jacob joked. Then he tested the temperature of the bathwater with his hand. "Is it alright?" he asked. "What do you think?"

"They say to test the water with your elbow; it's more sensitive," I answered knowledgeably as I rolled up my sleeves. "I think it's too hot. Add a little more cold water." Jacob poured in some cold water and I tested the temperature again. "No, you've added too much! Now it needs a little more hot water." We continued adding quantities of hot and cold water until we finally concluded that the bath was the perfect temperature.

I unwrapped the baby and began to lower her into the bath. "Stop!" Jacob shouted suddenly. "This seems like an awful lot of water for a little tyke like her." He picked up the bath in order to empty some of it out but on his way to the sink he tripped, causing half of the contents of the tub to spill out on the floor.

My hands were trembling by that time. "I'm afraid to put her into the water," I confessed. "She may drown!"

"How can you be so childish?" my husband retorted impatiently. "Give her to me and I'll bathe her."

"Oh, no!" I shrieked. "You don't even know how to hold her properly."

What seemed like an eternity later, we were finally through with the ordeal. I started to dress the baby while Jacob mopped the floor.

"I never realized what babies we ourselves are," Jacob remarked. We looked at each other in despair. But a minute later I looked up and saw that Jacob's eyes were sparkling with laughter as he watched me dress his little wriggling daughter.

"Thank God we've gotten this far already. By this time tomorrow we will be with the Bitters in our new home."

Late that afternoon, we were standing in the foyer with our forged papers in our pockets, rehearsing possible ways of leaving the building without wearing the yellow star. Finally we decided that Jacob would hold yesterday's newspaper in such a way that it would cover his chest, leaving it to everyone's imagination whether he was wearing the star or not, while I would hold the baby over my chest in a similar position.

"You look fine," we told each other encouragingly, knowing perfectly well that we did not. We were both reluctant to venture out.

"Now is the time," I declared without warning. "One, two, three, ready!" I flung the door open wide. Immediately, I shut it again. Two men and a woman were standing in the hall outside our apartment, and now they began pounding at the door with all their might.

"Who are they and what do they want?" I moaned, dropping into the nearest chair.

Jacob put his ear to the door. Then the color returned to his face. "It is my sister Minda," he said, his eyes shining luminously as he reached for the doorknob.

"Don't take chances!" I cried. "Let me open it!" And I quickly chased poor Jacob under Vera's bed. I looked through the peephole and sure enough, there stood Minda and her husband, Chuna, whom we had heard was deported a week ago from the Ujhely ghetto. They were talking to someone who was a stranger to us.

"What should we do now?" Chuna asked. "They aren't home."

Minda started to cry and wring her hands desperately. "Oh, my God, where can we go?"

I opened the door. "Leichi!" Minda cried, tremendously relieved to see me. "We thought you lived in *this* apartment. We were so scared when no one answered." She paused briefly.

"Where is my brother?" she cried.

"He is in the work-camp," I whispered, not trusting the stranger with our secret.

Chuna noticed me glancing at the man who accompanied them. "Leichi, meet Mr. Heves," he said. "He has a heart of gold. Not only did he hide us the entire week, but he also escorted us to the city." Then he whispered in my ear, "Can you please pay him for us?"

"With the greatest pleasure," I replied as I went to take some bills from my purse. "Would you like something to eat, Mr. Heves?" I asked, inviting them all inside.

"No, thank you. I must hurry to see my sister. She lives at Angyalfold, and I haven't seen her or her family for ages." The next minute, he was gone.

For a long while, we just stood there crying. Then Jacob walked into the room. Minda turned to me, puzzled. "Why did you tell us that my brother was in the work-camp?" I didn't answer. "Well," she said, filling up the awkward silence, "what's the difference? The most important thing is that you are well and that you have managed to stay out of the Nazis' deadly web."

"Leichi doesn't trust a soul," Jacob interjected, with a trace of exasperation in his voice.

"You don't trust Mr. Heves?!" Chuna exclaimed indignantly. "He saved us from the ghetto. He hid us for a week in his vineyard. And every day he brought us food."

"Do you know who he is?" Minda added, turning to Jacob. "Remember our old neighbor, Csaba Heves? This man is his second son, Bernát."

"Of course I remember him," Jacob answered. "We used to play together as children. He's about my age." Then Jacob started bombarding them with questions: "Who else escaped? Is anyone else coming here?" They shook their heads and started crying all over again.

"I can't bear this any more," I announced. "I am going downstairs to buy a comb and brush for the baby at the drugstore around the corner — I hope it's still open."

When I entered the store I grabbed the first little hairbrush I saw, quickly paid and started running home, suddenly overcome with anxiety and berating myself bitterly for having left my baby. What if something happens to me or, God forbid, to her? How could I have let her out of my sight? How? Frantic with worry, I didn't even wait for the elevator. I ran up the three flights of stairs and burst into the apartment, gasping for breath.

"Is she alright?" I asked anxiously. "Why are you diapering her when I diapered her just five minutes ago? Was she crying?"

"Listen, Leichi," Jacob began. "There is some trouble..."

"The baby? What happened?" I cried, hysterically grabbing her from him.

"No, no, the baby is fine, but while you were gone the police came here looking for you."

"For me? Why? What did I do wrong?"

"Bernát Heves apparently went directly from here to the authorities to report our guests' arrival."

I turned to Minda and Chuna. "Then why are you still standing here?" I asked. "They must be after you."

"No, Leichi," Jacob replied. "The SS isn't interested in them."

"How do you know?"

"I heard them talking," answered Mr. Antique, whose presence in the room I hadn't even noticed until that moment. "I happened to be in Mr. Bogar's apartment when the two SS men arrived. I hid in an adjoining room, while Mr. Bogar invited them in, offering them mugs of beer in order to give you time to escape. His performance was so convincing that if I didn't know him, I would have thought he was the worst kind of anti-Semite. He told them: 'I would like to see you catch those two shameless escapees,' while he continually refilled their mugs with beer. 'No, sir,' one of them answered him, 'we aren't looking for little worms like them. There is no time for that. We think this woman who lives above you is part of a large ring with high connections and big money, whose aim is to help the Jews escape from the ghettos. We have the Jews under arrest already, but we want to get our hands on some of that money. Just think, after the fifteenth of June they will all be in the ghetto,' he chortled. 'So let's drink to it!' "

We all just stood there in shock as Mr. Antique told his story. A short time later, Mr. Bogar came running into the apartment. "Quick!" he whispered. "They are in the bathroom now. Go! Go!" he ordered me, as he dashed out again.

"I am going now," Mr. Antique announced, and he, too, quickly left us.

As soon as he was gone, Minda gingerly lifted a light blond wig out of a box that was on the kitchen table and put the wig on my head. Everyone was startled by the difference it made in my appearance. "Here, take a look," Minda said, thrusting a hand mirror at me. "Do you recognize yourself?"

"I look like a clown!" I cried. "That can't be me!"

"No, that's not you," my husband replied. "That's Zsuzsi Kovacs. Remember, your address is Dombalya Utca 5. And make sure you're familiar with all your forebears' names, too. Go now!" he said, handing me the baby and turning away abruptly.

"Where shall I go?" I asked, still dazed by the sudden turn of events. "It's nighttime already."

"Go to your cousin Helen's house."

Minda pressed a package of baby clothes into my arms. I turned to Jacob. "I am not going if you stay here," I cried frantically.

"Go!" Jacob whispered, his tone now urgent. "The faster you go, the faster we will also be able to leave."

"Where are you going?" I asked.

"To Mr. Antique's house." Then he opened the front door and firmly guided me out. "I'll see you soon," he whispered. "Your sister will call for you tomorrow morning. Just stay calm. Nobody will recognize you, especially not the SS. Believe me,

Leichi, I myself have a hard time believing this is really you."

The door slammed shut behind me. I stood there, stupefied, clinging desperately to my baby and clutching at the little package of clothing Minda had given me.

Moments passed, and then, as if propelled by a force outside of myself, I descended the steps rapidly, repeating my husband's parting words: "Be calm. No matter what, keep on moving. You will make it." Soon enough, I reached the ground floor. Then I saw him: standing by the main entrance was a man wearing high shiny black boots and the unmistakable uniform of the SS. Only two things can happen now, I told myself: either he will recognize me or he won't, and either way, it's out of my hands now. I headed straight for the door, chanting silently over and over: be calm, keep moving, be calm, keep moving...

"Pardon me," I said to the man as I reached for the doorknob.

He eyed my professionally, taking in my appearance at a glance from my shoes to the top of my blond tresses. Then he held the door open for me, gave me a wolfish grin and started whistling the popular melody: "It's not my fault, my dear brunette, a platinum blonde has stolen my heart..."

I walked through the great front door and away from the dangerous spot, relief flooding my entire being. Suddenly, I heard footfalls behind me. He came after all! He suspects! Goose bumps formed at the nape of my neck and chills ran up and down my spine. I felt the man's steady gaze burning a hole into my back, and I doubled my pace, willing myself with all my might not to look back at my enemy. I spotted a streetcar on the opposite side of the avenue and I began to run toward it frantically, just to get out of sight. But as luck would have it, the traffic light changed and the heavy flow of traffic began again, leaving me standing helplessly on the street corner.

Anger engulfed me, and in my frustration, I raised my fist and shook it at the traffic light. I jerked my head around toward my pursuer. But to my utter surprise, I saw that the SS man was not behind me. Only fear had followed me — fear, the steady companion of my troubled days.

I am safe! I am safe! I repeated those words to myself over and over again. Then I headed straight for the streetcar that would take me to the Jewish section of town.

An hour later I was standing in front of my cousin Helen's house. I knocked loudly on the door. Moments later, Helen appeared, wearing a long robe of green and white polka dots. She looked at me with a blank stare. "Who are you looking for?" she asked politely. Suddenly a spark of recognition lit up her dark brown eyes. "Leichi! What is this? Why the blond wig? And what are you doing here?"

"Please let me come in and I'll explain everything."

She opened the door and I stepped into the narrow foyer, but she stood in my way, effectively blocking my entrance into the room. "What is this all about?" she demanded, and I quickly told her my story.

"You mean to tell me that the police are looking for you?" Helen shouted hysterically. "You couldn't find anybody else to pull down with you besides your own cousin?" Then her face turned crimson. I knew only too well what that meant: Helen was about to have one of her temper tantrums. Oh no, I thought, not today. I was so weak and completely drained of energy. But beggars can't be choosers, I told myself, feeling faint with weariness. Just bear it and hope that she won't turn you out. But I was still unprepared for what followed.

"Heavenly Father," she screamed, her whole body shaking like a leaf in a storm. "The police are after you and you came here to implicate me?" Her voice had reached a high-pitched cry, and as she shouted, she banged her head against the wall in anger. "What a dirty trick! A trick! A trick…" I stood there, mesmerized, and wondering: Where shall I go? After a while, her anger spent, she started to cry softly. Then she dried her eyes.

"Helen," I said after a short silence. "I am very sorry that I frightened you so badly. But your worry is totally unfounded. I haven't put you in any danger. I promise you that nobody knows I am here. Nobody followed me — I'm sure of it. Please, let me just spend the night in your house, and first thing in the morning I'll be gone. Just tonight," I begged. My baby began to cry. "She is hungry. Please, let me feed her."

"A baby!" Helen cried in surprise. "Why, I didn't even notice her. How old is she?"

"She is exactly eleven days old."

"Oh, the poor thing," she exclaimed compassionately as she ushered me into her living room. Gratefully, I sank into a tapestry-covered love seat by the fireplace.

When the baby had finished her feeding and her face bore that sleepy-satisfied expression, I placed her on a double bed next to the wall. Helen stood next to the bed watching her intently. The lamp on the nightstand illuminated my cousin's flaming red hair, which seemed to sizzle in the soft light, and I watched in wonder as the faintly tinted freckles on her transparent skin seemed to spring to life, one by one. It reminded me how her contemporaries back home used to rave about her flawless beauty.

"Can I please pick her up?" she asked, her face now radiating love. I nodded. She held the baby up high for inspection. "What a precious handful," she exclaimed, tears now shining in her eyes. "Oh, for years, how Imre and I have longed to have a baby of our own. And God only knows how many tears I have shed over not being able to bear one. But now I thank the Lord because it hurts so much more to have children at a time like this, with things as they are here in Europe. I'm not crying for myself now," she sobbed. "My tears are for you. Oh, Leichi, what on earth will you do?" She held the baby close for a moment, and then placed her gently back on the bed. Within minutes Faygele was fast asleep.

I lay down alongside my daughter, trying to draw some comfort, but to no avail. A thousand images rushed into my mind, torturing me mercilessly. What if the police have searched Mr. Antique's apartment? Or, who knows, maybe Jacob never even made it there. I should never have left without him! But then everything had happened so fast, so very fast, and I hadn't had time to think. I was literally pushed away, just as baby birds are pushed out of the nest. It wasn't even a comfort to think that those baby birds always seem to make it — they seldom fail because it is the best and only way. I, too, would have to learn to fly on my own.

"Leichi? Have you fallen asleep?" Helen asked. "You know, when I talk about Imre and our hopes and dreams, and the ambitions we shared, I realize that all the dreams are gone now. There is but one wish we cling to: the will, the hope, to survive, oh, just to survive!"

On the banks of the Danube the birds merrily sing
In the year 1944, Budapest in the spring.
The trees stand tall on warm balmy nights,
You can almost see them growing with your naked eyes!
But all this beauty is not for me, O not for Jews
For all that we see are the posters, the news.
O for us, for us tormented Jews
Only notices sprout on the walls with the morning dew;
Little innocent-looking notices so subtle and demure,
Bringing orders each day more cruel than the day before.
But today's spits venom so dreadful. It says
Each and every Israelite, young and old,
Must wear a Star of David made from Yellow cloth.

Seething in anger, trembling with fear,
But erect and tall and gritting my teeth,
As under the threat of imminent death,
In the grim shadow of murder and theft,
With my brethren's bones heaped up, innocent, white,
And myself steps away from the fiery death,
I pick up the Yellow Star to mark myself.
The Yellow Star sizzles, sizzles in my hand,
And as the red-hot branding iron scorches my flesh,
I bow beneath the weight of such cruelty in men.
"O why? O why O why O why O why?"
Seems to echo from near from far,
As if the seas, the skies, the earth with me cry: "O why?"
Trembling and crushed under the weight of my words,
And the world of my childhood, the world of my youth,
Tears stream wildly from my eyes,
And the seas, the earth, the skies with me seem to cry:
"Who am I to ask? Who am I am I am I am I?"

Book Three

27

I LAY VERY STILL in the dark, unfamiliar room, wide awake in the middle of the night. I could tell from Helen's rhythmic breathing in the bed next to mine that she was asleep. Quickly, I got out of bed and began to pace the floor nervously, unable to escape the terrifying question that all night had plagued me constantly: Did my husband and our guests manage to get away? Feeling faint, I walked to the window, opened it, and inhaled the warm night air deeply. I stood there, gazing out on the pitch-dark street, trying to find an answer to this and other worries as well: Where will I go from here in the morning? I knew very well that go I must.

I don't remember how long I stood there, lost in my misery, when I noticed a light on the horizon. I watched as it turned into glittering hues of gold and red before my very eyes. "Red," I muttered as I stared out at the sky, "like the blood of our people that flows so freely in this hateful time." Blood and gold — the two forces behind all this destruction.

Just then the sun forged its way out of its heavenly meadow, its rays blinding me with their brilliance. I covered my eyes. "Lord!" I gasped in wonder. "Is this all the time You need to chase the dreadful, dark night away?" Every atom in my body responded to the light and I knew in that moment that the darkness wouldn't last forever. Dawn would break, chasing even the darkest of nights away. Just, please, my God, I silently prayed, show us how to survive until then. I pulled the heavy blackout curtains wide open. Light flooded the room, and with renewed hope I climbed into bed next to my sleeping, unsuspecting little darling and fell asleep in an instant.

Hours passed. I was sleeping so soundly that I did not hear the doorbell ring. I awoke to the sound of the door bursting open and my sister's worried voice. "Are Leichi and the baby here?" she cried. The next minute both of us were weeping and laughing as we embraced one another.

"Oh, what a night this has been!" she exclaimed.

"But how did you know what happened? How did you find out where I was? Where is Jacob?"

"I'm so sorry — I should have told you the moment I stepped through the door that everything is alright. Your husband arrived at Dombalya Utca last night carrying a big, empty cardboard box. He had posed as a delivery man in order to enter the house unnoticed. We had been expecting you all day and were frantic with worry. Karoly, our good angel, went to pick up Chuna and Minda. So now they are all there safely, but extremely anxious about you and the baby."

Helen, who had been standing in the room during our whole conversation, finally spoke. "I will dress the baby," she volunteered eagerly, trying in vain to suppress the note of relief that crept into her voice at the prospect of getting rid of us.

Somehow, I managed a polite reply. "Cousin Helen, how can I ever thank you for what you did for us? But then, how does one thank someone for the gift of life?"

"Come on, enough of this," she retorted with annoyance. Then a wistful expression crossed her face. "This house will soon be part of the ghetto," she said, somewhat embarrassed. "Leichi, when you are ordered out of your lodgings, would you mind moving in with me?" She raised her head and looked at me pleadingly. "I live in a nightmare just *thinking* of having strangers living here." Then, before I could even think of an answer to her request, she turned to my daughter. "Yes, Faygele, my dear," she cooed, "you will make us forget our troubles. You will make us laugh."

I opened my mouth to thank her for her generous offer, to reassure her, but I could not utter a sound. How could I promise to stay with her? How could I say that I would come when just then I was preparing to go into hiding exactly for that reason: to avoid the ghetto and all of the horrors it signified. But that was a secret I could not divulge, and I searched rapidly for a plausible answer to give her.

Helen misinterpreted my silence. "I see," she said with a sigh. "Me and my silly temper. I see that I frightened you last night and that you won't even consider my invitation."

"No, no! It isn't that," I protested, finally finding my voice. "It's just that I happen to know that the Nazis won't let us state our preferences. We will be ordered to move wherever they see fit. The animals!"

My sister interrupted me and indicated that it was time for us to go. As we were leaving the apartment, she whispered, "Leichi...I mean...Zsuzsi, do you have your new papers with you?"

"Yes," I said, fighting back the tears, "and it frightens me to no end. How will I be able to be somebody else, to live a lie constantly, day in and day out?"

My sister gave me a hard look. It was clear from her expression that she had no patience for my existential questions. "You'd be surprised, sister dear," she replied harshly, "what people are capable of doing when their lives depend on it."

I decided not to pursue the matter further. "Did you get rid of your yellow star?" I inquired. She nodded. "Me too," I responded quickly, eager to show her that practical considerations were foremost in my mind too.

"So, let me introduce myself," she said lightly. "Anna Shipoc!"

"It's a pleasure to meet you," I answered wryly. "Zsuzsi

Kovacs!" And we climbed onto the trolley.

Looking around the crowded streetcar, I began to tremble with fear. I felt like a fugitive from the law. Why is that woman looking at me so strangely? I wondered. Is she searching for my missing Star of David? Of course she is, I concluded. Wasn't I always called "a dark-haired Jewish girl" by the many people who recognized at first glance that I was Jewish? And the man in the next seat — why is he staring at me so intently? And this woman with the colorful print dress? And the next passenger, and the next? I looked down at the floor and pressed my baby closer to me in a vain attempt to shield her from harm, as all the passengers seemed to melt into large accusing eyes, and countless upraised fingers seemed to point to me, demanding to know: Where are you going without your yellow star, Jew?

I couldn't bear the tension any longer. I clenched my teeth and, after what seemed an eternity, I mustered the courage to glance around me. I saw, to my surprise, that most of the passengers had already disembarked, and I was relieved to discover that a stout, red-faced mother surrounded by her brood now sat next to me.

"Look, quickly," she exclaimed loudly to her children. "We are nearing the prettiest spot on earth!" The children ran to the window and I, too, automatically turned my eyes toward the scene. The beauty of the landscape overwhelmed me as the mountain of Buda came into view from across the sunbathed blue Danube.

"It's breathtaking! It's majestic!" I gasped, awestruck. All at once, the instinct to live stabbed at me with a fury. I will never give up! No, and again no! I will fight to stay alive, I vowed.

Suddenly everybody was screaming. Smoke was rapidly filling the trolley car. "Fire! Fire!" the passengers cried. "Open the door!"

The trolley stopped abruptly, causing people to lurch into one another. The conductor quickly made his way up the aisle and opened the door. "There's been a short circuit in the wires," his voice boomed, "and it won't take long to fix. But in the meantime, you can steal an unexpected little holiday."

We all piled out of the streetcar. I sat with Anna and the baby on the bank of the blue Danube, on a soft carpet of silky green grass.

"Poor Jacob," breathed my sister.

"Iztvan," I corrected swiftly.

"All right, let's call him Iztvan. All I wanted to say was that I am really angry that this silly trolley had to break down, causing us a further delay just when he is so worried about you and the baby. Well, at least *I* know that you are safe, but he must be crazed with fear by now."

I heard a commotion and looked up to see the children who had been sitting near me in the trolley come running toward us, squealing with delight, followed by their harried mother. She held a baby in her arms and could scarcely keep up with her lively lot. Suddenly the children flopped down in the grass right in front of us, calling for their mother to follow. She looked so helpless that my heart ached.

"How gladly would I help her watch her children if I weren't afraid of calling attention to myself," I whispered in Anna's ear.

A thin, graying woman in a light beige linen suit and a brown striped blouse approached the little group, obviously prompted by the same feeling of compassion. She sat next to the woman on the grass and put her hand reassuringly on the woman's shoulder. "What a beautiful family you have, my dear," she said. "Would you feel imposed upon if I offered to amuse them for the time being?"

The woman's face lit up. "Oh, thank you!" she replied. "No, I wouldn't mind at all." Then she turned to introduce her children. "This is Miklos, my eldest," she said, pointing to a husky boy who was almost colorless, apparently an albino.

The boy stood up and bowed respectfully. "I am Miklos Hegedus and I am twelve years old."

"I am Mrs. Losonci," the woman replied, "and I must say that your mother is certainly raising you right. You have extremely nice manners. It's a pleasure to meet you." The boy blushed bright red and sat down.

"This is Bela, my second son," the proud mother continued, "and these are my daughters, Erika and Marta." The two little girls curtsied, their long wheat-colored braids shimmering in the sunshine. "And these are our twin boys, Peter and Paul," she said pointing to the two freckled, chubby little boys with identical, upturned noses. "And this little one is baby Eva."

Mrs. Losonci acknowledged them all with a smile. "All right, Miklos, Bela, Erika, Marta, Peter and Paul, I have a pair of binoculars in my bag that I think will come in very useful now. I have a nice game made up for you. Now stand up. Look over there," Mrs. Losonci said, pointing toward the calm, blue waters of the Danube. "See all those boats anchored near the shore?"

"Yes, yes," they cried out with excitement.

"Now, each of you, starting with the eldest, pick a boat and pretend that it is yours. Then the next time you come here with your mother, you can look for it again. I think it will be fun."

Miklos pointed to a large, white boat with red, white and green sails. Mrs. Losonci handed him the binoculars. "I can see it! I can read it. It says *Attila the Hun.*" The woman took a sheet of paper from her bag and, amid the cheers of the youngsters, wrote "Attila the Hun." She folded the paper carefully and handed it to Miklos. Miklos puffed out his chest proudly like a man who has just purchased his first car, but in this case, it was his first boat.

"I've picked mine already," called Bela impatiently, aiming the binoculars at a motorboat named *Wild Fury*. He called out the name so that the woman could write it down for him.

"You made up the name," Miklos taunted him, and the bickering began. Finally, peace was regained.

"I've picked the one over there," Erika said with delight, "the one with the name *Hope*."

"Hope," Mrs. Losonci repeated, her voice shaking.

"*Hope*!" the children's cries echoed along the banks of the Danube.

Yes, hope — the only possession of the oppressed Jew, I thought, as my sister blew her nose vigorously into her little lace-trimmed hanky, a gesture I had learned meant that she was experiencing tumultuous emotions. After a while, she whispered in my ear, "Zsuzsi, look at the tender expression on their faces. Those people actually have feelings! Did you see the faraway gaze in their eyes when they said 'Hope'? And I thought that they were carved from stone, devoid of all human feeling."

"Funny, I was thinking the same thing," I confessed. It made me feel good to see that they were not the monsters I had thought they were. They were simply clay in the hands of the media, with all the inciteful literature and slogans and propaganda which had inured the citizenry to our suffering. Hitler knew that the masses don't think; they follow. He threw us at their mercy so that the world wouldn't notice, until he had succeeded in stealing the entire globe from under its nose.

"Attention! Attention, passengers," a voice thundered through a bullhorn. "Take your seats in the trolley, and thank you for your patience."

28

THE CONDUCTOR announced, "Next stop: Horthy Miklos Korut," and Anna murmured, "This is our stop." She stood up and I immediately followed suit. We alighted from the trolley and began walking. I suddenly felt very anxious as I thought about the importance of the impending meeting with the superintendent of our new apartment. It was well-known in the city that the government enlisted the help of superintendents in tracking down suspects. They would call to the SS's attention the presence of any new tenant in their building.

"Here we are," Anna said after a few minutes, stopping in front of the only house on the wide-open meadow. If my sister hadn't stopped I never would have seen the building, since it was almost completely hidden behind a cluster of purple and white lilac trees.

"Oh, how lovely," I cried, stunned by the beauty of the flowers.

"You've finally noticed!" Anna said. "I've been trying to show you these wild flowers that grow in abundance here, but you didn't respond at all. You really worried me."

We walked to the front door and she placed her finger on the bell, but I stopped her. "Don't," I said. "Let me look around first."

"That is where we live," she said, pointing to the top floor, "and this is our terrace." I noticed that the terrace was on the south side of the building.

"Excellent," I whispered. "Another route of escape."

She took my hand and led me around the house. "And there is another porch in the back of the house. This one is adjacent to the Bitters' bedroom."

"And there is tall grass all around," I remarked, my thoughts still focused on possible means of escape.

"Don't be so pessimistic. Let's just hope that we will never need the porch or the tall grass. The only help we need comes from Above."

A tall, middle-aged woman appeared, wearing the traditional garb of the Hungarian peasant — a long, gathered shirt atop countless petticoats, and a dark, print bodice. She extended her hand and welcomed us warmly. "Wait here," she said. "I'll call my husband." She disappeared behind a door which had a little sign that read: "Janos Horvat, Superintendent."

"Isn't it peculiar that our superintendent is so old-fashioned?" Anna commented. "In that peasant outfit, she looks as if she has stepped out of another time."

"Yes, it struck me as odd, too. But as far as I'm concerned, that's where the similarities between her and the peasants begin and end. Didn't you notice her face, how proud and intelligent it is? And what is more surprising is her manner. She completely lacks the deference for which our peasants are so well-known."

The door opened and Mrs. Horvat appeared with her husband, a tall, slim, handsome man with sandy hair faintly streaked with silver at the temples, lending dignity to his appearance. He approached us with the sure, long stride of a man accustomed to wielding authority. I began to feel suspicious and frightened. This man was no superintendent. He must be a detective, or worse, an SS man. Chills ran up and down my spine.

"Welcome," he said simply. "I heard that you have a baby. May I see him?"

"It's a she and her name is little Zsuzsi," I said, placing her in his outstretched arms. He looked at her warmly, the deeply-etched laugh lines at the corners of his eyes magically animating his tired features.

"A baby is all my husband needs," Mrs. Horvat laughed. "I don't think that there is a man who loves children more than this big hulk of a man of mine does. It's just too bad that our only child, a boy, isn't married yet and hasn't produced little copies of the Horvats, which would delight his father so." Then, with tears glistening in her eyes, she added, "I don't have such high expectations. All I pray for to God is that He bring our son home safely from the war."

At the mention of Janos Horvat Junior's name, Mr. Horvat's smile disappeared. Wordlessly, he gave me back my little girl and then he began to rummage through the briefcase which lay next to him on the floor. Out came an official-looking paper. "Here," he instructed me, "fill this out and I will take it to the precinct to register your new address."

I took the paper from him, and with trembling hands I wrote: Name: Zsuzsi Kovacs; Nationality: Hungarian; Religion: Catholic. My baby began to cry and I started to fuss over her, which gave me time to pull myself together. When I handed back the documents and thanked him for taking care of my papers, I was thrilled to hear that my voice sounded perfectly natural.

"How nice they were to us," I said to my sister as we mounted the steps inside the house. "But can you just imagine what their reaction would have been had our true identities become known?" I hissed. "Oh, those dirty Nazis!"

"Don't jump to conclusions," Anna replied. "They haven't given us the slightest reason to believe that they are Nazis. Why not give them the benefit of the doubt?"

"Because I have the eerie feeling that something is very

strange here," I said as we approached our new apartment. "Didn't you notice how intelligent they both look? And their self-confidence. Mr. Horvat must have work experience beyond simply mopping floors as a maintenance man. The only logical explanation I can think of is that he is some kind of bigwig in the local Nazi party. Don't you think I have a point?"

"Well, if you really want to know what I think right now," Anna retorted, "I think that you are absolutely crazy!"

The door opened noiselessly. Jacob, Minda and Chuna stood together at the entrance to the room. My husband came running forward, and I ran toward him as fast as my legs could carry me.

"Leichi! Faygele! How long it has been! Oh, what torture it was not knowing for sure that you were both safe!"

"And add to it the guilt of knowing that it all happened because of our carelessness," Minda sobbed. Chuna stood next to her, tears streaming down his pale face. "But how could we have foreseen that the man who hid us in a wine cellar on the slopes of the Tokaj Mountains, at the risk of his own life, would turn informer the minute the money was in his pocket?"

"By the way," I said, "that brings up another question. What is the general consensus about Magda? Can we trust her?"

"Yes, yes," Minda replied.

"You don't sound very convincing."

"She really is the nicest girl you can imagine. But then again, we trusted Bernát Heves, too."

Jacob consulted his wristwatch. "They will be here any minute now and you can form your own opinion."

"They just turned into our path," Anna called. "Come quickly and you can see her." I reached for the cord to draw up the venetian blind, but Anna grabbed my hand. "We never pull up this shade because the window opens onto the balcony we share with our next-door neighbors."

"You mean to tell me that they can overhear us?" I was

beside myself, but Anna didn't notice how upset I was, and she kept pushing me toward the spot where one of the slats was broken.

"Here, look," she insisted. I peered through the tiny space as Anna continued to talk. "This is the spot where each of us stands sentry, taking turns throughout the day. We have a regular spying system," she giggled, "and we call this our observation tower."

"Be quiet for a second. I am so excited. This is the first time that I've seen Magda."

"Isn't she beautiful?" Anna remarked.

"I've never seen such a stunning couple before in my life. If I had the talent, I would paint a picture of them, just as they look right now." I watched as the tall, chestnut-haired Karoly approached the house with his tall and lovely blonde wife, who walked with the grace of a princess as she carried their six-month-old daughter, Macika. "She is so pretty!" I exclaimed.

"Yes," Anna agreed, "but the best part of it is that both of them are as beautiful inside as they are outside. And the baby — I just adore her!"

I heard the large, wrought-iron door slam shut, followed by the sound of running. The next minute they were in the room and we were hugging each other. "Oh, Zsuzsi!" Karoly and Madga cried happily. "Thank God you're safe!"

"It's so good to be here! It's so good to be here!" I repeated over and over.

We sat and chatted for a while and then, as it began to get dark, everyone became involved in preparing supper and feeding the babies, so we separated. But soon I heard Magda's voice coming from the terrace. "Anna, Zsuzsi," she called, "come sit with us. It's a sin to stay inside on a night like this."

It really was a perfect spring night. The mild May breeze brought with it the heavenly scent of blooming lilacs, and the stars shone like a million lanterns from above. "How beautiful and peaceful the sky looks," I sighed. And yet, I thought, those same stars are shining over Hitler's gas chambers. The pain of that knowledge stabbed me like a knife, and countless questions arose inside me: Stars, what are you seeing right now? Instantly, I came up with the answer: They see a new transport arriving and the people are now being marched up to the door of the ovens. I closed my eyes to shut out what the stars were witnessing, as I sat shivering in the enchanting warmth of the night.

"A penny for your thoughts," Magda said, smiling pleasantly at me.

"She must be exhausted," Anna answered, looking with worried eyes in my direction. I nodded gratefully toward my sister.

"The beauty of this night overwhelms me," Karoly said. He took a deep breath of the fragrant air and smiled. "You know, the scent of the lilacs reminds me of those rare occasions long ago when I would sit under the lilac trees in the moonlight with my parents and enjoy the Hungarian spring night. I used to watch my parents fall asleep sitting upright in their chairs. My father would mildly protest staying up so late when soon dawn would break, bringing with it a new work day. And my mother would plead: 'Please, Miska, work well! Do more than enough before harvest time.' But nothing will bring back this heavenly smell after the lilacs fade away." Karoly sighed. "My dear parents. They do not have an easy life. They work from sunrise until sunset. Nevertheless, they managed to provide me with a very happy childhood."

"What nice recollections," Magda said. "But to me, the smell of lilacs brings back the most unpleasant memories." She shuddered involuntarily. "I can't describe how miserable I was during those few weeks that I stayed with your parents."

"Tell me, my dear," Karoly said, gazing lovingly at his wife. "What is it that you disliked so much?"

"I can tell you not one, but three things without even thinking," Magda giggled. "Number one, you weren't there with us and I missed you so much. Number two, your mother *was* there and I would never have missed her. And number three, I am a city girl. Budapest is in my blood. I could never fit into a small community!" She looked out upon her new surroundings. "But this place has the best of both our worlds. It has the wide-open space of your dreams, and I just have to go around the corner and I have my city. And, best of all," she concluded, "we have each other," and they both laughed.

"Oh, Magda," Karoly whispered. "I can't tell you how much I missed you." They were so wrapped up in each other that they didn't notice when Anna and I tiptoed from the balcony into the house.

I stumbled inside, weary from the day's events. "Which is my bed?" I asked, exhausted.

"Why, in there," my husband said, pointing to the alcove adjacent to the living room. It must have been designed originally as a music room, but now it served as a makeshift and overcrowded bedroom that housed our twin beds along with our most prized possession: the little crib with our sleeping infant in it.

"How did you fit so much furniture into this three-by-nothing hole?"

"It was a real challenge," Jacob answered, "but I succeeded. And now, watch this." To my amazement, he fell to the floor and rolled swiftly under the bed. "Can you see me?"

"No," I said, incredulous as I realized that even without the bedspreads to cover the sides of the bed, the three walls surrounding were enough to keep my husband out of view.

"But what about the rest of them?" I asked. "Where will they sleep?"

"Never mind," Anna laughed, moving together two of the dining-room chairs near the wall. "Isn't this perfect?"

"And Chuna and I have the living room with the divan," Minda said matter-of-factly. "And, of course, some help from chairs. So don't worry. We are all set."

Magda and Karoly passed through the living room on the way to their quarters. "Come, Zsuzsi," Magda prodded me, "let me show you our room." And as Karoly stopped to talk with

Jacob, I followed her. Magda turned on the light. "Look at the size of this room," she exclaimed. "Did you ever see a closet this big? I wish I had clothing enough to fill even half of it. And wait until you see this place in daylight — it is so bright and sunny. And the most important thing," she continued happily, "is that we have our very own porch here behind this blackout curtain. I am so happy and I love this place with a passion!"

Magda's elated cries touched a familiar chord in my heart, as I recalled the time when I walked through our first apartment babbling with joy, pointing out to my husband its virtues and raving about our private porch. How happy I was then! When was that? Could it be that it was only last June, not even a full year ago? How did everything happen so quickly? Why didn't I see it coming? But Jacob did, and he prepared. How would we be here now otherwise?

Yes, my husband is quite a man, I thought with admiration. Hot tears flooded my eyes. How dearly I am paying for those happy moments, and how greatly it hurts to love during times like these. And poor, dear Jacob. What a weight, what a burden he is carrying by holding himself responsible for our safety. As I stifled the cry that was rising in my throat, Macika stirred in her crib, and her mother hastily switched off the light, thus saving me the unpleasant task of having to explain my tears to her. As we tiptoed out of the room, I vowed that never again would I look back, squandering my energies on things I couldn't change. I would look forward, not behind, just as our Sages taught. Still, I couldn't help wondering how any of them managed to live by this useful doctrine.

I was so lost in thought that I didn't hear a word Magda was saying. Suddenly, she poked me in the ribs. "What's the matter?" she asked. Alarm was written all over her childlike face. "I'm speaking to you, and you seem so far away."

"Oh...what did you say?" I stammered, hoping she wouldn't ask me too many questions.

"I said that it is very important to remember that I told everyone who lives here that you still haven't heard any news from your husband at the front. We've got to stick to the same story." And with that, she said good night and left me.

Finally, the house fell silent, and only my husband and I were awake. This was the moment I was waiting for, the time to ask and tell each other a million and one things, to fill one another in on every minute since we parted. But neither one of us could utter a single sentence. We gazed at each other wordlessly and wept with happiness. Then, as if enchanted by magic, we both whispered simultaneously: "What a nightmare it was not knowing if you were safe." Then we burst out laughing, whispering nonsense as if we didn't have a care in the world.

Jacob broke the spell. "How did the Horvats impress you? Do you think they will be alright?"

"We'll only know that they aren't informers if the police don't come for us in the near future." I was content to leave the discussion at that, and I began to tell Jacob of other things in order to divert his attention from this subject. There was no point in going on until I could confirm my suspicions about the Horvats.

"Can you imagine how I felt when I filled out my forged documents?" I asked my husband.

"Were you scared?"

"No, but every atom in my body sprang alive to taunt me. It was as if an inner voice were accusing me: You threw away your name and the names of your ancestors, names you have always been proud of!"

Suddenly the wail of sirens shattered the quiet of the night. I turned to Jacob and cried, "I am not going down to the shelter! I can't leave you here unprotected."

Then Karoly ran into the room. "Please hurry," he said, "and don't wait for the superintendent to come for you." Reluctantly, I picked up my baby and we raced for the shelter.

"Here it comes — the big confrontation," Anna whispered through pale lips. "We are going to meet the whole lot of them in the shelter." Panic gripped me. I can't face them! I thought. I can't! I entered the shelter and sat down on a bench next to Anna. Together we listened to the reverberating thuds and blasts. How frightened the men must be up there, I thought. I was so possessed with fear that I couldn't even think.

That awful, crippling terror brought back words that my grandfather had spoken to me so long ago. I could hear his voice in my mind: "Look your fear in the eye!"

All at once I was a child again, and I was crying from a nightmare. "A bear, a bear is in the room! And it is coming to get me!" My screams brought my parents running to the room, and because we were vacationing in my grandparents' house, they came in too.

Finally, they all managed to convince me that it was only a dream, and I went back to sleep. A short while later, I awoke as my grandfather came back into the room holding a lit kerosene lamp. He approached my bed. "Put on your dress," he commanded. "I've come to teach you a lesson which I had to learn on my own. It may come in handy to you someday."

Thinking back, I could almost feel the warmth of his large hand closing over my small, trembling one as he guided me to each and every corner of the room. He even shone the light under the bed. "Look," he said. "I want you to see that there is no bear there," and he stood there until I worked up the courage to look myself. Then he sat down, lifted me onto his lap and whispered, "Fear is a very useful emotion, provided you use it wisely. Its main function is to call your attention to approaching danger and make you act instantly to preserve your safety. Look fear straight in the eye, and you will reduce it to size. Do you understand what I'm telling you?"

"Yes," I answered shamefacedly, thinking of how I had screamed from under my bedcovers that night, not daring to look.

"I once felt as you did tonight," he continued, "but luckily I forced myself to look at my fear and I will tell you what happened. You will be able to see the consequences for yourself. You know that I used to earn my living as a *shochet*. Since the town we lived in was too small — the people were too few and too poor — to pay me a salary by themselves, it shared my services with the next town. These two towns were divided by a large forest which I had to cross by day and by night, in sunshine, ice and sleet.

"On one moonlit night when I was about to enter the forest on my way to the neighboring town, I looked up and saw a man hanging from a tree, his arms and legs waving and kicking. Fear got the better of me, and I bolted into the forest just to get away from the cursed spot. I ran with all my might until my conscience prodded me: How could you have left him hanging there while he was still alive? Go back and rescue him! Don't abandon him. Nevertheless, I kept on running.

"Finally, I couldn't think of any more excuses for letting the poor man die alone, and I turned around and started to head back to him as fast as I could. When I reached the tree, I was relieved to see that he was still moving. I was far too scared to look up, but somehow I mustered the courage and did it. And what did I see? Well, lo and behold, the man I had come back to rescue turned out to be a soiled white tablecloth, obviously left behind by some careless picnickers and carried up into the branches by the wind. I was so overcome with joy that I started to cry on the spot.

"Now, just think — what if I had never gone back? What if I had never found out that the 'man' was just a dirty tablecloth? Can you imagine how I would have felt for the rest of my life, thinking that I had succumbed to my fear and left a helpless man to die?"

I thought of my grandfather's words now as I stared at the grim, frightened faces around me in the shelter, and I was suddenly devoid of fear. I realized that my potential enemies, who were the cause of my fear, were too scared for their own lives, too absorbed in their own troubles to be interested in mine.

I almost smiled then when I recalled how, the year after my nightmare, Grandfather came visiting and I gave him a little white envelope. In it was a sheet of paper on which I had written:

> Look your fear in the eye,
> And most of the time all you will meet,
> Is your own inflated imagination,
> Looking back at you, my dear!

I trudged alongside my mother as we walked Grandfather to the train station at the end of his visit. My heart was pounding wildly. Will he say anything about the poem? I wondered. Will he be pleased that I still remember what he told me? We were approaching the train station when he stopped.

"Our little philosopher," he said to my mother, and he gave her my note to read.

The "all clear" siren wailed. Grandfather dear, I thought, I do remember! I picked myself up before anyone could move and I strode from one person to the next, extending my hand and introducing myself. "I am Zsuzsi Kovacs and this is my daughter, little Zsuzsi. This is my sister Anna Shipoc." Luckily, my voice sounded as natural as though I had nothing to hide.

In a few minutes I finished the introductions, and I headed for our room with my baby, my sister and Magda. We had hardly closed the door behind us upstairs when Jacob, Minda and Chuna began bombarding us with questions. "How was it?" "Was it scary to meet them?" "Was it as bad as you had anticipated?"

"Never mind," Magda said with obvious admiration. "Not only was Zsuzsi not afraid of the bombing, but she seemed completely relaxed and at home with everybody there."

"Tell me everything," Jacob urged me. "Who lives in this house? Please be specific. Don't leave anything out. I must know as much as possible about our neighbors." Minda and Chuna joined in with similar questions, so that even though I was so tired that I was almost numb, I had no choice but to begin my descriptions.

"Well," I said, "from what I could tell, an old woman and

her married daughter live here."

"No," Anna corrected me. "The old woman's grandson, Lasi, told me that she is his *father's* mother, not his mother's mother."

"Alright," I said, "so it's an old lady with her son and daughter-in-law and their only child."

"What do they look like?"

"Well, the grandmother is a short, white-haired woman with brilliant, dark eyes and firmly set lips. Her son is a physician, Dr. Nagy, his wife's name is Ersabet, and their son is called Laslo, or Lasi. The doctor does not resemble his mother at all. He's a stocky man of medium build, with blond hair and blue eyes. And his facial expression is blank, devoid of all emotion."

"I guess he's wearing the mask of the physician," Anna interjected.

"What about the wife?" Jacob asked.

"She's very pretty and extremely well taken care of."

"She has skin like alabaster," Anna commented. "And did you notice her hands? They are so well-manicured. I could tell that she has nothing else on her mind but taking care of herself." The contempt in Anna's voice was evident.

"Why not?" Chuna remarked bitterly. "She doesn't have your problems!"

"I liked her," I insisted. "She looks very sensitive. But anyway, how much can one tell from only one meeting, and under such trying circumstances at that? Oh, listen to this: we have another doctor in the house. This one is a dentist and he lives right beneath our apartment!"

"How fortunate we are!" Minda exclaimed. "We are surrounded by professionals. It's certainly not bad to have help ready and available in times like these."

Exhaustion was getting the better of me by this time. "Please let me go to sleep now, before I collapse on the spot!"

"One more minute, please," my husband begged me. "Just tell me how the group as a whole impressed you."

"I think we all looked scared and tired. That's all!"

That last remark of mine succeeded in halting further conversation on the subject, and everyone agreed it was time for bed. Just as we were all about to separate and get ready to go to sleep for the night, Anna made one final comment. "Just remember, not only can the people living downstairs overhear us, but they can hear every step we take. That's right — every one!"

Chuna's pale skin turned even whiter. "It's a good thing you mentioned this," he said. "Supposedly, only two girls and the Bitters live here, so we must take special care to walk around as little as possible and then, only in our stocking feet."

"You know," Anna announced, "I like Erika."

"Who is she?" I asked, certain Anna did not mean the child from the trolley.

"Don't you remember? Erika is the daughter of Endre Kerekes, the dentist. Julyanna is her mother."

"Oh, you mean the tall, young girl I spoke to? She looks very pleasant."

"She's about my age," Anna said. "I hope we will become close friends."

Jacob, who had been listening to our conversation, interrupted loudly. "Wait just a minute," he exclaimed. "That's all we need right now — a friend in the house, someone who will be coming to visit often — just what we need!"

When Jacob and I were finally alone again, he persisted in questioning me about our neighbors. "Now, tell me the truth. Was the encounter with the new neighbors as bad as you feared it would be?"

"No," I replied. "I found that I am much more nervous anticipating things than actually facing the music. Then, it seems, I manage just fine." And with that, we settled down for the night.

29

AS THE DAYS PASSED, we slowly settled into a routine. My sister-in-law Minda became the "chatelaine" of our fort; Anna became our food gatherer; I became a full-time nanny who was devoted exclusively to the care of my child; and the men tried to pass the time by learning, reciting *Tehillim* or playing game after game of chess. These distractions kept them in their chairs for hours at a time, thus reducing their walking around or talking and the risk of being heard by our neighbors.

Anna's job was a very hazardous one, and backbreaking as well. She had to be outdoors, and was therefore extremely vulnerable as she went shopping for food with her forged documents and her forged ration tickets. With time, she too worked out a routine. In the morning she went shopping at one bakery in our neighborhood, using her ration tickets and mine. In the afternoon, she walked to another bakery several blocks away from the first, where she shopped for the three illegal members of our household, whom we called "the ghosts." Thus she was constantly lugging packages of food through the long meadow separating our house from the local shopping areas, while I stood watch at our "observation tower" from the minute she left until she walked through our door. And even after she had returned safely, we always wondered whether the storekeeper had realized that she was using forged tickets. Fortunately, we didn't have to concern ourselves with shopping in the grocery store because there was hardly anything to be bought. Occasionally, my sister picked up a little flour or oil there, but for the most part, we lived on bread and a thin gruel that Minda made with the little oil and flour we were able to obtain.

We became so accustomed to our new life that we never made mistakes anymore. No one ever called my husband Jacob. He was Iztvan and I was Zsuzsi. Nobody called my sister Esty anymore. She was Anna. Chuna became "Pali" and Minda was "Rozalia."

One evening, Anna came in from the terrace giggling. "What's so funny?" I asked.

"It's Lasi. Guess how old they say that hulking six-footer is?"

"Twenty."

"That's what I thought. But they say he's thirteen!"

"Well, I suppose his mother and grandmother know his age better than we do."

"No, I think they're lying about his age."

"Why?"

"Because he is retarded," Anna concluded.

"What makes you think so?"

"You should see how his family hovers over him. They treat him like a baby. They even answered for him when I asked him how old he is and if he's still in school. You should have seen how confused he became and how pleadingly he looked at his mother until she spoke up for him." Anna started to giggle again.

"Come now," my husband retorted indignantly. "Don't make fun of other people's tragedies."

"I didn't mean to. It's just that he looked so perfectly normal until then. See for yourselves," Anna urged us. "Then you will understand what I mean."

"What for? What difference does it make to us?"

"Well, for one thing, we can't leave our little Zsuzsi or Macika out on the terrace unattended for a second until we are absolutely sure that he's normal."

"Did you ever see your sister without the baby in her arms?" Iztvan asked with a wry laugh. "It seems she doesn't trust any of us — not even the crib!"

Iztvan's words stabbed at my heart. I wanted to scream: How can you understand me? How can you know what I am going through? How can you possibly know about the nightmares that haunt me, that have transformed into dread and fear the secure feeling I had before our baby was born? For then I knew that if our Jewish origin were discovered and they came to arrest us, they could only take you and me away! Now I know that those sadistic Nazis could grab little Zsuzsi, tear her from my arms....

But I didn't say a word. I simply began my nightly ritual. I lifted my baby from her crib and put her in my bed. Then I looked out the window to make sure that all was quiet outside. I was surprised to see that dawn was breaking over the tops of the lilac bushes, and from its purple loveliness came the alluring song of the birds. Despite all this beauty, I still went to sleep with a heavy heart.

Later that morning, I stood at our observation tower as usual, waiting for my sister to return from her shopping trip. All at once Ersabet Nagy caught my attention. She was placing three large terra-cotta flower pots filled with purplish-red azaleas on the ledge of her terrace. Suddenly, she stopped fussing over them and leaned over the ledge, watching something intently.

I followed Ersabet's gaze, and to my great shock and surprise I saw my sister walking down the path flanked by — yes, I was seeing correctly — two SS men! I bit hard on my finger to stifle the cry of horror that rose in my throat. Iztvan was at my side in an instant. Immediately, he grabbed the baby from me with one arm and steadied me with the other. I was speechless with fright and gesticulating wildy toward the path in the large, open field.

"Zsuzsi, it's alright!" I heard my husband say, as if from a distance. "Everything is alright! They are not Nazis. They are only our friends masquerading in Nazi uniforms. Can't you see? Don't you recognize the thin man? That's Mayse Cohen. And you don't even have to look to guess who the other one is. It has to be Abe Swarc. Who else but those two would have the nerve to walk around in their enemies' uniforms?" I looked more closely this time, and I saw that the two "officers" were indeed Iztvan's former schoolmates.

Soon I heard the unmistakable sound of army boots on the staircase. "I thought that number three was Zsuzsi's door," a voice shouted arrogantly.

"No, not that one," Anna said. "Please, ring number four. That's where we live!"

I opened the door. When they saw me, the two "Nazis" jumped to attention, clicking their heels together in characteristic SS fashion. "Heil Hitler!" they proclaimed in unison.

"Heil," I repeated with the same vigor, as I motioned them inside.

"Look!" the two men gasped as the door closed behind them. "It's Minda and Chuna!"

"I am Pali," Chuna corrected them, "and my wife is Rozalia."

"I am Misi Bartok, and this is Geza Bajor," Mayse answered with a mock salute. Anna burst out laughing.

"What's so funny?" I asked.

"Just try to imagine how our neighbors would react," she said, pointing to the wall, "if they were to witness this!"

"Well," Misi remarked, "I hope these walls will keep our secret."

"Tell me," I asked them, "how did you two find us, and where did you get those uniforms?"

"I gave them this address," Iztvan confessed in a small voice, "so that they would have somewhere to run to in case the everyday dangers became life-threatening." Then he turned to them. "Are you being pursued?"

"No, we're not, thank God," Misi said. "We have to admit that we took advantage of your generosity. We live as sublessors with an Aryan family. Our documents say that we are working in a municipal plant."

"Oh, I see," Iztvan murmured. "You need a legitimate excuse for not serving in the army."

"Right."

"But I still don't understand what this has to do with your visit," I insisted.

"Don't you see? Our 'job' requires us to be out of the house from early in the morning until late at night. We've spent the better part of the last few days in dark movie theaters, but how long can we get away with claiming to be on sick leave from work? And we feared that someone might suspect us, because one doesn't see too many men out on the streets nowadays. So, after spending hours pondering what to do, Geza came up with this brainstorm: we would come here a couple of times a week to visit and spend the day. At the same time, we could be of some benefit to you. Having such elite Aryan friends would enhance your credibility in the eyes of your neighbors." He winked and then looked at us pleadingly, waiting for an answer.

"Let's say you were to come here twice a week," Iztvan proposed. "What would you do during the remaining five days?" He looked down at the floor as he spoke, as all our angry gazes screamed: Don't endanger our lives with them!

"First of all," Misi answered, "Feri has surfaced in the last few days and he is busier than ever. He works day and night forging documents. He wants to fulfill his dream: to free as many men from the *munkatabor*s as possible and to find places to hide them. We usually spend two or three days a week there planning, and we run some perfectly 'legal' errands for him as well."

"Like what?" I gasped.

"Look," he said with a grin as he produced an envelope

from his uniform pocket. "We were about to deliver this document to a Jewish soldier, but we came too late. His unit was moved during the night to Bekescsaba. You know him too. Herschel Rubin."

Iztvan opened the envelope. "Father's name, mother's, the whole works!" he exclaimed admiringly. Then he pulled out another paper from the envelope. "I've never seen the likes of this!" It was a special document attesting to the fact that its bearer was on a secret assignment for the Hungarian homeland.

"Feri certainly has a sense of humor," Rozalia chuckled.

"I would call it *chutzpah*," Pali said.

"And some might call it contempt or rebellion," Geza added. "But what's the difference?"

"I think it's too dangerous for us to carry these papers in our pockets," Misi considered, speaking almost to himself, "especially since we're carrying our own forged documents as well." Then he turned to Iztvan. "Could you possibly hide them somewhere until I ask Feri what to do with them?"

"I hide my *tallis* and *tefillin* inside this wood stove," Iztvan volunteered, "and if anyone finds them, God forbid, I don't think that these papers could make things any worse for me. I'll put them in here if you like."

For appearances' sake the wood stove was densely stuffed with firewood. Iztvan started to remove it now, piece by piece. Out came the wood, which he stacked in neat piles on the floor. A stifled cry rose from the lips of the startled visitors as Iztvan's religious articles became visible at the very bottom of the hearth. A great hush fell over the room. Then Geza stretched out his bony fingers. "May I please use the *tefillin*?" he asked. "It's been so long..."

I couldn't tear my eyes from him as he removed his jacket, rolled up his sleeve, and carefully wrapped the black leather strap around his arm. Then, still wearing his black SS cap, he began to recite the opening lines of the daily *shacharis* prayer: "*Mah tovu ohalecha Ya'akov*! How beautiful are your tents,

Jacob! How holy are your dwellings, Israel!"

Listening to this man offering praise for the Jewish way of life, while wearing the emblem of the anti-Semites, the black cap of the Nazis, on his head, reminded me of the origin of this prayer, recorded in the Bible. Balak, the jealous king of the Moabites, enlisted the services of Bil'am, the priest, to curse the children of Israel. The priest rode to their encampment to observe their way of life, and as he watched from the hills above, he secretly marveled at the beauty of Jewish family life. He saw that the tent, the home, was the focus of each Jewish family. It was their inspiration, their strength, and their unity. It was a place where fairness and love prevailed amid the unshakeable faith in the One God.

Yes, Bil'am thought, that is what I shall destroy: their tents! That is the secret source of their power! He raised his hands and pointed towards the children of Israel and their dwelling places, ready to curse them. But as his voice rang out loud and clear, he was most amazed to hear his own hidden envy and admiration rise to the surface, and from his lips everyone heard: "*Mah tovu ohalecha Ya'akov*! How beautiful are your tents, Jacob!"

A great longing gripped my heart, and I prayed fervently: Oh, dear God, God of our fathers and our fathers' fathers, please give us back our humble, love-filled tents so that we can worship You proudly once again. Please thwart the Moabites, the Bil'ams, the Hitlers, and all the enemies of Israel who, from ancient times to our present day, try to destroy us and the source of our strength, our homes.

I heard the door slam on the wood stove, and the spell was broken. "It's five to eleven," somebody in the room said, and the electrifying message ran through the air: "The Voice of America!"

Iztvan jumped up as though he had been shot from a cannon. "My watch stopped!" he cried. "We would have missed it!" Instantly, he crawled under his bed and emerged holding a shortwave radio, ownership of which was strictly forbidden for one obvious reason: it could receive foreign stations.

All of us sprang into action. Iztvan hastily set up the shortwave radio on the table while a second radio — a legal one — was placed just a few inches away, its volume turned up high to drown out the forbidden sounds. Rozalia plugged in the shortwave while Pali ran for the blankets. I took up my post standing by the door in the entrance hall, and Anna faced me at the dining-room door.

The hushed room was filled with excitement as we all waited for the voice of the free world to penetrate our oppressed environment, to make us aware of the lies of Hitler's successes which were announced day after day in the heavily censored local newspapers and radio. The censorship kept the masses in the dark about the real events because Hitler knew, as did all dictators before him, that he owed his power to those who don't think, but merely follow blindly.

When Iztvan gave the signal, Rozalia covered the four men with the blankets. She turned to watch Anna, who was standing with her back to her, watching me intently. My part in this elaborate security play was to signal to Anna if I heard anything unusual outside. She, in turn, would signal Rozalia, who would immediately pull the cord from its socket, thereby prompting the men to hide with the radio. This well-rehearsed routine would take but a few seconds.

The men listened while we stood sentry, and soon they emerged from under the blanket. The moment I saw their faces, I knew that today something extraordinary had happened. The other women noticed it too.

"What is it?" we all cried at once.

"The Americans are coming!" Iztvan said. His face shone and his eyes were full of laughter.

Anna looked around, dazed. "Where are they?"

"Here, right here," Misi joked, and we burst out laughing. The men told us the wonderful news: the Americans had landed in Normandy!

30

I WALKED MY "SS" friends to the door. "I think we made enough noise here to wake the dead," Misi whispered in my ear, but he obviously wasn't convinced that our superintendent was aware of the source of the noise, because as the two boys passed the Horvats' apartment, he yelled back to us at the top of his lungs, "Anna, are you coming with us tonight to the SS meeting at Andrássy Utca 60?"

Back in our apartment, we looked at each other with astonishment over what had just happened. Not a word was spoken as each of us tried to assess the significance of our friends' visit. How would it reflect upon us? Iztvan broke the silence. "Leave it to Misi. Only he would think of ringing our neighbors' bell deliberately, 'by mistake,' to call their attention to our pure, Aryan visitors." We all laughed.

"You Jews!" Magda chuckled. "It is amusing how your minds work. I would never have thought of such a thing."

"You would have," Rozalia said with a sigh, "if you belonged to a people that has been persecuted as much as we have been. You'd be surprised at how this sharpens one's mind and makes one resourceful. It awakens the pure animal instinct that has become second nature to us during all the years we've had to struggle for survival."

"Tell me, Magda," Anna blurted out unexpectedly, "why do the Gentiles hate us so?"

Magda was taken aback. "I hope you don't think that Karoly or I..."

"Oh, Magda, how could you ever say such a thing after all that you and your husband have done for us? But I am sure that you are aware of the hatred." Magda didn't answer right away, so Anna persisted. "I know that you understand. Please tell me. What is it?"

"Well, for one thing, if you must know," Magda began, "my friends and I resented your overpowering, overprotective Jewish mothers. They made such a fuss over you as children. I guess it made us jealous."

"Oh, how absurd," I cried. "Tell me, Magda, now that we are both mothers, is there a difference between my behavior toward my child and your behavior toward yours? Do you feel that I love my baby more than you do yours?"

"No, no!" Magda exclaimed. "There is no greater love in the world than the love I feel for my child." She hugged her baby tightly. "No one could love anyone more. But now that I think about it, I can see a great difference in our behavior toward our children. I can also see a reason behind it, though. It seems," she said in a whisper, "that you try to make up for all the hatred awaiting her out there."

"You have a point," I said thoughtfully. "I never realized why I am so demonstrative, why I keep reassuring my baby the whole day long how much her father and I love her. For centuries, we have faced the problem of having to cope with varying degrees of anti-Semitism, some more violent than others. Our parents did their utmost to try to mitigate the impact it would have upon us, and I think you're right — that we try to do the same for our own children."

"But I think this approach has backfired on you," Magda commented. "You and your people have felt so loved that none of you could believe that there exists such a deadly hatred toward you."

"That's right! And when we woke up from our dream-world, it was already too late."

Pali saw it differently. "Do you think that Hitler, with his hoards of murderers, could have succeeded if God had not decreed our downfall beforehand?" he said angrily.

Magda stood up. She was dumbfounded. "Do you mean to tell me that Hitler is an innocent pawn who, against his will, is fulfilling a command of the God of Israel to maim and kill His children?" she asked. "Why should God bring this curse on you?"

"To punish us for our sins."

"I don't understand," Magda said, galled by Pali's reply.

"Let me explain then. We Jews blundered. We drifted away from the path of our fathers, especially in Germany where there was a lot of intermarriage. We began to assimilate at an alarming rate. Consequently, there arose a man by the name of Hitler to remind us that we are Jews even if we choose to throw away our religion."

"You make it seem so simple."

"It is, but the idea that Hitler is an unwilling participant is not correct."

"Well, then, how do you explain it?"

"It's simple. God allowed the evilest of all evil men to have his way. But someday the Germans will pay for their crimes. And just as God taught us how to create justice on this earth through His Law, so too does He judge us from Above in His infinite wisdom. One day, the descendants of this hateful nation will perish in fire, just as they have decreed that the Jews shall burn now."

"On what do you base this prediction of yours?" Magda asked him.

"On the history of our ancestors. Didn't mighty Pharaoh of Egypt decree that all male Jewish babies be cast into the Nile? And what actually happened? The Egyptians themselves were drowned in the Red Sea and we escaped."

"Well, I think that the comparison is not altogether accurate. I hate to remind you, but the victims of the gas chambers and the crematoria will never escape."

We were so engrossed in the discussion that we didn't hear the footsteps approaching our door. The doorbell rang, and I went to answer while the "ghosts" hurried to their hiding places.

Uncle Yidel, my father-in-law's youngest brother, stood at the entrance. I quickly ushered him in and closed the door.

"What took you so long to answer?" he cried, looking around wildly. "Where is Cheskel?"

"Why, how should I know?" I replied.

"He left the *munkatabor* long before I did."

"When did you see him last?" Rozalia asked. Upon hearing her uncle's voice, she had come out of her hiding place in the closet.

"You don't understand. He set out for here at least two hours before I did."

"Did Cheskel have the correct address?" Anna asked nervously. "Did he have the proper directions?"

"Last night, when we heard that our unit was going to be transported to Germany, Cheskel and I decided to escape and come here. We went over every detail several times, even though we didn't need to, since I believe we would have been able to find this house in our sleep. You see, we always lived with the notion that someday we might have to seek out this place."

"Don't worry," my husband comforted him. "Cheskel will surely be here soon." But the sound of his voice was not convincing at all, and I felt a terrible foreboding as I stood there, peering out to the path outside. If I were to see him coming, I would have been surprised beyond words.

[In fact, I didn't see Cheskel coming and neither did anyone else. None of us ever saw him again. Yidel had been the last to see him, when he watched him enter a public toilet earlier that day while Yidel marched on toward his destination.]

Later, sitting in the bomb shelter after an air-raid alarm, I wondered uneasily: What if someone saw Uncle Yidel enter our apartment? What if they ask me about him? What shall I say? Worse yet, maybe somebody knows that he is still upstairs. Yes, and the superintendent will go up and fetch him.... Don't think, I scolded myself. Why torture yourself? Go and talk to somebody.

I pulled my chair closer to Erika Kerekes, who was speaking with my neighbor, Mrs. Nagy. "Would you believe it?" she commented sadly. "I am always hungry these days. And to think that not very long ago," she added wistfully, "my parents would invite my friends over for supper, hoping that their undernourished darling would eat better in the presence of company!"

I saw Erika's mother and Ersabet Nagy look at each other for a fleeting moment. The two women's eyes met in an intimate glance that only people who are very close to each other exchange. Was it fear I saw in their eyes and in the deep silence that followed her outburst? But the next moment, the two women were laughing. Ersabet fished through her apron pocket. "Here, take this," she said, popping a candy bar into Erika's mouth, "and stop complaining!"

As we left the shelter and headed for our apartment, I told Anna, "I forgot to tell the Horvats about the hot water. Go upstairs and I will be there in a minute." I turned back and knocked at the superintendent's door. There was no answer, but I heard voices coming from inside. I was accustomed to letting myself in, and since the door wasn't locked, I marched inside.

"Who's there?" came Mrs. Horvat's frightened voice from within.

"It's me, Zsuzsi," I said, stepping into her dining room.

"What's the matter with me today?" she sighed. "I seem to be seeing things that aren't there." But she did seem to have fear written on her face, and her voice sounded so strained....

I was confused and tried to mask it by admiring a picture on the wall.

"That's a beautiful painting," I remarked. "Even as a child you seem to have had this amazing self-confidence combined with the sensitivity which I find so interesting."

"Why, this portrait isn't of me," she replied, turning crimson. "I bought this picture at a flea market and I have no idea who it is." She ushered me into the kitchen without offering me a seat. "What can I do for you?" she stammered.

It's obvious that she's very proud of her spotless home, I thought, marveling at the starched, white kitchen curtains, but it is even more obvious that she desperately wants to get rid of me. But why? Why does she own a portrait like that anyway? Why did it scare her when I recognized that it was she in the picture? Stop it! Stop reading hidden meanings into everything today, something inside of me screamed. My God, am I going crazy?

Making a lame excuse about seeing to the baby, I quickly headed for the door. As if I wasn't confused and upset enough, I collided with Mr. Horvat on my way out. "Excuse me," I said haltingly. He merely threw a hurried glance my way and slammed the door behind him.

For several moments, I stood in the hallway outside the Horvats' apartment, trying to regain my composure. All at once, I heard loud voices coming from within. I couldn't make out everything they said, but clearly the Horvats were upset, and I had been the cause!

"Where is Erika?" I heard Janos Horvat shout. "Don't tell me that she ...while Zsuzsi was here?"

"Oh, what a scare I had!" Julia cried. "Zsuzsi stepped inside only seconds after Erika ...!"

"Do you mean to tell me that Zsuzsi ... What did she want?" he demanded angrily. He muttered something I couldn't hear, then "... despise them, and the Bitters as well. They had no right bringing co-leasers along."

"She also saw my portrait ...!"

"Why did we have to display it in the first place?" he roared. "I'm going to hide it...And I'm going right now. I have to know if Erika ...enter our house."

Puzzled and shaken by their conversation, I hurried to our apartment, with numerous unresolved questions whirling about in my mind.

31

> Judge me, O God, and plead my case against a nation which works not with lovingkindness;
> O, deliver me from a man of deceit and violence.
>
> *Psalms 43:1*

The next day the air-raid siren sounded once again, and I quickly ran downstairs to the bomb shelter. I had just taken a seat there when I became aware of an odd noise in the hall outside. With the reflexes of a hunted one who must always be on guard, I immediately scanned the faces around me to see if one of us was missing. No, we were all safe inside. A stranger? Who would be coming here? I didn't have to wonder for long, for soon the heavy iron door of the shelter opened and a short man wearing a soldier's uniform strode inside.

The man marched wordlessly up to the front of the room and introduced himself unceremoniously. "I am Sandor Tiszai from Balt Utca."

My eyes were riveted on him. What does he want here? I wondered. He must have read my mind, for he said, "I am sure that you are wondering what has brought me here. So let me tell you right now. I have come here in good faith to warn you, my dear Hungarian citizens, brothers and sisters, of the dangers involved should you unwittingly be sheltering any illegal elements among you!"

Mr. Horvat stepped forward. "I am the superintendent of this building and I am aware of the fact that some Jews are trying to outsmart us, and think they can fool us with falsified documents. But I can assure you, my brother, that I have checked the papers of these tenants meticulously. However, if you have reason to accuse any of those present here, out with it, brother, and I will take care of it!"

My heart began to race and my stomach turned upside down. My God, I cried inwardly, let them not notice what is going on inside of me!

Then I heard Ersabet's high-pitched voice above everything else. "It would be best for us, Mr. Tiszai, if you would wait here until we can all go upstairs to fetch our documents and you can check them yourself."

The man's dark eyes lit up. "That's not a bad idea, not bad at all." I died a thousand deaths until I heard him say, "But it won't be necessary, as Mr. Horvat is a Party member and I see that he is aware of the danger. I trust his judgment."

"There must be a reason for all this," Mr. Horvat said, echoing the thought that had crossed all our minds.

"You are quite right, my friend. There surely is. Let me tell you what happened in our building last night. I had just come home for a forty-eight-hour furlough." The little man straightened himself up to his full height. "Thursday morning, you know, I will be on my way with my unit. Yes," he declared proudly, "we are going to the front line to fight for the homeland so that you, my Aryan sisters and brothers, will be able to enjoy peace!"

From the corner of my eye, I saw the old lady raise her hand and hold it high in the Nazi salute: "Heil Hitler!" she cried, with the enthusiasm of a young girl. Following her lead, we all shouted at the top of our lungs, as though we wanted to outdo one another, "Heil, heil!"

"But Sandor Tiszai is not about to offer his life on the battlefield," he continued, "without fighting for it on the home front as well. I am always on the lookout for what I can do for my beloved country. Sure enough, in the shelter last night, my gaze fell upon a lonely-looking man sitting in a corner of the room. Then I noticed that the man had a very prominent Jewish nose. I asked my wife who he was. 'I've never seen him before,' my wife whispered. Hmmm, I thought, he must be a Jew! But when I stood up to approach him, the man, realizing my intent, ran straight for the door and darted heedlessly into the darkness."

A bomb exploded next to our shelter with an unearthly roar, followed by heavy artillery fire. People screamed, but this didn't seem to bother our visitor who stood there, unruffled, his dark eyes shining with a mysterious fire, his voice full of contempt as he removed his service revolver from its holster and raised it high in the air. "But I ran after him, and I got him!" he cried. "I got the Jew! And this is the very same gun I shot him with, shot him to death!" He stopped speaking and stood there proudly, waiting for our response. Suddenly the room erupted with applause and while we shouted out our approval, he stood erect and haughty, as though he had built the world from rubble instead of having murdered an innocent man.

Nechy tossed and turned in her bed, trying in vain to keep her eyes closed. Although she was exhausted, she was restless and her eyes opened as if of their own accord. All the horrors of ghetto life came back to haunt her at this hour. What a miserable day yesterday was, she thought, with rain falling continuously, forcing us, oh Lord, all twenty-seven of us, to remain here in these five rooms with all the children and all the noise. She threw off her covers and got out of bed, remaining barefoot so as not to waken the children. She tiptoed to the window to see if the rain had stopped. As she pulled aside the mandatory blackout curtain, the moonlight's glare blinded her momentarily. After a short while, her eyes became accustomed to the brightness, and she looked out at the full moon and the thousands of glittering stars which had replaced the weeping gray skies of yesterday.

It's going to be a nice day, she thought. That should fill me with thankfulness, at least. Please, Nechy, feel something! she prodded herself. Don't be so indifferent. You have little children, you must go on. You are needed! But still, no matter how hard she tried to cheer herself up, her heart remained as cold and closed as a tomb.

She consulted her wristwatch in the moonlight. My, she thought with surprise, only one-thirty, and at twelve o'clock I was still washing out the children's things in the kitchen. Then it occurred to her that the teapot she had put on the stove might still be hot. Maybe I'll drink some tea and that will help me sleep. She had guessed correctly, for the water was still steaming. She spooned a few tea leaves into her tiny colander, placed it over her cup, and poured the hot water over it. But as she watched the liquid darken to a golden brown and tried to bring the cup to her lips, she was unable to force her hand to move. She was overwhelmed by a fear she had never experienced before. The heavy sense of foreboding which had descended upon her precisely at the moment when her brothers and sisters living in the ghetto had grasped at a last hope, left her paralyzed with gloom. Now, alone in her misery, she sat hunched over the table and recalled the episode.

It was July 8, 1944, and Chaim had burst into her room. "Nechy, where are you?" he called. "What are you doing here when everybody is outside? The mailman has just brought three letters. Everybody is thrilled."

Nechy's eyebrows shot up in surprise. "Are they from some of our missing men?" she asked hopefully.

"No."

"Then what's all the fuss about?"

"Oh, Nechy, don't you know? All three letters were sent from Germany. Now at least we know what happened to our people there!"

Reluctantly, Nechy went out into the courtyard with Chaim to the crowd of people that had gathered there. "Well, Chaim certainly didn't exaggerate," she muttered. "I've never seen so many people here."

The air vibrated with the sound of excited voices: "At least we know that we are being told the truth by our captors," someone said.

"So what?" another retorted. "I am itching to work, to do anything to earn some money to support us."

"Are you sure, Mrs. Hartstein, that this is your sister's handwriting?" a woman asked. "Can you verify it?"

"Of course I recognize it," Mrs. Hartstein replied indignantly. "I *am* her sister!"

The postcard was passed from hand to hand until it finally reached Nechy. She looked at the picture of the blue mountains, and all at once, a choking sensation gripped her. She imagined that all the mountains in the photograph were going to tumble down upon her, on her children, on all of them. Even before she read the postcard, with all the smiling faces encircling her, a sixth sense told her that this was the forerunner of their doom, and was meant to appease them, to make them docile.

"Hey, why don't you read it?" she heard people call. "Don't you see we are all waiting to see it, too?"

She turned the postcard over obediently and began to read it:

Waldse, Germany

My dear sister Chany,

Please forgive me for not writing sooner, but I must tell you that it has been hectic here. Imagine, so many of us arriving at once! But now things have turned out pretty well. Miriam and Elky are working from early morning until nightfall in an ammunition plant, coming home only at night, but we have gotten used to it. I keep house and try to make the children happy in their absence.

Write to the above address. I hope you are well. Give my love to the whole family.

Kisses from your sister,
Goldie

With a forced smile on her lips, Nechy thrust the postcard in the direction of the nearest outstretched hand. All she longed for was to be in her room and away from the crowd before she lost her composure and started to cry, which, she feared, would give away everything. Then it occurred to her that maybe everyone else also suspected the truth, and they were just putting on a show for the benefit of the others. She wished with all her heart that she too could put on a show, but tears were rolling down her cheeks, and she ran to her room.

Chaim followed her and found her lying on her bed, sobbing into the pillow. "Chaim," she cried, "tell your friends to be ready. The time for your disappearance is nearer than you think!"

The next day, early in the morning, Nechy stood by the window as she usually did at this hour, staring out into the still empty courtyard. She kept her eyes on her brother Shimon's room, expecting to see him come outside with Rifky any minute. Soon the door opened and Shimon limped out. He stopped to hold the door for Rifky, and she emerged carrying a large pail of laundered diapers. She proceeded to hang up the clean diapers as she did every morning at the crack of dawn, while the inhabitants of the ghetto were still sleeping and the arguments over who would use the clotheslines had not yet begun. Rifky couldn't take any chances, not now with her two-week-old twin sisters who, she had discovered, needed an enormous supply of clean diapers.

All at once, Shimon grabbed Rifky by the shoulder, causing her to spill out all the wet laundry onto the pavement, quickly dragged the startled girl into the house and slammed the door shut. Then Nechy saw it: pushing their way through the great oak door of the ghetto and into the courtyard were German and Hungarian officials.

The shock almost paralyzed her, and she fell onto the bed next to her two little boys. She covered her face with the blankets and prayed in the dark, "My dear God, I know that we are doomed. But please, don't let our enemies rejoice in our humiliation, in our suffering! Grant us the kindness You bestowed once, so long ago, upon Samson. Please bring this building down on us now and let our enemies die with us!"

Nechy stood in line holding onto her two little boys, one on either side of her. The children were frightened and she tried desperately to reassure them.

"Nechy!" her aunt Brandl cried in horror. "You forgot to pack your knapsack. What will you do without a change of clothing for the children, and where will you get a blanket to cover them with?"

She almost told her aunt Brandl that they wouldn't need anything, but she caught herself in time. "Chaim is carrying our things," she lied.

"Well, where is he then?" Brandl asked with irritation. "Why isn't he staying next to you and helping with the children?"

"Shut up!" an SS officer barked. "What do you think this is, a social club? No talking! Come on. Move back. Don't stay here so comfy. Move! Move, move!"

Little Avromi and Shmully began to cry and Nechy took a candy from her pocket which she had hoarded in order to make her children's last ride as sweet as possible.

32 | July 9, 1944

I, CHAIM EINHORN, arrived in the basement located directly under our school building where, during the course of the past few months, we have managed to complete this bunker. The six of us have worked hard and we now consider it to be a secure place for hiding out. If God watches over us, we will be safe. I glanced at my wristwatch and saw that it was exactly five-forty A.M. After opening the immense door of the matzah oven, I jumped inside and got down on my belly and crawled. In the pitch darkness, I felt for the entrance to our hideout. When I reached it, I removed the large piece of cardboard which we had painted to match the bricks of the oven and substituted for the oven's original back door, which we had torn out. I heard two voices breathe, "Welcome!" and quickly recognized them as belonging to Majs Morgenthal and Shmuel Porgesz.

"We can replace the cardboard shortly," I said, catching my breath. "I couldn't convince the other two to come with me. God knows, I tried."

"I understand," Majs replied. "Both of them are the oldest children in large families. Yes, they couldn't abandon their mothers at the last minute."

"And Nochem Baum is still delirious from his high fever,"

Shmuel added, "so it looks like, of the six of us, only we three are going to stay here. Let's close the back of the oven now."

Our bunker is located at the corner of Thokoly Imre and Brenner Janos Utcas in the heart of the ghetto. This morning we heard our brethren marching right over our heads. Panic and guilt overwhelmed us, and before we knew it, all three of us began to cry like babies. "You too?" we whispered to each other, and, not knowing exactly what to do, we shook each other's hands. "Welcome to the club," Shmuel laughed weakly.

"What's that noise?" Majs asked as the grandfather clock chimed twelve.

"Oh, I'm sorry," I said. "I forgot to tell you. Nechy gave me her clock last night all wrapped up in her husband's feather quilt. She wanted me to bring it with me to the bunker because it needs to be rewound only every six months."

"That reminds me," Shmuel cried. "I have a surprise for you." The bunker was filled with the sound of rustling papers. "I relieved an SS officer of his identification papers on my way down here," he stated simply. "They may come in very handy someday."

"You did *what*?" I asked, not believing that I had heard correctly. "How on earth did you do that?"

"Don't believe him," Majs warned me. "He's teasing us."

Shmuel clarified the issue. "Don't think he was in his jacket when I removed them," he explained. "I saw this jacket draped over one of the benches in the empty synagogue and I didn't think twice. I stole it, so that if we find life intolerable here..."

July 10, 1944. So far we have not left this black hole for the bathroom, and the stench in here is unbearable. We are frightened and our ears are glued constantly to the brick wall, our sole connection to the world outside. There is no doubt anymore. There are definitely people out there. We can hear them walking above our bunker, but we can't make out what they are saying.

July 11, 1944. There is no air in here at all. We argue constantly about opening up the tunnel to the bathroom, but so far I am still outnumbered two-to-one. I am secretly contemplating pouring out the little drinking water we still have left in order to force my point, but so far I have restrained myself. It won't last much longer anyway.

July 12, 1944. We ran out of water today and everybody agreed that we should open up the tunnel. As soon as we did, light and, God in Heaven, air rushed into the room and we ran to the faucet to drink and drink and drink. I stood on the toilet and located the two little cracks that we had labored so hard to make between the bricks in the wall. First I looked through the crack that opens to Brenner Janos Utca. The street was deserted. But I heard voices and so I stretched over to the second opening to view Thokoly Imre Utca. I saw nothing. I stepped down. "I hear voices but I can't see anything. Majs, you're the tallest, maybe you will be able to see better."

Majs climbed up to take my place. For several minutes he just stood there silently as he peered outside, periodically looking down at us and shaking his head. Then his whole body tensed up, and he turned around and got down from his observation post, looking as if he would faint. "Armed soldiers!" he gasped as Shmuel took his place at the wall.

After a short while, Shmuel stepped down, his face contorted with rage, his fists clenched. "They're carrying bundles of clothing and suitcases," he whispered.

"The animals!" I cried. "They must be caching the belongings they've stolen from the Jews in the *shul* buildings. The thieves! The murderers! They made sure they would not be robbed by the rest of the hordes!"

July 13, 1944. They arrived today at six in the morning. I saw them. One of them is tall with a long, bony face, dirty blond hair and nondescript features. The other is of stocky build, and the thing which stands out most about him is his Hitler-style mustache. I quickly named him "Hitler" and his partner "Goering," and if hate could kill, they would both be dead in an instant. We have decided to spend our days from now on in the bathhouse where we can hear everything they say.

At six P.M. another two soldiers arrived, and our jailers of the day left without exchanging a single word with their replacements. We heard them marching back and forth ceaselessly. Late this evening, Shmuel crept down from his post. "I think they went to sleep for the night," he reported excitedly. "Nevertheless, let's keep them under surveillance so that we can learn their habits. It may be useful one day." And as Shmuel finished speaking, I thought enviously of his SS documents.

August 1, 1944. We sat in silence in the bathhouse listening to "Hitler's" and "Goering's" conversations outside our bunker. Our pants pockets were filled with shelled nuts, an open package of matzah lay on the floor by our feet, and we munched nonstop. Our supply of these two foods, which constitutes our diet, is quite adequate, for it was planned to last for a six-month period for six people, and we are only three.

August 2, 1944. The day began as it always does, with us sitting and listening to the guards' discussions as we chew away at our provisions. Our ears pricked up when we heard them discussing the condition of the ghetto in Budapest. It was thus that we learned that our brothers in the city are still there and still alive. "Alive, alive," we all whispered, and we pinched each other to make sure that we weren't dreaming. Then Shmuel pulled us away to the opposite wall. "If that's the case," he whispered, "I'm going to break out of here and try to make it to the ghetto in the city."

August 3, 1944. We didn't sleep a wink last night. Majs and I are opposed to Shmuel's plan, but he is adamant about leaving.

The atmosphere in the bunker is charged. We can't afford the luxury of fighting with words, so we have resorted to shoving angry notes under each others' noses. "Fools!" Shmuel wrote in an angry scrawl. "Do you think we can stay here undetected forever? Sooner or later we will have to make this move anyway. Why don't you give me the encouragement I need? I am afraid, but I am going."

Reluctantly, I wrote back: "You do what you want!"

Shmuel took several small slips of paper from his pocket and counted them carefully. "Write your names on them," he said. He took off his yarmulke. "I will send you the documents back as soon as I can," he breathed. "Now we must decide who will use them first." He collected the scraps of paper, folded each one and put them in his yarmulke. I picked one and so did Majs. I held my breath. Both of us picked my name. There was a long silence, and I felt a mixture of relief and guilt. Majs was visibly upset. Then a paralyzing reality hit me. I took a piece of paper and wrote, "I left my 'modern' suit back home. I forgot to bring it with me!"

"You can't leave in your black suit and hat," Majs whispered, and I hated him for the obvious relief that I heard in his voice.

Shmuel felt the tension. "I'm sure that our brothers in the Budapest ghetto will help me get both of you out simultaneously," he reassured us repeatedly. "I promise to do my best. Pray for me," he whispered as he crept into the matzah oven toward the tunnel which led to the world beyond our bunker.

August 10, 1944. Today, as every day since Shmuel left, our ears were glued to the agreed-upon spot at the appointed time, hoping desperately to hear the password. But nothing. Again nothing. My nerves are strained beyond endurance. It was late and Majs was sleeping. I don't know how he does it. I am so envious. Not only does he sleep through the night, but he dozes off as soon as his duty by the wall is over, while I pace the floor night after night, thinking ceaselessly. What can I do? I asked myself. How can I escape? If only I had a different set of clothes, I would break out of here even without papers. Nothing would keep me back, nothing!

Then an idea struck me. Why hadn't I thought of it before? I quickly ran to see where the guards were standing but all I could see were their trousers and boots on the floor near the oak door where they usually slept. With great determination, I crawled through the oven and made my way to the synagogue, where I remembered having seen piles and piles of mens' clothes strewn across the floor.

I couldn't think clearly. Even though I knew very well that I should consult with Majs before taking such a drastic step, I couldn't stop myself. My legs took command of me and I ran up the steps. Then my hands took over and I opened the door. There I stood, at the courtyard, on the very same soil where I had grown up. I was blinded by the moonlight and by my tears. After a while, I became accustomed to the light and I saw what I wished I hadn't seen. The courtyard was filled with our people's belongings. I realized with a stab of horror that people had been working here all the time and had sorted out our things. There, right in front of me, covered by canvas, lay countless men's suits.

I raised my hand to select one, but I stopped, my hand still in midair. All at once, in the white light of the moon, everything seemed to melt into white bones, the white, dried-out bones of my murdered brethren. I looked at them, mesmerized. Under the starry sky, the nearby chestnut trees swayed in the mild summer breeze and their leaves rustled above the piles of clothing. It seemed to me as if at any moment, vultures would descend upon the bones of my dead brothers. And I could almost hear voices screaming at me, "You, too?" I covered my eyes, and my hand fell to my side. I couldn't touch a thing. Then, like a wounded animal, I bolted for my cave. After I entered it, I threw the cardboard back quickly to lock out the bones which seemed to be following me all the way back to the bunker.

August 11, 1944. So far I haven't told Majs what I did last night and I have no intention of doing so. Today seemed endless, but as night fell, I was able to tell myself with a little more confidence that the journey had remained my secret. Nevertheless, I was convinced, now more than ever, that we had to get out of here without delay, and I kept prodding Majs to consider leaving.

August 12, 1944. It's happened, it's happened, it's happened! The tapping on the agreed-upon spot sounded again and again tonight. My heart felt as if it would burst! Majs was half-crazed with excitement. "Majs, Chaim — Shmuel sent me!" we heard a voice whisper.

"*Shalom, shalom, shalom*!" Majs said the watchword in response.

Everything seemed to be in order as I made my way to the iron door on the Brenner Janos Utca side of the building. The night was pitch black but my frayed nerves picked up the raw animal fear emanating from the stranger on the other side of the gate. Despite the darkness, he obviously sensed my presence as well, for the moment I thrust my hand through the gate, a package was placed into it. I hoped he would not be detected, and I prayed *we* would not be detected. The fact that the watchman might have seen me made me shiver as I crept close to the wall on all fours and back into our hole.

As soon as I was back in the bunker, I tore open the package and found clothing and a note written in giant letters:

The train runs on the same schedule as usual. Hurry, don't miss it! Memorize your aliases. I will be sitting in the third car in a light beige suit. Don't talk to me! Just follow me closely. In Budapest, I will lead you to your sister.

P.S. If, for any reason, you can't make it today, start out tomorrow and the Number 5 streetcar will take you into the ghetto. Don't worry. We'll be in touch.

Was I dreaming? I rubbed my eyes, but I had no time to ponder. Majs had changed his clothes and now appeared fully dressed in his modern suit. "I'll sort out the documents," he said. "You go and get dressed." In a wink, I was ready and both of us started to memorize our new names.

"Let's go," I cried.

The time is twelve-thirty. I, Chaim Einhorn, together with Majs Morgenthal, am leaving our bunker. I am not afraid, for God is my Shepherd....

"Count the steps," Majs cautioned as we mounted the stairs. "There have to be fourteen of them." We felt our way along the wall for direction. Suddenly, the warm night air struck my face and I realized that we had reached the open door. My heart was pounding with fear and excitement. In my confusion, I didn't know which way to turn. I knew that if we followed the correct course, the wrought-iron gate, through which we were hoping to escape, would be to our right. If we made a mistake, we would head straight to our jailers. I stopped and tried to get my bearings.

Within moments, I was able to orient myself. I pointed to the right. "This way," I whispered.

Majs held on to me tightly. "Hurry!" he ordered me impatiently. "We have a train to catch!" He prodded me fiercely with the oversized, wrought-iron key.

The night engulfed us in deathly stillness. We chose our steps carefully, tapping the wall to find the gate. Finally, I recognized the texture of the wrought-iron gate to the courtyard. I took a breath and stepped back. "Open it fast," my friend hissed. The ironwork of the gate was wrought in a lacy pattern which I used to love. Now, however, the beautiful design became our deadly enemy, because its intricacy made it next to impossible to find the keyhole in the dark.

"Let me try it," Majs whispered.

"Be careful not to drop it," I warned him as I handed over

the key. I had hardly uttered the words when the heavy key fell from his hand and landed with a loud ring on the concrete floor. My blood froze and we both just stood there, scared to death.

"Fast, fast," I breathed as I pulled Majs along with me toward Aunt Brandl's door. I found the knob and turned it. "Luck is with us! It's yielding!"

The next minute we were both inside. The key which Aunt Brandl always kept in the lock was still there. I turned it, ran to the window at the opposite end of the apartment, and threw it open. We jumped through and ran heedlessly in the direction of Brenner Park.

Once at the park, we stopped to catch our breath. Our lungs were nearly bursting. We realized, to our utter relief, that no one was following us, but in our excitement, we had completely lost our sense of direction. Then we heard the sound of an oncoming locomotive and immediately ran in the direction of the noise. We had scarcely jumped onto the second car of the already moving train, when it began to pick up speed.

Soon, the door to our compartment opened and the conductor walked in. By the dim light of his flashlight, I saw that Majs was sitting next to the man who had written, "I will be wearing a light beige suit." Terrified, I repeated over and over in my mind: My mother's name is Emma Csardas. The conductor checked the stranger's papers, then Majs' without asking for clarification. My name is Lajos Toth, my father's name is Lajos Toth, I said to myself as the conductor stopped next to me and barked, "Ticket!" I shoved the ticket into his hand. He tore off the upper half and returned the stub to me without a word and walked away. I sat there, drenched in cold sweat, my heart pounding loudly in my ears.

33

THE NEXT MORNING, all our weariness from the sleepless night we'd had disappeared the instant we spotted Karoly, in his beige suit, turning into the path with Chaim, in modern attire, at his heels.

There are no words to describe the joy we felt as they entered the room and collapsed into our outstretched arms. "Oh, Karoly," I cried. "You did it! You did it again!"

"Please tell us about it," Iztvan said. "Tell us how it went."

"First, allow me to introduce myself," Chaim said, smiling broadly. "I am Lajos Toth. How do you do?" Then he pointed to the radio. "Turn down this noisemaker," he complained. "I can't hear my own voice."

"Shh!" Iztvan hissed. "That's the whole idea. We can't let our neighbors know how many of us live here." Chaim's eyes grew huge with worry as he looked from one face to the other.

"Good heavens, Anna," Magda exclaimed, changing the subject. "Your brother is the image of you, the exact duplicate of you in a male version."

August was extremely hot and dry. Here and there, arid, yellow patches appeared in the lustrous green meadow surrounding our house. The leaves on the trees were turning yellow, too. This did not prevent "Lajos," who had spent so many weeks in a dark, dingy, underground bunker, from admiring the beauty of the world. He stood for hours peering through the little crack in the venetian blind and gazing at the scenery. He talked endlessly about our sisters and brothers, and the children whom, we knew deep down, we would never see again. My helplessness and guilt surfaced with renewed strength. We did not do enough, I said to myself. We did not do enough.

On the twenty-ninth of the month, Horthy, the Regent of Hungary, surprised us by having a rift with the Germans. He withdrew his troops that had supported the German army in their battles against the Allied forces and appointed one of his more liberal cabinet staff members, General Lakatos, as the new prime minister of his newly-formed, less-radical cabinet. Most important, Horthy flatly refused the Germans' request that he authorize the deportation of Jews from the ghetto of Budapest. The news spread like wildfire through Jewish circles, and it brought renewed hope to the sixty-three thousand Jews who still languished in the ghetto. Even the most skeptical ones whispered a hesitant "maybe" to the unexpectedly good tidings.

Our food ration tickets were dwindling to a dangerous low, and the knowledge that sooner or later my husband would have to go to the ghetto to obtain more of the precious slips of paper was hanging over our heads like a sword. There lived in the ghetto a man by the name of Godinger whom the Jewish underground entrusted with supplying the likes of us, members who weren't registered and thus were not eligible to receive the life-sustaining forged ration books.

All too soon, the dreaded day arrived. "Relax, my dear," my husband said as he prepared to leave for the ghetto. "You know how much more lenient the new regime is toward us. Please don't worry. We'll be alright." He turned to Anna, and the next minute they were off, my sister carrying a shopping bag in which she hoped to store the dangerous items.

As they got off the trolley on Andrássy Utca, Iztvan said, "Let's explore for a little while."

"I'm not interested in touring this neighborhood," Anna replied, "and I dread seeing the ghetto. Let's just hurry. You know what a bundle of nerves your wife is, so let's not waste any time."

"Who wants to waste time?" Iztvan retorted. "I just want to point out to you the shortcuts you can take so that you'll be familiar with them if you need to get away quickly." He pointed to the building directly in front of them. "We will walk into this house, exit by the back entrance and we will be in the Dob Utca."

The building they entered was a large tenement which was bursting at the seams with people. In each and every room of this dilapidated structure lived another family. The dark courtyard which they entered next was almost impossible to cross as it was so full of people of all ages. This did not stop the children from running around noisily, completely engrossed in a world of their own.

"Let's go," Anna insisted, as she trembled and cried out of pity for the conditions under which these Jews were living.

"Alright," Iztvan agreed. "Let's get away from here."

He led her to a side door which opened onto a narrow back alley. The alley was packed with garbage cans, most of them uncovered, and it was swarming with big black flies that traveled from one heap of refuse to another, their shimmering transparent wings reflecting a spectrum of colors.

"How much further?" Anna was by now nauseated by the foul odor of the garbage.

"We have to cross through only one more house and we will be at Godinger's," he answered her.

The back alley lead into another house with many doors. "Once I counted its exits," he whispered, "and I came up with no less than six, leading to four different locations. Here we are," he said with a sigh.

They crossed the street and entered the building in which the Godingers lived. They ran up the steps and Iztvan stopped outside an apartment on the second floor. The door had once been painted gray, but now the paint was mostly chipped off and the door looked as depressingly neglected as the rest of the building.

Anna watched wide-eyed as Iztvan knocked three times. He waited a few moments and then rang the bell once. Soon they heard footsteps approaching the door and someone peered at them through the tiny peephole. Iztvan knocked again and the door was opened. They entered an equally neglected little vestibule where an older woman stood, wearing a drab dress and what appeared to be men's shoes without shoelaces. She fit into the environment so perfectly that it appeared as if she had no existence apart from it.

They stood gazing at her wordlessly. "Call me Kati," she said after a while.

This brought them back to the present. "And call me Marrano," Iztvan replied hastily.

"Come with me," the woman said, and she escorted them to another room where an old man, obviously her husband, was sitting and learning Gemara. They stood there respectfully, waiting for him to address them. After a few minutes he looked up. "They are Marranos," the woman whispered.

"Just how many of you are there?" he asked. "And how many do you need?"

"As of now, there are five of us who are not eligible for the ration books," Iztvan replied, "but I have two brothers in the *munkatabor* who may have to join us in the future."

"And I have one brother who will find us one of these days," Anna interjected, the tears glistening in her eyes. "And let's not forget about our SS friends who frequently spend the day with us," she added.

"God bless you all," murmured the old man, and he stood up and slowly walked out of the room. He reappeared in a short while carrying a wad of the priceless yellow papers. "Here," he said, his faded gray eyes glinting. "I hope the war will not last as long as these can keep you."

"Open up, Jew!" someone shouted in fluent German,

almost knocking down the door in his impatience.

"He is probably looking for my brother's son," Mr. Godinger explained quickly. "My nephew is a rich and powerful man who escaped with his family to Switzerland during the very first week of the German occupation. The Nazis come occasionally to interrogate me. They desperately want to find him."

"Hide me!" Iztvan begged his hosts. "Please hide me!"

Mrs. Godinger opened the door to the adjoining room and motioned to Iztvan to enter it. "And you," she whispered to the terrified Anna, "you can say that you live in the next building."

Iztvan stumbled into the room trembling with fear. He frantically searched for a hiding place, but to his dismay the only pieces of furniture in the little two-by-nothing room were two cribs. There wasn't even a closet in which to hide.

He crouched behind the crib, shaking and frightened. Suddenly, the door burst open. In the doorway stood a big, fat, uniformed Nazi. "Hey, who is this?" he bellowed, pointing at Iztvan. Iztvan's blood froze in his veins. "Who are you?" the Nazi demanded again, coming closer. Then Iztvan noticed that he had left the door to the foyer open. He didn't hesitate for a moment. With giant strides, he fled from the room and out of the apartment.

"Stop!" the officer shouted. "Stop or I'll shoot!"

Iztvan was almost at the front door when a shot whizzed past his head. He lunged for the door and almost managed to escape, but just as he reached the entrance, large hands grabbed hold of him and pinned him to the floor.

The German stood over him as he lay there dazed, with the second man still holding him down. Then Iztvan heard the officer praising the other man, whom Iztvan assumed to be the superintendent of the building.

"I was sitting, breaking bread with my wife and two little girls, when I heard the shot," the superintendent explained. "I jumped up, warning them to stay put. 'They must be killing some Jews. Don't endanger yourselves,' I told them. Then I came here and saw this man trying to escape. I could not believe the nerve of him."

"You did an excellent job," the Nazi commended him.

"Just doing my duty," he replied proudly.

"Get up!" the Nazi ordered Iztvan as he yanked his arm and smacked him hard across the face. "Where are your papers?" he demanded.

"Here," said the stunned Iztvan. His mind was working fast as he tried to figure a way out of this. He stood up with difficulty, moaning with pain.

After examining his papers and learning that Iztvan wasn't Jewish, the Nazi asked, "What are you doing visiting these Jews?"

"German people, nice people," Iztvan answered with a great grin on his face.

"Why did you run? Tell me, why did you run?" the Nazi demanded.

"German people, nice people, smart people," he muttered between moans.

The German turned around and faced him. "You'll have to come to headquarters if you won't cooperate with me here. Tell me, did you bring a message from a relative of this Jew?"

The reality of the danger he was in penetrated Iztvan's consciousness. Oh my God, what shall I do? he thought in desperation. Suddenly a picture formed in his mind's eye, a vague picture of a dimly-lit room where the Ratzfelder Rebbe sat, his big dark eyes burning with fire. "And what would you like me to bless you with, my child?" the Rebbe asked. Rivka Leah answered in a small, scared voice, "I don't know. Rebbe, what has God written in our book? Are we to survive, or will we succumb to this purge? Just promise me that come what may, my husband, unborn child, and I will never be torn from each other." He could hear the Rebbe's voice loud and clear despite the commotion around him: "You will make it," he had promised. "Just hope and pray and never give up!"

The Nazi gave him a push, interrupting his reverie, and indicated that he was to cross the street to number Sixty

Andrássy Utca, the SS headquarters. The headquarters, with its infamous inquisition chambers, loomed ahead. From the corner of his eye, Iztvan noticed the house with the many exits that he had pointed out to Anna when they first arrived.

As he limped along, Iztvan was sure that he had succeeded in fooling the Nazi as he had planned. The German seemed genuinely convinced that Iztvan was lame and in pain and that he was a slow-witted idiot. They stood on the street corner and watched as the oncoming cars passed quickly by. Iztvan waited until an approaching car was a few meters from him. Then, with the swiftness of a deer and the courage of a lion, he darted across the street. Brakes screeched, people screamed. Before anyone knew what was happening, Iztvan ran into the house with the multiple exits and disappeared from sight.

34

AUGUST PASSED and so did the better half of September. The air grew chilly in the evenings, and even though the sun still shone brightly at noontime, it had lost its ability to awaken the curled-up petunias on our terrace. At sunrise frozen dew glittered like precious jewels on each blade of grass in the large, open meadow surrounding our hideout.

"Autumn is here and there's no doubt about it," my sister announced one day.

"And so is Rosh Hashanah upon us," my husband sighed.

"Remember our Hebrew teacher, Miss Jenya?" Anna asked with a wink. She stood up, put her two hands on the table and looked directly at an imaginary classroom, just as Miss Jenya used to do back in our childhood. Then, mimicking our teacher's voice perfectly, she started to preach. "And these are the days when our Creator judges us according to how we conducted ourselves during the past year." Here she stopped momentarily and gazed briefly upon the "girls." "And in front of Him two great books are opened — one for life and the other for death." I remembered how we would shiver, our innocent childish pranks looming like deadly sins.

Then Anna spoke encouragingly, just as Miss Jenya would do at this point in her lecture. "And these days should remind us all to strive for new strength of character, for personal growth, and to resolve that in the coming year we will be helpful and compassionate to even the tiniest creature of the Almighty." Here Anna stopped her mimicking and her voice became deadly serious. "And now that our fate, which God decreed last Rosh Hashanah, has befallen us with all its unprecedented horrors, I tremble with fear. We must search our souls as never before, in order to learn what angered our Father in Heaven and made Him turn away from us. Yes," Anna wept, "and we must try to correct our wrongdoing!" We stood there trembling as we contemplated our tremendous task.

"I cannot imagine praying at home this Rosh Hashanah," my husband stated decisively.

"What do you mean?" I asked him.

"Why, it's simple. I want to go to the ghetto and pray with our brethren."

I could not believe that I had heard correctly. "Go into the ghetto?" I exclaimed. "Have you lost your mind?!" But then I saw tears shining in my husband's eyes and I stopped my angry tirade, for I only wished to cheer him up. "Of course, Iztvan," I soothed, "there has never been a greater need in our history for repentance than there is now."

Then the bickering began between each and every member of our household. Not even the pleas of Karoly and Magda could make my husband abandon his plan. He stood his ground, insisting, "I must go. I must." There was nothing to do but enlist the help of a very reluctant Misi to find us a place to stay for the two-day holiday.

On the eve of Rosh Hashanah, I hastily packed the barest necessities into my oversized bag, and the four of us — my husband, my little girl, my sister and I — set out for the ghetto.

We arrived just before nightfall. We found our accommodations easily and were warmly welcomed into a flat which housed three families. "Please feel at home," our hostess said cordially, "even though all we can offer you is a place in the kitchen." She pointed to a corner where our beds were made up on the stone floor.

"That's what I call sharing," my husband said approvingly. With a sigh of relief that we were finally here, I laid little Zsuzsi down on the mattress and tucked her in for a nap.

Early the following morning we went to the building next door to pray. My husband *davened* among the men in a downstairs apartment, while we women prayed in an adjoining room. From behind sheets of thick mesh we could see the Rabbi conducting the services.

Shortly before noon the morning services ended, and the *gabbai* announced to the sobbing audience that an hour of intermission would precede the *musaf* prayers, the highlight of the day. As the weary, downtrodden congregation started toward the door, I stood up to follow them. All at once, someone grabbed me from behind and I heard a tinny voice begging, "Please don't go yet. I want to talk to you."

Startled, I turned around and gazed into the woman's face. She must have been very young, perhaps even younger than I. Her childlike features were distorted with fear, and her almond-colored eyes looked at me pleadingly from beneath her dark brows. But as she spoke, her words were cold and detached, as if they came from the grave.

"I watched you the whole morning. You were praying."

Her words confirmed what I had been thinking about her. She was mad. I started to push my way through the crowd in order to get away from her. "What other reason would I come here for, if not to pray?" I retorted angrily. She didn't answer, but her eyes filled with such indescribable pain that I changed my mind and slowly sat down in my seat, ready to listen.

"I can't pray," she sighed. "I feel I have no right to." She stretched out a hand as if to touch little Zsuzsi who was dozing in my arms, and I instinctively drew back. "You have a beautiful baby," she said so softly that I had to strain my ears to hear her.

"Thank you," I whispered, spellbound by her tormented features.

"A boy or a girl?"

"A little girl, five months old."

The place was half-empty now and I willed my trembling legs to get up. "I must be going now," I told her.

She didn't answer but her eyes held mine steadily. "I should be expecting my baby by now," she said. Her eyes were blank and her face a mask of stone.

"Why, what happened?" I asked.

The girl's eyes darkened, making the deathly pallor of her face seem more unnatural and frightful. "I…I…I…," she stammered. "Oh, this horror, this crushing sin!"

I gaped at her, and, with an involuntary movement, I bent over my baby protectively and slid as far away from her as I could.

"Tell me about it, my dear," someone behind me said gently, and I realized that there was another person present in the now-empty *shul.* I recognized the woman instantly as the wife of our Rabbi. "Tell me what happened. You can talk about it," she repeated over and over, as she stroked the girl's limp hands. Her face radiated warmth and motherly love, and her voice was full of lovingkindness.

The girl averted her eyes and buried her face in the Rebbetzin's shoulder. Her words came out in broken syllables. "He was my life and I loved him more than anything in the world. And they tore him from my side. Then he was no more. Then he was dead. My father and mother and sisters and my little brother were all deported, leaving me all alone in the world. No, you can't have the baby, too, I vowed. You can't take more from me. Nothing, never."

"Calm yourself, my dear," the older woman soothed. "It's all over and done with. The only thing you can do now, my lamb, is to pray, and I will pray for you and so will the Rabbi."

In my heart a prayer on behalf of the suffering girl rose with such force that I began to cry again, and, blinded by the tears, I ran out of the *shul* and headed straight for our lodgings. Neither my husband nor my sister were there, so I went outside to look for them.

A crowd had gathered on the far side of the courtyard and I

saw a man speaking, surrounded by a circle of onlookers. Soon I spotted Iztvan and Anna. Don't go there, common sense cautioned me. Nevertheless, I edged up behind my sister. "Who is he?" I asked in a whisper.

Anna's eyes were red from crying. "I don't know his name," she said softly. "He is from Pressburg, and he is talking about how the Nazis destroyed his beautiful Jewish community, about the great suffering there and about his family's miraculous escape."

Go away, don't listen, I prodded myself again. But of course I couldn't tear myself away from the scene.

The man's voice trembled with emotion. "And that's how it happened in the end," he cried. "As I mentioned before, the secret warning had reached the three of us. We learned from England about the liquidation of the Jews of Pressburg, and, after the initial shock, all three of us reacted. We and our families all had papers to make it to Budapest. But Bernát Leitner and his wife lost the courage and stamina to flee. They said that they could not face life as fugitives, and no amount of begging or reasoning could change their minds. Later we learned that they stayed to help people escape and were subsequently caught and deported to Auschwitz. Then, who could have known that little Medy, Albert Hausner's little girl, would come down with appendicitis and have to go to the hospital?"

The man was crying unabashedly now. His short, stocky body trembled and the tears in his sky-blue eyes shone like gems in the sunlit yard. "Albert tried to make his wife see that if they fled with the others, at least they would be able to save themselves, but she wouldn't hear of it — how could she leave her daughter behind? The next morning, when dawn was breaking over the Danube, Albert spotted the black limousine speeding across the shiny bridge over the river. He panicked, and as the Nazis approached his house, he fled through the back door."

"He is here in the city," the man said, tears flowing from his eyes unchecked. "I saw him last week. He is a shadow of his former self. As soon as I spotted him, I quickly turned and walked in the opposite direction. Because, as God is my witness, this man has a heavy enough burden to bear without my reminding him, by my mere presence, of what might have been." His voice cracked, and he stopped abruptly, looking around helplessly.

Suddenly, a cry pierced the silence. It was a cry that left us shaking in its intensity. A young man pressed both hands to his lips in an unsuccessful attempt to stifle the sound, and then he hastily bolted from the crowd and disapppeared from sight.

"Who was he?" the words rang through the crowd as we scanned each other's faces for some clue as to the young man's identity.

"May the Almighty forgive my sin," our orator cried. "Who knows what memories I have awakened for him!"

"No, no," said an old woman who was wearing a long, white, gathered skirt, and a white kerchief on her head. "He was brought to the city just a few days ago, where he learned of the fate of his family, his wife, his children." We looked at her, flabbergasted. "They had been assigned to work in the fields of Grof Burgli, where they lived in complete isolation from the outside world. No mail, no newspapers, nothing. And then they were all taken away...He is one of the men from the *munkatabor* who detonated the bomb last night." She pointed toward the sidewalk where countless workmen were laboring to clear away the debris from last night's air raid.

"I must go and feed the baby," I whispered to Iztvan, for I was anxious to get away. We started walking to our lodgings.

"Just compare the lot of these two men," my husband said. "One knew and tried, but failed, and the other went with his family wherever he was ordered, and now they are in the same boat. Both have lost their wives and children."

"But compare the futures these two will face," I cried with

sudden awareness. "Now I understand what people mean when they say that they won't exclude themselves from the fate of the fold, and whatever is good for their own is good enough for them, too. Unconsciously, perhaps, they are wise enough to realize this." I rambled on, not giving Iztvan a chance to speak. "Who will fare better in the long run? The ones who went with their brothers and shared their fate, without guilt and self-hate gnawing away at them, or those who saved themselves but failed to save their families, and who will carry their guilt with them throughout their lives? Oh, what an onus! For the penalty for failure is life! Woe for those so condemned!" I wailed.

Iztvan glanced at his wristwatch. "I must go back to *shul*," he said, "and you'd better go too, because in twenty minutes they will blow the *shofar*."

My baby grasped my finger with her tiny hand, reminding me of her presence. "Oh my darling," I cried after my husband, "can you see it? Can you see that we also took a chance? We took the chance with her. Oh my Lord, have mercy upon us!"

After I was seated in *shul*, I turned around just in time to see the door open and the imposing figure of our Rabbi walking in. My heart ached as I looked at the man with the long, silver beard wearing the traditional white *kittel*. He walked slowly, weighed down by all the misery which had befallen us. It seemed as if the entire congregation held its breath. The Rabbi laboriously climbed up the steps leading to the Ark, where on a table, covered with a sparkling white cloth, lay the Torah. The holy scroll of the Torah was also draped in pure white, as was the curved ram's horn alongside it.

The Rabbi picked up the *shofar* and we all trembled. Raising it high in the air, he cried, "This *shofar* is to remind You, my God, of how our forefather, Avraham, took his only son, Yitzchak, to give him to You as an offering on the altar at Your command. But You, my God, had pity on them, and when Avraham was ready to slay his son, whom he loved more than life itself, Your Heavenly voice rang out: 'Halt! There is a ram in the bushes. Offer it to Me and spare your son, for I only wanted to test you, Avraham, my servant.' And sure enough, caught by its horns in the brush, was the ram. And yet, my God, when Your children are dragged away to be offered at the flaming altar of anti-Semitism, there is no ram! Please, oh God, have pity on us and forgive our sins. Please have mercy on us and don't let us all perish in the flames!"

By this time his words were drowned out by the wailing of the worshipers, and the clear, loud sound of the *shofar* rang through the air, piercing our wounded hearts.

35

> Hide me from the secret counsel of evildoers
> From the tumult of the workers of evil.
> *Psalms 64:3*

OCTOBER ARRIVED on the wings of a downpour, and all we could see in the fields surrounding our house was mud and more mud, as each day brought heavier rains than the day before. But that did not discourage our SS friends from visiting us. Life in Dombalya 5 became much more peaceful during this blessed period which began on August 29, 1944, when Prime Minister Lakatos was installed into office. The police became more lenient towards the Jews and the dreaded street *razzia*s were halted. Because of this, our friends in SS uniforms came to our house more often than ever, and the Jews in the ghetto breathed a sigh of relief. But on October 15, this short-lived time of relative tranquility ended abruptly, when the repressive Salasy regime took over.

The day had begun happily, with little Zsuzsi performing a new trick. "Iztvan, Iztvan! Come quickly!" I called excitedly. "Look! Our baby is sitting! She sat up all by herself!"

Everybody came running to witness the miracle. Her father lifted her from the crib. "So, you can sit," he declared, beaming as he tickled her under the chin. The baby started to laugh and all of a sudden the pale, apathetic faces around her came to life with joy. "Let's see if she can do it again," Iztvan suggested, putting her back into the crib. Little Zsuzsi started to cry, and with her two little arms raised in the air, begged to be picked up.

"You can't put her down," I teased him. "We all know how you feel about your daughter."

Iztvan was puffed up with pride. "Come, sit up again," he cooed. "Show everybody that you can do it. Come on, don't make your daddy a liar." And as if she understood his words she suddenly rolled over on her tiny belly, supporting herself with one little arm and pushing against the mattress. She twisted herself around, and the next moment she was sitting up and looking at us triumphantly.

"Let's see, how old is she now?" I wondered out loud. "What's today's date?"

"The fifteenth of October," Lajos volunteered.

"She was born on the thirteenth of May." I started counting aloud on my fingers. "So that would make her exactly five months and two days old!"

"She is so quick," Pali commented, "and so friendly as well."

"Well," I said, hiding my pride, "she isn't the first baby who learned how to sit up, but I'm sure nobody ever did it with such ease and grace."

After a while she tired of the new adventure. I watched her tenderly as, exhausted, she drifted off to sleep.

Magda was still excited and proposed a celebration. Following her lead, I made a suggestion. "I know what we'll do. Little Zsuzsi and I are going to play hooky."

Anna, who took everything so seriously, looked at me in wonder. "What do you mean?"

"I mean that, air raid or no, I will sleep the whole day long." I threw myself on my bed to prove I meant what I'd said. "I don't want to even go near those hideous shelters!"

"Sure, sure," Anna laughed nervously, "and tell me what excuse we will give to the others living in this house with us."

"You could tell them that I went to the dentist and took my baby along."

"Why not say that you took little Zsuzsi for a checkup?" Magda played along earnestly.

"And what if they ask for the name or the address of the doctor?" Anna asked fearfully.

"Oh, Anna, how can you be such a killjoy?" I cried. "Let me at least pretend." I turned to the wall, closed my eyes and pulled the covers over my head.

"Zsuzsi, Zsuzsi," Anna whispered a few moments later, tugging the covers from my face. I still did not open my eyes. By then, the room was silent. No radio. Not a sound. Although I was awake, the unusual quiet gave the place a dreamlike quality.

I smiled with still-closed eyes. "Let me sleep," I murmured.

"But, Zsuzsi..." She sounded as if she were on the verge of hysteria. I opened my eyes and saw my sister's terrified expression.

"What's wrong?"

"There is an intermission now," she said softly, "and we were told to call our neighbors, anyone who does not have access to a radio."

Then we heard the announcement. "Attention! Attention! At the request of our beloved Regent, Miklos Horthy, every Hungarian citizen is to stay within hearing distance of the radio for further orders." Then we heard a "click." We remained standing next to the radio, looking at each other wildly for some reassurance, for some possible clue. Before any of us could find his tongue, Lajos placed a finger on his lips, his blue eyes wide with fear. He pointed frantically to the wall and whispered, "Without the blaring of the radio, they can hear us on the other side of the wall."

"What does this announcement mean?" I asked softly.

"Have patience," Karoly snapped.

"Oh, Karoly," I said, "you cannot understand our fears. To us, a change in government, *any* change, for that matter, automatically brings to mind the question: 'How will this affect the Jews?' "

"The radio!" Anna cried as the broadcast began once again. But it was just a repeat of the former message.

Then several minutes later, as we stared at the silent radio, it came to life once more.

"Attention! Attention Hungarian citizens. Please stay tuned, because in the course of the day, the Regent will be issuing very important orders."

The announcer's closing words hung heavily in the air. An important message. What could this be? we pondered. The suspense grew with each passing second.

"Maybe he wants to blow up the ghetto," Rozalia said, her brown eyes wide with horror, "and the Regent will advise his Aryans to vacate their homes and stay away from the area at a specified time."

"She may be right," Pali whispered with restrained emotion, and two bright red spots appeared on his pale cheeks. "It is an open secret that the ghetto is wired with explosives hidden underground!"

"I think I've heard enough," Karoly exclaimed, visibly shaken by this exchange. "Never in my life have I heard such a crazy idea — that the Regent would issue an order to blow up even the tiniest part of our beloved Budapest, the pride and joy of the homeland?!" Then he added in a soft, fatherly tone, "As if it won't be damaged badly enough by the enemy. Now stop working yourselves up into a state of hysteria, before I really get angry!"

It occurred to me that he too was frightened. I wondered briefly, if the Regent personally urged people like him and Magda to turn in the Jews they were hiding, whether they'd comply. Then, in the silence of the room, I recalled the announcement made many months ago, just after the ghetto was closed: "Attention! All Aryans who are harboring Jews illegally: give them up or suffer the consequences!" Later it mentioned the horrible punishment that awaited those who failed to do so: "You will be made to witness the brutal deaths of your wife and your children. Then, and only then, will you receive the *coup de grace* to relieve you from your misery."

And Karoly and Magda, shaking clenched fists at the radio, had turned to us and said, "Fear not, dear friends. We'll never give you up to those swine."

Hot tears flooded my eyes as they always did when I searched my soul and asked myself: Would I do this for perfect strangers, as Karoly did when he appeared at our door in the dead of night and offered to rescue my sister from the Szombathely ghetto? And from millions of contradicting voices in my soul, the only one which rang with the undoubtable truth was the one that asserted that they would never abandon us.

The air-raid siren wailed. I looked up and saw that my husband was missing. "Where is Iztvan?" I cried, suddenly terrified.

No one answered.

"Where is he?" I asked again, beginning to panic.

"Be quiet," Lajos whispered sharply. "I'll tell you. He went to bring his brothers Yudl and Herschel up from the *munkatabor*."

"He went out without telling me?"

"He didn't want to cause a row. He knew that you would be opposed, so he sneaked out."

I was flabbergasted. "Please, Zsuzsi, I beg you, don't worry," Anna urged me. "Everybody is in the shelter already. Come on, let's go!"

I felt my legs giving way under me, but nevertheless I followed Anna, who carried the baby.

"Good heavens!" Mrs. Horvat cried when she met us at the entrance to the bomb shelter. "What's the matter with you, Zsuzsi? You look sick."

"I must have indigestion," I muttered in a daze, taking a deep breath.

Several minutes after we entered the shelter, the radio went on. All the occupants of the room gathered around it anxiously, but it was the same message again.

"I feel so disappointed whenever I hear this," the elder Mrs. Nagy said.

"Me, too," Julyanna sighed.

"I could just scream!" Magda lamented in frustration. "Why can't they tell us what it is all about?"

"My nerves are so frayed that I'm afraid I'll explode," Ersabet whined.

"There is nothing to be gained from being nervous," the old lady added, more to herself than to the others. Then her expression brightened. "I have a good idea. Let's each try to guess what the Regent's message will be." Her words were met with silence. "All right, then," she smiled, her bright eyes full of mischief, "let's make up rules. Whoever comes closest to guessing will receive a prize — my sugar ration for the whole month of November."

"Oh, that would be just in time for Christmas," Erika exclaimed. "We could use some extra sugar, couldn't we, Mother?"

Julyanna smiled at her encouragingly. "Then show off your genius, my baby."

"Dear Regent Horthy," the old woman began, "you know how anxious we are to hear your speech. Please don't delay it any longer, because right now the whole nation is huddled together in the shelters." And as if on cue, the radio came to life, but it was only a repeat of the same message.

Erika stood up. "Please, Regent Horthy, don't let us wait so long for your speech. Please confirm to us all what I know in my heart."

"What do you know in your heart, Erika?" we cried. "Tell us, please."

"That we won the war! That the war is over!"

"Bravo, bravo! Tell us again, Erika," we shouted, clapping vigorously, and Erika, shy Erika, stood there looking at us triumphantly, and continued to say those wonderful words.

"It is an open secret. I saw it in the papers yesterday. About how our brave men pushed the enemy back at Szeged. It serves them right," she added with contempt, "those inhuman swine who bombed hospitals and schools."

"Can it be," Magda asked as if in a dream, her beautiful face radiant with excitement, "that soon we will learn that the war is over?"

"And peace will follow," Ersabet mused, rolling her huge, brown eyes heavenward, "and our men will come home and there will be no more air raids."

Will my husband come home safely with his brothers? The thought stabbed me with renewed force. Please, Father in Heaven, bring them back safely, I prayed. Please bring my husband back. Please, please!

I became aware that the old lady had started a conversation with Maria Vasvary, who was sitting with her husband in the far corner of the room next to a little bassinet where their infant son lay. Now I was all ears, for I hadn't the slightest idea who these people were. I did know that they had paid rent on the apartment from the time the house was built, but they had actually moved in only a few days before. No matter how much I wanted to get to know them, it was impossible to get close to them, as they indicated from the very beginning that they preferred to be left alone.

"They may be Jewish," I told my husband excitedly the first day I saw them.

"What makes you think so?" Iztvan asked me.

"A lot of things," I replied. "First of all, why would they pay rent and not live here? Who knows, they may have moved into the ghetto and kept this place ready to flee to in an emergency."

"They even look Jewish," Anna added. She had also tried to strike up a conversation with them, but had failed.

"If that is the case, stay away from them," Iztvan cautioned. "What if they are discovered, God forbid? Better to keep your distance."

But now Maria was responding to Mrs. Nagy's question about Horthy's speech, and I listened attentively.

"Look at those shiny, golden-brown eyes," I whispered to Anna.

"They're just like doe eyes," she agreed.

"Well, I really don't know what to think," Maria was saying slowly, "but I wish with all my heart that I could share Erika's optimism, because to me it seems that the hardest days are still ahead of us."

She knows, I concluded. She didn't swallow the propaganda of the press. She probably doesn't even read the papers. Her information must come from the "Voice of America." I made a fast calculation. They live under the Kerekes' apartment and right above the Horvats' — between two bitter anti-Semites. Panic gripped me. What if one of them were to overhear the forbidden "Voice?"

"The radio! The radio!" people began to yell. We all ran to it.

"Ladies and gentlemen. In sixty minutes Regent Horthy will be on the air."

The shelter was filled with excitement. People ran around heedlessly. Only I remained sitting, clutching my baby nervously and crying silent, bitter tears. Where is my husband? I wondered. Oh God, where is he? Is he safe? What difference does it make what Horthy says if anything happens to my husband? If anything happens to him, then for me the war will be lost! And as I watched the excited bunch buzzing around, from the corner of my eye, I slipped back into my horrifying fantasy world.

I saw Julyanna Kerekes clearly, her face full of contempt, saying, "I overheard the Vasvarys listening to the forbidden 'Voice of America.'"

Frozen silence. Everybody was gaping at her, their eyes almost popping out of their sockets. "The traitors! The traitors!" they cried.

"We must inform the authorities!" someone shouted.

"I did," another voice exclaimed. "Of course I called the police right away!"

The police! Oh my God, the police! I bit my hand in an effort to choke back the cry, "Where will I hide my people?"

Fortunately, at that point, the all-clear siren sounded its harsh blare, shocking me back into realityand away from my dreadful fantasy.

I was the first to arrive upstairs, anxious to see if my husband had come home while we were in the shelter. I slammed the door behind me impatiently.

Can it be true, or am I still daydreaming? I wondered as my husband, followed by Herschel and Yudl, rolled out from under the bed.

"Didn't I promise you?" my brother Lajos laughed, his pupils enormous in his huge eyes.

"Thank God!" I cried with tears of relief.

The room vibrated with excitement, because most of those present believed that Horthy was going to instruct the Hungarian citizens to turn against the Germans and drive them out of the land, just as the king of Roumania had done a year ago in his country.

"And what a great success it was," my husband commented. "It went so quickly. Before the Germans realized what was happening, they were relieved of their firearms and taken prisoner by their fellow soldiers. And so, too, were the civilians held by their former friends, and then given over to the authorities."

"Why does he have to keep us waiting so long?" Lajos said, his eyes glittering. "Why won't he make his announcement already?"

Suddenly the haunting melody of the Hungarian national anthem filled the room and all of us sprang up and stood at attention.

"Fools! Fools!" my brother-in-law Herschel raged, pushing us down angrily, one after the other, into our chairs. "Why?

Why this blind devotion? Why the respect for this land or its government? Tell me, what did this land give us? Tell me, what?" he repeated, trembling visibly. "From me, it only took," he cried. "It took everything. It took all I had!"

A hush fell over the room, and while we stared at him in shock, Anna stood up, her large green eyes shining with tears. "You are right, Herschel," she murmured. She stared at some invisible object in her clenched hands, and with a faraway look on her face, she sobbed, "Just like a bubble, a bubble which has burst. Oh, how painful is the realization that this land, this glorious country which I so fiercely loved, was never for an instant really mine!"

With the final strains of the anthem, Horthy began to deliver the long-awaited speech.

Hungarian Brothers and Sisters:

Ever since the will of the nation put me at the country's helm, the most important aim of Hungarian foreign policy has been...to repair...the injustices of the Peace Treaty of Trianon. Our hopes in the League of Nations in this regard remained unfulfilled...

Hungary was forced into war against the Allies by German pressure...we were not guided by any ambition to increase our own power and had no intention to snatch as much as a square meter of territory from anybody.

Today it is obvious to any sober-minded person that the German Reich has lost the war...

Conscious of my historic responsibility, I have the obligation to undertake every step directed to avoiding further unnecessary bloodshed...

...After having received a firm promise by the Fuehrer of the German Reich that he would cancel acts that violated and restricted Hungary's sovereignty...I appointed the Sztojay Government.

Yet the Germans did not keep their promise. Under cover of the German occupation the Gestapo tackled the Jewish question in a manner incompatible with the dictates of humanity, applying methods it had already employed elsewhere. When war drew near our frontiers, and even passed them, the Germans repeatedly promised assistance, yet again they failed to honor their promise.

During their retreat they turned the country's sovereign territory over to looting and destruction...

I decided to safeguard Hungary's honor even against her former ally, although this ally, instead of supplying the promised military help, meant finally to rob the Hungarian nation of its greatest treasure — its freedom and independence.

I informed a representative of the German Reich that we were about to conclude a military armistice with our former enemies and to cease all hostilities against them...

Commanders of the Hungarian Army have received corresponding orders from me. Accordingly, the troops, loyal to their oath and following on Order of the Day now issued simultaneously, must obey the commanders appointed by me. I appeal to every honest Hungarian to follow me on this path, beset by sacrifices, that will lead to Hungary's salvation.

Then the announcer said, "Please stay close to the radio for further information and for the repetition of the speech at half-hour intervals."

There was a click and the machine was silent. We stood there gazing at it, choking and gasping for breath.

Karoly jumped up, drunken with happiness. "Sweetheart," he cried, sweeping the dazed Magda high into the air, "our troubles are over. We are free! Free, free!"

"Free! Free!" a jubilant Magda echoed, and the next moment we crowded around our wonderful saviors, crying with happiness.

Iztvan lifted his tear-stained face, but his eyes were laughing, just as they were the first time I saw him. "Karoly and Magda, my sister, my brother! Please let me try to convey to you our profound gratitude for what you have done for us!" His lips parted to say more, but he had to grope for words and then he fell upon Karoly's shoulder. "But how does one say thank you for the gift of life?" he sobbed. "How? And how can I express my admiration for your fearlessness and loyalty?"

"Stop it, my friend," Karoly laughed and the next minute we were all laughing and crying before these two most extraordinary people.

Then my brother Lajos appeared in the room, carrying knives and scissors, his eyes flaming. "Out to the streets to fight!" he shouted. "The time for revenge has come!"

"Shh," we hissed, pointing, horror-stricken, to the wall. But Lajos was beyond reason. "Come on," he urged, "let's go!"

Magda saved us by starting to sing and Anna clapped to the tune. "Oh, how we miss you," she said, pointing to the radio, "you silly noise machine!"

Meanwhile, the rest of us tried to calm Lajos down and remind him of the dangers of giving our secret away prematurely. "Can't you hear me?" my husband whispered angrily. "Sit down and be quiet, unless you want to pull all of us down with you."

"No, I can't hear you," he answered in a slightly more subdued tone. "All I can hear is the tap-tap-tap above my head in the bunker, and how the sadistic Nazis drove our brothers from the ghetto. And how they laughed. My God, how they rejoiced in our pain." He looked from one to the other. "Cowards, all of you!" he sneered as he realized the overwhelming opposition to his plan. Dejected, he hurried back into the kitchen.

Soon our two SS friends, Geza Bajor and Misi Bartok, arrived, each of them carrying packages in their hands. "Who did you rob?" we asked jokingly.

"These are our civilian clothes," they explained. "We brought them along in the hope that the city will turn against the Nazis."

"And so will we," the men replied in unison.

"This can't go on," Iztvan exclaimed impatiently. "We must remember to mind our neighbors on the other side of the wall."

The room was charged with emotion and it was so crowded

that we were practically breathing down each other's necks. "I must escape from here," I said to Magda, biting my lip nervously.

Magda pulled Rozalia up from the couch. "Come on, let's go into my bedroom." She picked up her little girl and held her close. "Poor darling," she cooed. "I forgot all about you in the midst of this excitement. You must be starving by now."

"How lucky we are to be blessed with such angelic babies," I remarked as we settled ourselves in Magda's room. "It's long past little Zsuzsi's feeding time, too. It's as if they understand, and they never complain."

"That's a daughter for you," Rozalia whispered, looking at the babies wistfully. "Will Pali and I ever be granted the privilege of having a family of our own? To have sons and daughters? To live a normal family life?"

"Why doubt it now, when it's only a matter of hours before the Germans will be driven from the land?" Magda commented. "Here, hold the baby for a moment while I prepare her food. That will cheer you up and bring you to your senses." She placed her little one in Rozalia's arms and went into the kitchen. Soon she returned with the baby's food. Little Macika held her arms out to her mother, who promptly began to feed the hungry child. Then, obviously satisfied, she sat down on the floor and, smiling contentedly, pulled off her mother's shoes and tried to put her tiny feet in them.

The conversation drifted back to the topic of the Regent's speech. "It breaks my heart to think of Horthy crying as he related how he was forced by the Germans to sign the deportation order of Hungary's Jews," Magda said. "He was so sorry he'd had to do that."

I felt the blood racing to my head. "Sorry? Do you believe he was sorry? He is a liar!"

"And I say," Rozalia cried, "that he knew perfectly well that the Germans would never so much as touch his son, Miklos Junior. I think he spread that rumor himself. Do you imagine they would take the chance of incurring the wrath of the

Hungarian people, whose sons bled for them? Nor are they in a position to antagonize our people, because there is hunger in our land now, and the German officials are searching out the hidden produce of the poor Hungarian farmers, taking it by force and sending it to Germany, leaving nothing for us."

"Oh, Rozalia," Magda cried, her voice quivering with emotion, "this is something that only a mother or father can understand. Oh, Macika, my little darling," she cried, pressing her little one to her chest, "how fortunate I am that I was never asked to make this choice!"

"But you were," I sobbed. "You were, my friend!"

I listened to the two women talking softly while I sat in the far corner of the room, nursing my baby, and my awareness of the love between mother and child overwhelmed me. I shivered as I asked myself what I would have done in the Regent's position, as a parent. But then a picture leaped into my mind from out of the past, reminding me of Horthy's anti-Semitism, and I felt just as I did when it happened long, long ago.

The fire was burning in the fireplace and my mother sat in front of the hearth, the yellow-red glow of the fire illuminating her beautiful face. We all sat around her — there were seven of us at the time. I could still feel the warmth, the serenity of the hour. "Mother, please tell us a story," we begged, as we usually did on long winter nights such as those.

"Which story shall I tell?" she asked, rocking Meyer, the youngest, in her lap.

"Whichever one you want," we sang in a chorus.

"No, Mother, please tell us about the year that Father and you got married and moved to Szombathely," my sister Tzivia urged her.

My mother paled. "I'd rather not. Those were very trying times for your father and me."

"But you promised you would tell us," we protested. "You promised. You said you would!"

My mother stood up. "Well, a promise is a promise," she said, her eyes clouding. "Let me put the baby into his crib."

I could almost hear her voice now and feel the warmth of her presence, and see the tears shining in her eyes. "I've told you about the difficult times we, as Jews, lived through during the World War, in addition to the suffering that all Hungarian citizens endured." She looked beyond us and into the burning fire, tears dropping in quick succession down her pallid cheeks.

"Mother, please tell us what happened to you and Papa. Please go on!"

"I will," she said with a forced smile. "Isn't it silly to cry over what has passed so long ago? Yes, it has passed, just as your father said it would." She ran out of the room in tears. I saw her go to the kitchen sink and wash her face. When she returned she tried to look cheerful. "Where was I? Oh, yes. It was a bitter, cold night when I was awakened by the sound of people in front of our house. I ran to the window, just in time to see the president and vice-president of the congregation, flanked by two policemen, being led into our yard. Before I had time to collect myself, there was a loud knock at the door. 'Open up! It's the police!'

"Your father ran to open it. One of the officers pointed his finger at him and bellowed, 'We have come to arrest you!'

" 'Arrest me?' your father asked, his face turning white. Then the absurdity of this scene became apparent to him. 'Why me? I've committed no crime,' he said. 'There must be some mistake, Officer.' Straightening himself up to his full height, he looked at the policemen and asserted himself with conviction. 'Officers, you have come for the wrong man!'

"'There is no mistake,' the officer declared."

"Was he afraid?" my sister Tzivia asked.

"Was he afraid?" we mimicked in unison.

My mother did not answer. She took Tzivia's pale face between her hands. All of us watched her expectantly. "Four officers surrounded him," she whispered, "each with a loaded rifle pointed at Papa's head, and they took him out into the yard. And it was such a bitter cold night, very, very cold." We just gazed at her in horror, none of us able to utter a sound.

My little sister Surele, who was all of three at the time, stood up. I could still see her in my mind's eye, her brown, curly hair framing her pale, freckled face, looking around questioningly with her sky-blue eyes.

"Was it as cold as it is today?" she asked innocently.

"Yes," my mother answered, her eyes shining with love. "It was as cold as it is today," she said, picking Surele up, "but right now the house is warm and your father is sitting securely in the next room studying the holy books, thanks to the good Lord."

I was the first to find my voice. "Mother," I cried, "what did they do to Papa?" Frightened, I threw myself into her lap and hid my face.

"You see, I should not have talked about this," my mother said, patting my unruly dark hair. "I really don't know what made me do it against my better judgment."

"But what happened to Papa?" we demanded in loud, anxious voices.

"I'll tell you. Yes, yes, I still remember it exactly. One of the policemen struck a match to light a candle, and in the soft light the officer read his arrest orders while we held our breath in panic: 'Rabbi Abraham Einhorn, you are under arrest in the name of our newly elected Regent, Nagybanya Miklos Horthy.'

" 'Why? Why?' I cried in terror. But my words left the man of the law totally unmoved. He continued to read in a self-important and very authoritarian tone, and named an astronomical sum of money for the ransom of your father.

"The officer turned to the two other men they had arrested, who stood there frozen with fright. 'And if by nine A.M. tomorrow morning, you do not come up with the money,' he boomed, 'then it will be just too bad! We have strict orders to pull the trigger at the appointed time. So now, gentlemen, start knocking at the doors of your fellow Jews and collect the money!' "

"And did they come up with the money in time?" I asked, stammering in terror.

"Of course they did, silly girl. Can't you see that your father is alive and well, thank God?"

Lost in my memories, I didn't notice when my husband noiselessly entered the room in his stocking feet. "Iche just turned into our path," he said to me softly.

That quickly brought me back to the present. Iche was a friend of Misi and Geza who had also begun to make visits to our house, posing as a Nazi. Still dazed, with the measured steps of a sleepwalker, I carried my baby back into our room to put her down in her crib, and then went into the hall to wait for our guest to arrive.

Iche came up the stairs, his appearance disheveled, fright etched on his face.

"Iche, what happened?" I exclaimed.

He looked at me skeptically. "I am scared, of course. Don't you know? The whole town is talking about it."

"What is everybody talking about?" I asked, feeling faint.

"The radio! The radio!"

I looked at him uncomprehendingly.

"Don't you know that they skipped the three-thirty and four o'clock repeats of Horthy's speech?"

"Horthy?" I asked with contempt. "Who cares? Who's interested in him or his hypocrisies anyway?" All my pent-up emotions began to escape, like lava from an erupting volcano, and I ranted on angrily. "First, he uses us to gain the friendship of the Germans, and now that he sees that Hitler is finished, he goes and digs out our charred bones from the gas chambers, to wash his face with in order to appease the Allies!"

Iche looked at me in bewilderment. "How blind can you be?! Zsuzsi, don't you see? I really don't understand you." His eyes were glazed and his face burned from some inner fire. "Can't you see?" he demanded again, angrily. "If he will manage to save the ghetto," he whispered, "oh, God, if he manages to save the last remnants of Hungarian Jewry, Miklos Horthy will be my hero forever and ever!" He ran toward our door and I followed him, stupefied.

"Iche, how is the city reacting?" Pali asked excitedly as all eyes focused on our friend. But one look at Iche's face told them that something was wrong, *very* wrong. At that moment it seemed to me that they all became like puppets. Their bodies tensed, their faces revealing a mixture of bewilderment and terror. It was as if some invisible hand had changed the lighting and cast upon their faces a uniform shade of whiteness. Quickly, our optimism and high expectations disappeared and were replaced by the terrible, gnawing fear of the unknown. A sense of foreboding descended upon us like a leaden weight.

At exactly five P.M., the radio returned to life, and without any explanation, the Regent's speech was broadcast as if nothing unusual had occurred in the interim. "It must have been some technical difficulty in the studio," we whispered to each other, elated with renewed hope. Our happiness, however, was short-lived. Abruptly and without warning, the program stopped, but this time we heard angry voices in the background. The tape of the Regent's speech was playing continuously over the din, but it could not mask the angry voices of interference. There was no doubt that a fight had broken out in the studio.

We shivered with fright. "Do you hear?" I cried. "Do you hear the footsteps? My God, more and more people are running into the station."

"It seems that there is a battle being waged over the National Broadcasting System," my husband whispered. Then we heard even more footsteps, and by then we had no doubt that indeed Horthy's opponents were storming the studio.

"Open the door!" we heard the mob demand coarsely. "Open up or we'll break down the door!" Their demand was met with silence. "You have five minutes to act!" No answer. "Fools, open up and save your lives!" came the warning.

"Over my dead body, you traitors!"

Then came the splintering sound of doors being smashed in, and the victorious cries of the invading mob rose to a crescendo and mingled with the terrified cries of Horthy's loyal defenders in the studio.

"Long live Horthy!"

"Long live Hungary!"

In answer, a gun battle erupted. And amidst the chaos and the agonizing death cries of the heroic few, there burst from a thousand throats, the most formidable of slogans a Jew could hear.

"Heil Salasy!"

"Heil Hitler!"

"Heil! Heil! Heil!"

And as we felt the very earth shake under us because of this unpredicted turn of events, the mob became drunk with the promise of more Jewish blood to be shed by the German-installed puppet government, headed by the most bigoted, narrow-minded of men, Ferenc Salasy.

36

> Thy word is a lamp for my feet and a light for my path.
>
> *Psalms 119:105*

HIDDEN BEHIND rosebushes on a manicured lawn stood a large, whitewashed house. The house resembled the other well-kept villas surrounding it in the plush Rozsadomb section of the city, but if one looked closely, one could find a shiny little plaque discreetly mounted next to the door bell, beneath the climbing ivy on the wall, bearing the inscription: VILLA MARIA MAGDALENA, VISITING HOURS: 10 A.M. TILL 4 P.M. ON SUNDAYS. This cheerful-looking house sheltered women who had suffered heartache and disillusion, and desperately needed some support. The owner of this house was a kind and beautiful baroness. She opened her doors and her heart to these troubled mothers-to-be and spent most of her time, as well as her sizable fortune, easing their plight.

The affluent neighbors resented the influx of common people into their privileged domain. But then, still untouched by the terror of the war, living in their tightly-knit society of glitter, how could they understand the emptiness in the soul of the owner of this villa? The baroness' life had been shattered when her only son, the dashing young baron, gave up his life "for the glorification of the homeland." Then, out of the dark cloud had come a ray of sunshine. Vivian, her French-born daughter-in-law, moved in with her to await the birth of her first child.

This incident made the baroness aware of the plight of other unfortunate young women in similar situations, and prompted her to open her heart to women whose husbands had succumbed to the ravages of war and who had no family to turn to. So one day, to the chagrin of the neighbors, the little brass plaque was mounted on the wall.

The news traveled by word of mouth, and soon a steady stream of broken, terrified young women were flocking to the estate where they were welcomed by the kind baroness. She consoled them and provided for them until they were strong enough to face the world alone with their infants in their arms.

It was to this house that Bracha Fendrich headed, armed with Aryan identification papers and a false army report stating that her husband was missing in action. Monika Halas, she repeated to herself, reviewing her alias in her mind as she nervously approached the house.

She had had the most miserable morning before she arrived. She had said good-bye at the train station to Meir, her husband of eleven months. He was being transported that day to a work-camp which was known to be run by hateful and sadistic men. It was referred to as "the work-camp of no return." She felt her heart breaking with anguish.

"Meir," she said, trying to smile through her tears to lift her husband's spirits, "I'll do as you have said: From here I am going straight to Villa Magdalena and I'll wait there with our baby for your return."

"And I will do my utmost to stay alive for you and our baby, so help me God," a tearful Meir murmured in reply as he was swept away with the crowd of bewildered *munkataboros*. Then he disappeared with all the rest into an overloaded wagon.

Bracha stood there with tears in her eyes, hoping to catch a last glimpse of the man whom she adored more than life itself. She stayed long after the wagon disappeared behind the tall, green trees of Buda. Meir's words still rang in her ears: "Don't go back to the ghetto. Seek asylum in Villa Magdalena!" As if in a trance, she went to the ladies' room to bathe her red-rimmed eyes and to unfasten her yellow star. She lifted the insole of her shoe and quickly hid the incriminating yellow badge under it, as Meir had instructed her. "You may need it, you can never tell," he had said.

She picked up her valise, and, trembling, she wearily walked to the trolley stop to take the streetcar to Rozsadomb. It was the beginning of fall, but the sun still shone in all its brilliance as, heartbroken and stumbling, she walked down the beautiful villa row of the privileged few.

Suddenly a group of small children ran out from one of the gardens and the oldest among them, a boy of about ten, glanced at her. It made her feel uncomfortable even before she saw that the youth was pointing her out to the younger boys. Still, she was not prepared for what followed. The boy emitted a loud whistle as a sign that another stranger had arrived. This signal brought more and more children of all ages who, with insults and malice, threw pebbles at her as she made her way to the entrance of the villa. Petrified, she reached for the knocker. "Oh, what a cruel, cruel world," she sighed.

The door opened noiselessly from the inside and she nearly fell through the doorway and into the outstretched arms of a tall woman.

"Welcome, my dear," the baroness greeted her, kissing both cheeks. Gasping for breath, the girl fell on her shoulder and began to cry bitterly. "I saw," the baroness said after a while, "and I am sorry."

"They...they threw pebbles at me," she stammered, horror-stricken.

"And they ridiculed you," the woman said, her beautiful

face reflecting deep concern, while Monika struggled to gain control of her turbulent emotions.

Oh, you rotten little urchins, she thought to herself. If only you knew how grateful I am for your making this dreaded arrival so much easier for me. But aloud she said, "Forgive me, I haven't even introduced myself. I am Monika Halas," and she placed her identification papers into the woman's long, graceful hands.

"That's all we'll need," the baroness said. "We will take care of registering you and applying for your ration books." Having said this, she put her finger on the bell. "I will summon a girl to show you around."

Soon a shortish girl with platinum blond hair appeared in the doorway. "My name is Irma," she said, embracing Monika warmly. "We saw you coming and we're all anxious to meet you." She led Monika through a long and narrow corridor to the dining hall. Here, all the residents, in various stages of pregnancy, lined up to welcome her. As Irma introduced the new arrival, each girl hugged her and tried to make her feel at ease.

"Thank you, girls," Monika said with tears in her eyes. "You are truly making me feel as though I have come home."

"Well, this *is* your home now...your home away from home!" Irma said. "We will try to replace your family since they are so far away. In any case, we are your friends!"

"I was told that this place was overcrowded, and I was so afraid of being turned away because I have nowhere else to go."

"Well, don't worry, you've made it," the girls sang. "Welcome to the club!"

"The last empty bed is in my room. Come," Irma said, "I'll show it to you."

"Thanks. Thank you very much," she whispered hoarsely, and, unable to contain her emotions any longer, she burst into a torrent of sobs.

The air turned cool at night and the girls lit the fireplace in the sitting room to chase the chill away. "We always come here after supper," Irma informed her. "The girls are nice," she added. "I hope you'll like it here."

"I already do," Monika assured her, "I really do!" How strange the smells from the kitchen are, she said to herself, nauseated at the mere thought of having to eat non-kosher food. Aloud she said, "I'm starved. When will they serve supper?"

"We will be summoned to the table in a minute," Irma said, glancing at her wristwatch. Shortly afterwards, a woman emerged from the kitchen and announced that the meal was being served. Monika sat next to Irma and listened to her friendly babbling. "We're having pork roast tonight," she said, taking a deep breath and inhaling the strong aroma coming from the kitchen.

"Oh, what a royal treat," Monika exclaimed, but the knowledge that she had no alternative but to consume the forbidden food made her stomach turn.

Four girls wearing white robes, their hair tucked under red and white polka-dot scarves, appeared in the doorway, each carrying a tray laden with bowls of steaming hot soup. "Each week four different girls are the waitresses, while another four wash the dishes, clean up, and so forth," her new friend told her. "Those two are Aranka and Mary. They always work together, though I can never figure out their friendship. Mary is so jealous of Aranka. She can't forgive her luck."

"Why is she jealous?" Monika asked. "I personally think that Mary is rather cute, while Aranka is nothing really special."

"I agree, but there is an awfully big difference between the two." She moved closer to Monika. "Aranka is the lucky one," she whispered, "since she received news that her husband was found in a hospital, wounded but very much alive. And better yet, he'll never be back in uniform again, because his injury disqualifies him. Lucky girl, she has everything to look forward to in life. And what do we have to look forward to? What, I ask?" Irma continued to gossip between bites at a dizzying speed. "Do you see that blonde with the long, straight hair? She is the beauty queen among us." She chatted on about all the other residents while Monika finished her meal.

This food is making me sick, Monika thought in a panic. "Going to the lavatory," she whispered with great effort.

"I'll save you a seat next to me in the sitting room," Irma called after the departing girl, who hardly had time to lock the door behind her before she became violently ill.

"I hope nobody noticed," she prayed afterwards, leaning heavily against the wall and watching in the mirror as the color slowly returned to her cheeks. Then she gave a quick glance around to make sure that no telltale sign of her ordeal remained.

When Monika entered the sitting room she found the girls sitting around the fire, talking wistfully about what might have been if not for the war. She sat among them tearfully bemoaning the loss of her beloved husband and venting her fears about the future.

"This is how it goes, night after night," Irma whispered to her. "There is not a night that we don't ask ourselves, Why on earth did I get married and become pregnant in times such as these?"

Suddenly a gong sounded, which sent the girls scurrying to their rooms and then to line up in front of the bathrooms, toothbrushes and towels in hand.

"Goodnight, girls. It's bedtime," the baroness' voice came through the open door.

"Goodnight, baroness," everyone replied in chorus.

Within minutes, all the women were in their beds. "Lights out!" someone called. Monika heard a shuffling sound, and as she looked around in the dimmed room she saw that all the girls had lowered themselves to kneeling positions next to their beds and had begun to pray, just as the baroness had taught them, since the good woman was a very religious soul.

Monika lay in bed wondering how long it would take until she, too, would be expected to talk about her past. But why worry about that now? she thought. That will come to pass on another day. The most important thing was that the first day, the day she had so dreaded, had come to an end. And lying on the strange bed, she offered a special prayer of thanks to Hashem for making her entrance to this place so much easier than she had anticipated.

37

> He alone is my rock, my salvation, my high tower, and I certainly will not be swayed.
> *Psalms 62:3*

IT WAS THREE A.M. on a cold October morning and everyone was sound asleep at Villa Maria Magdalena — everyone, that is, except for Monika and Irma, who were rushing down the stairs toward the kitchen to take up their assignment of the week.

"Brrrr, it feels like the middle of winter," Monika whispered, trying in vain to make the ends of her sweater meet around her heavy body.

"I'm freezing, too," Irma responded through chattering teeth. "It's a good thing we prepared the firewood last night."

"Yes! We only have to hold a match under the paper," Monika said, opening the oven door, "and in one moment it will be warm!" The girls watched with anticipation as the paper began to burn.

But when Irma brought out the iron kettle from the pantry and placed it on the range, she discovered that the stove-top was ice cold. "God in Heaven," she cried, "the fire went out!"

"Don't panic," Monika said. "I can fix it." She knelt down and peered inside the oven. "This wood was chopped too thick, and it's also very wet," she explained. She reached under the range and removed a handful of thinly chopped wood which had been stored there to dry properly so that it could be used to start the fire. Then she put the wood in the oven, wadded up some paper, lit it, and slid it under the twigs. "It's burning!" she exclaimed. She began to blow on the wet wood until her face was purple and she was coughing uncontrollably.

"Get away before you choke," Irma warned, firmly pushing Monika aside and shutting the oven door. But when she opened it again, heavy, black smoke came billowing out at her. She slammed the door shut and ran toward a window, gasping for breath.

"What are we going to do?" they moaned while rubbing their hands and hopping around to warm their frozen limbs.

"Look!" Irma cried suddenly, pointing to the red flames licking at the edges of the oven door. "It's burning! Now just let me wash my face before we start sifting the flour."

"Oh, no!" Monika cried. "Old Maid Bozsi will be here any minute now and all we've done so far is start the fire!"

But when Bozsi Eger, the cook, stepped through the door at four A.M., they had everything under control. The flour for the bread had been sifted, the sourdough had risen properly, and the girls were secretly delighted with themselves. They suppressed a smile as they watched the hefty brunette squeeze her bulk into her white uniform.

Bozsi scrubbed her hands quickly and started kneading the dough, while keeping both girls on their toes with her orders. "Don't forget to flour the dough before you cover it, Monika. Come on! Move! Bring the down comforter. Don't let the dough cool!" Her arms were elbow-deep in the second kneading bowl. "Pour some warm water in here, Irma. And throw some more wood on the hearth. We want this dough to rise!"

When Bozsi finally took a last fistful of flour to rub her hands dry from the dough, huffing and puffing from all the activity, and flopped down on the bench, the girls breathed a sigh of relief. Now, completely relaxed, they tidied up the kitchen.

After a while Bozsi stood up, her dark, button-like eyes seeking theirs in secret alliance. This was the moment they had all been waiting for. Monika ran to the oven without a word, fished out six giant-sized baked potatoes and placed them on the three plates on Irma's tray. Then Bozsi shut the pantry door and turned the key. And before they knew it she was standing before them, holding in one hand a ball of sweet, fresh butter hidden between large grape leaves, and in the other hand a small pitcher of milk which she had stolen from the girls' meager weekly allotment. The two girls squealed with delight as they ran toward the washroom, where, hiding in a dark corner, they finished the food down to the last morsel.

It will be five weeks today since I first stepped through the doorway of Villa Maria Magdalena, scared to death and wondering about my future, Monika thought smugly. "Do you want to wash or dry?" she asked Irma, pointing to the pile of the evening's dirty cups and plates awaiting them on the counter by the sink.

"What do I care?" Irma snapped. "I hate doing either."

Monika washed the dishes while Irma dried and stacked them neatly in the cupboard, talking and complaining nonstop as usual. "Oh, that Aranka, how I hate her. She treats us like dirt. Yes, plain dirt under her heels!"

"What did she do this time?"

"Well, Mary Ann had simply remarked about the weather, saying, 'It's raining cats and dogs,' and you should have heard how she jumped at her. 'What's your problem? Your visitors won't come?' Irma mimicked Aranka's high-pitched voice perfectly.

"Oh, how cruel. Everybody knows that Mary Ann hasn't had a visitor yet," Monika muttered. "Poor Mary Ann!"

Irma's eyes threw sparks of fire. "The bigshot! Who besides her has visitors anyway? Tell me, who? Aranka and her pathetic invalid, Pityu." She spat in contempt.

"Invalid?" Monika asked, taken aback. "Who told you so?"

"Do I have to be told everything? Am I not entitled to form my own opinions once in a while?" Monika looked at her, dumbfounded. "Why else do you suppose his parents come to visit her so often," Irma explained matter-of-factly, "if not to blackmail her into staying with their one-legged son?"

How blessedly simpleminded she is, Monika thought, to occupy herself with such frivolities while the whole world's eyes are at this very moment focused on Budapest and its fate, ever since Salasy's unexpected coup.

But by now Irma was gossiping about her next victim, and the next after that, driving Monika to despair. But why complain, Monika reasoned, when the girl's pettiness keeps away all the others like the plague, which suits my needs just perfectly. Monika continued listening intermittently to Irma's tirades, nodding occasionally to give the impression that she was still following her. In reality, however, she was thinking of the recent changes in the government and worrying about their impact upon her and her fellow Jews. Suddenly she became aware of Irma looking at her strangely. "I am talking to you," she said indignantly. "Don't you hear?"

No, I can't hear, nor can I think straight any longer, she said to herself. "My feet are killing me," Monika moaned and lifted up her long white apron, revealing legs that were swollen and covered with ugly, purple varicose veins. Irma made no comment and completely ignored her. She was too preoccupied with her own thoughts.

Moments of silence passed between them, and then Irma snapped her fingers in excitement, her dark eyes flashing under her bobbed platinum-colored hair. "I have it!" she cried. "I have it! How could I have ever missed it? Of course, she is a Jew. There are no two ways about it! She is a Jew. Saints preserve us — there is a Jew hiding among us!"

"Who is hiding?" Monika cried, looking around wildly. "Where is she hiding? I see nobody here but us," she said with disappointment, trying to sound and look natural while the whole foundation of the earth shook beneath her trembling legs.

"Don't be silly," Irma laughed. "Not here in the kitchen. How thick-headed can you be?"

"Then don't talk in riddles. Explain what this is all about," Monika demanded.

"You know how I dislike Lenke," Irma began. "She is so strange, so...different."

"I don't like her either. So what?"

"So what? I will tell you what. She is a Jew!"

Monika thought she was going to faint. She held on to the sink to steady herself, and then began scrubbing away furiously at the pots and pans. For Lenke was indeed a Jew, a friend from her childhood, and also the one who had suggested that she come to stay at the Villa Maria Magdalena long before her husband had mentioned the place to her. Until now, they had studiously ignored one another, pretending to be strangers. I must be calm, Monika told herself sternly. I mustn't panic. "What makes you think so?" she asked Irma.

"I don't know how it came to me. It just hit me, right out of the clear blue sky! I first realized it yesterday, when we were listening to our new fuehrer on the radio. You know how we looked."

"Glowing with pride, if that's what you mean," Monika said, as a sharp pain suddenly stabbed through her abdomen.

Irma continued excitedly. "Right, that's just what I mean. But Lenke was so unnaturally pale, almost fading into the wall, in contrast to the glowing faces of the rest of us. At first I thought she was sick, and I started to walk toward her, but then we all began cheering and I got caught up in the mood and forgot about her. It was much later that I remembered about her, and by that time she looked fine."

"Oh, Irma," Monika cried, "if what you say is really true, can you imagine what fun we will have?"

"Oh, yes," Irma replied, jumping up and down with excitement, and the two girls immediately began to discuss whether to squeal on Lenke first or take the matter into their own hands and interrogate her for their own pleasure. In the end they decided to do the latter.

"I am so thrilled," Monika exclaimed, "and nobody else knows about it. It makes me feel like the two of us belong to an exclusive club."

"Imagine the look on the girls' faces when we tell them! And the baroness...what will she think? How will she react?" They continued chattering about it as they put the last dishes back into the cupboard and headed for their bedroom.

Once back in bed, Monika lay awake in a pool of perspiration. listening to the even breathing of the sleeping girls, straining her ears for the snoring which would tell her that Irma had also succumbed to sleep and that she could proceed with her plan. By the time Irma's faint buzzing reached her ears, she was almost mad with impatience. Every inch of her body screamed, Don't waste time! Don't waste time! But she waited until the snoring became stronger and there was no doubt that Irma was sound asleep. Then Monika got to work.

She removed her quilt, shaped it into a human form and covered the "dummy" with the striped quilt cover. Then she quickly stole into the bathroom, her body tense, her legs shaking like jello. Sweating profusely in the predawn chill, she dressed herself quickly and crept toward the bed where Lenke was sleeping peacefully. Her heart was racing as she placed her trembling hand on her friend's forehead. She waited until she saw by the little night-light that Lenke's eyes were open.

They stared at each other briefly and knowingly, and then Monika left the room noiselessly, satisfied that the girl fully understood the danger she was in, and knowing without looking back what Lenke was doing. Just as I did, she thought. Will the girls find the two dummies in the morning? Or will it be the two of us? The thought stabbed at her when the cold air hit her face as she stepped out the door into the darkness.

Away, away! she prodded herself, and ignoring her heavy

body, she plunged into the darkness, hugging the lamppost frantically to get her bearings, running, heaving and gasping for breath as she went in the direction of the trolley stop. She heard a faint noise in the stillness of the night. Is it the trolley? Oh, my dear Lord, please let it be the trolley, she prayed, frightened beyond words. The trolley came and she was aboard in an instant. Not until after the vehicle had turned the corner did she realize how fortunate she had been, for this particular line came very infrequently. She shuddered to think what would have happened to her had she been forced to wait a long time. But why worry? I am safe, she told herself. I am safe from the girls!

It was much later that the trolley stopped to pick up a lone passenger. She was an older woman who, much to Monika's horror, disregarded all the empty seats in the trolley, flopped down heavily right next to her and immediately started a conversation.

"It's my husband I am running away from," Monika heard herself saying to the stranger. "He came home violently drunk last night. I am heading for my mother's." And she listened to the old woman's horror tales about the pregnant women she knew who had given birth to malformed babies after being beaten by their drunken husbands.

"Oh, good riddance," Monika sighed with relief when the woman signaled the conductor to stop on the Pest side of the bridge, but as she tried to relax she realized that there was absolutely no point in ignoring the pain any longer. "I am going to have the baby, and I am only in the thirtieth week of my pregnancy!"

Suddenly the pain stabbed her with such intensity that it was hard to restrain herself from crying out. Of course, she thought in the intervals between pains, this started while I was washing last night's dishes. It was brought on by the shock of hearing that Irma had discovered our secret. Will I reach the Bethlehem Hospital, which was designated for us Jews?

She suppressed a cry as she felt her body about to explode

with pain. As the trolley approached the hospital, she thought, I must pin on my Star of David in order to be admitted here. Clutching the badge in her hand, she stepped off the trolley. She stood there, unable to move a step further. Then a pain ripped through her with such force that she keeled over and lay on the cold pavement and began to scream.

She soon became aware of people running toward her, and as if in a dream, she heard the words, "Blood — stretcher — hurry, fast!" She heard strangers trying to comfort her, and finally, she felt herself sinking into nothingness as they lifted her onto the stretcher and ran with her. Her head, heavy and drowsy, was buzzing with sentence fragments. Hospital... friends... relax... And then there were no more sounds, no more pains, only darkness and quiet.

38

THE GRANDFATHER CLOCK in the foyer chimed seven as Misi and his roommate Geza stole into the room adjacent to the entrance hall. They carefully locked the door behind them so as not to make any noise, and then they both heaved a sigh of relief. "We did it!" they whispered excitedly.

"She didn't catch us, the old witch!" Misi exclaimed triumphantly. He was referring to the landlady of their rooming house, who had the annoying habit of stopping them for a chat whenever they entered the foyer. This time, they'd taken a less obvious route.

"Using the chimney was a good idea," Geza said with a wink. He lay down on the bed while Misi peered under it, a security precaution he performed routinely. "Oh that tyrant! How he double-crossed us!" Geza raged. "And just when we thought it was all over." Suddenly he froze. "Shh! I hear someone coming!"

"The Gestapo! My God, the Gestapo!" They grabbed their coats, ran to the window and opened it. "We can't scale the wall. The street is full of people." It was only a short leap to the pavement, but they would be completely exposed to view. For moments they simply stared at each other in despair and panic.

"Listen! He's getting closer! Let's jump anyway. Maybe we won't be noticed in the dark!"

There was a knock at the door. "Are you in there? I can hear you! When did you come in?" It was their landlady. "I didn't hear you return, and Mr. Porgesz has been waiting for you in the kitchen for some time now."

When the two young men heard this, their relief knew no bounds. "Shmuel Porgesz!" they whispered jubilantly. "It's Shmuel!" They quickly put away their coats and opened the door to welcome him. Shmuel appeared to be in a very good mood. Holding a bottle of wine in one hand and wine glasses in the other, he announced, "I came to celebrate the victory of our new fuehrer!" He handed each of them a cup and immediately began to pour the rich, red Tokay wine, filling the goblets to the brim. "Come on, Paula *neni*," he called to the landlady. "Come and celebrate with us."

"No thanks, I don't drink," she said as she entered the room. "Wine makes me sad."

The men began singing the newest Salasy march, and then Shmuel raised his goblet. "To our new fuehrer!" he cried, and everyone applauded loudly. The wine glasses were filled again and again. The three men even succeeded in persuading Paula to have a drink, despite her weak protests.

"I have an idea," Shmuel cried. "Let's go out and see how the Jews in the ghetto are celebrating the installment of our new chief of state!"

"Good thinking!" his friends approved noisily, and they reached for their coats and hurried out, slamming the door behind them.

"I doubt that she will ever question our loyalty to Salasy or to the party," Shmuel whispered when they were a safe distance from the house. "We must be more careful now than ever."

For moments after the threesome's departure, the woman remained standing behind the closed door. "How self-assured, how self-important they are," she muttered, shaking her head disapprovingly and staring into the empty wine cup. Her mind was now clearer than ever before, with new ideas forming which she had never allowed to take hold of her before, for she never dared to question the law when she was sober. She raised her hand menacingly. There was no stopping her now. "May the good Lord strike all three of you dead, for helping this mad autocrat come to power, prolonging the war for your own selfishness. You are safe, far away from the horrors of the war. While my dear Rudi and Stefan tempt death twenty-four hours a day, fighting it, frozen and hungry, you have nothing better to do for your country than sing and celebrate!"

The men walked briskly in the darkness, their footsteps echoing in the eerie silence. After turning the corner without a break in their pace, they reached the signal point in a dark alley where Shmuel had said their two friends, Iche and Bala, would be awaiting them. Within moments, the two newcomers joined them, and, as if on cue, all five of them reached into their pockets and took out heavy woolen socks which they furtively pulled over their black boots to muffle the sounds of their movements. Then, without exchanging even a word among themselves, they quickly headed towards their secret meeting place in the Margitsiget. There, in the huge deserted park, they could talk freely without being overheard.

Breathing a sigh of relief upon reaching their destination safely, they turned toward the large open stretch of land bordering the Danube River, where the famous Cigany Zene Cafe stood. The coffeehouse had once been a center of Budapest night life, where the rich and famous danced to the music of the Cigany Rudyes Violin Orchestra on balmy summer nights, but now it stood dark and deserted in the October chill.

After making sure that they were indeed alone, the friends

quickly split up into two groups and carefully approached the old wooden building that housed the cafe. Once inside, they searched the place, making sure that everything was as they had left it, including the secret escape route they had constructed at the time they decided to use the place for their clandestine meetings. Then each of them dropped wearily into his usual seat without uttering a sound.

Misi broke the tomblike silence that pervaded the dark room. "I'm cold and I can smell snow in the air, he complained. "Will somebody please light a candle?" Then he cried out in despair, "What will happen to our naked and half-starved brothers in the *munkatabor* when the temperature begins to drop?"

Shmuel lit a single candle which cast a yellow glow on his pale, wasted face. His transparent skin was stretched taut over his high cheekbones, emphasizing his dark, burning eyes. In strange contrast to his lifeless form, those eyes were alive with excitement. The other boys gazed at him in wonder. "My friends," he said with great urgency, "I have obtained the Swedish citizenship papers from Feri!"

"How many?" they cried ecstatically.

"Thirty!"

"You mean there's hope for at least some men to escape the *munkatabor*?"

"Yes!" Shmuel said, and then he impatiently silenced them. "This was Feri's message: 'These papers are our last hope while there are still some men alive.' Now, before we discuss which methods to employ to free them and bring them to the 'safe houses' which our Good Angel, Raoul Wallenberg, has purchased for that very purpose, let us all rise in tribute to this heroic Swedish diplomat." His voice cracked and as he stood in the yellow glare of the candle, tears rolled down his pale face, and, turning crimson, he stammered, "You...you should see how authentic these documents look. I think even our Good Angel would have trouble recognizing them as fakes. Come on, boys," he cried, "we must pool our resources and decide how to execute our Wallenberg's will. For that is the only way we can thank him for his unsurpassed generosity. And," he added, "this is the very last opportunity we will have to save some more lives before Salasy does away with them all!"

Suddenly everyone started talking at once. "Calm down," Shmuel warned. "We will never reach a solution this way."

However, hours later, after abandoning one plan after another, the group realized that they were no nearer to a solution than when they had started. "It's no wonder," Misi commented. "How can we come to an intelligent decision on a day like today, the day that Salasy has taken power? Let us try again tomorrow when the initial shock will have worn off."

Iche pulled nervously at his Hitler-style mustache. Throughout their discussion, he had appeared tense and distracted. "Let me out of here!" he demanded hysterically. "Let me out before I go insane!"

"Go," Shmuel replied. "Go, before I lose my patience with you. Anyway," he added, unbolting the door, "the cold air may bring you to your senses and help you think of a solution."

Iche stepped out into the cold night. He stopped briefly to inhale the night air and then, by following the whispering sounds of the river, he found himself at its deserted banks. He stood motionless, gazing into the vast body of flowing water. He hoped he would enjoy its usual calming effect on him, but tonight the Danube did not offer him comfort. The river was dark and unfriendly, and its appearance made him feel even more troubled. He wearily lowered himself to the ground and sat down, his back supported against an old, dried-out tree stump. The familiarity of the scene overwhelmed him. He sensed a strange similarity to a night long ago when he had also sat propped against a tree stump, among weeping women. Now the whole episode came back to him.

It was dark when his father appeared on the large, green

lawn. He ran to him. "Father," he asked, "why are all the mothers and girls crying and *davening* and sitting on the ground?"

"Because, Ichele, my little one, today is the ninth day of the Jewish month of Av, which marks the destruction of our Holy Temple in Jerualem by the Romans long, long ago. And because, Ichele," he sighed heavily, "since then we have been in *Galus*!"

"What does '*Galus*' mean?" he asked in a fearful voice. "Father, what does it mean?"

"It's not for you to know about yet," he replied. "It's past your bedtime, Iche. Go run to your room." His father hugged him, his long beard tickling Iche deliciously under his chin as he giggled with delight.

As Iche ran past the weeping women, he noticed with shock that it was his own mother who sat in the middle of the semicircle, sobbing as she read aloud to the tearful group. His mother saw him, and, smiling between her tears, she motioned to him to go to bed, but, defying orders, he tiptoed to one end of the semicircle, and, unbeknownst to his mother, sat down on a tree stump to listen to the story:

> The Holy One, blessed be He, said to Yirmeyahu, "Today I can be compared to one who had an only son, and he prepared a wedding canopy for him, and the son died under the canopy. And you, you do not grieve, neither for me nor for my children! Go and call Avraham, Yitzchak, Ya'akov and Moshe from their graves, for they know how to grieve."
>
> Yirmeyahu said to Him, "Sovereign of the Universe, I do not know where Moshe is buried."
>
> The Holy One, blessed be He, answered him, "Go, stand at the banks of the Jordan and call, 'Son of Amram, arise and see your sheep who have been devoured by their enemies.' "
>
> First Yirmeyahu went to Chevron, to Me'aras Hamachpelah, and said to the Patriarchs, "Arise, for you are wanted before the Holy One, blessed be He."

"Why?" they asked him.

He said, "I do not know," for he feared that they would rebuke him, saying, "In your days has such sorrow come upon our children."

Yirmeyahu then left them and went to the banks of the Jordan and called, "Son of Amram, arise, for you are wanted before the Holy One, blessed be He."

Moshe said to him, "Why is today different from yesterday, that I am wanted before the Holy One, blessed be He?"

Yirmeyahu said to him, "I do not know."

Moshe left him and went to the ministering angels, who had been present at the time of the giving of the Torah. He said to them, "Servants of the Celestial Heights, do you perhaps know why I am wanted before the Holy One, blessed be He?"

"Son of Amram," they said to him, "don't you know that the Holy Temple has been destroyed and Israel has been exiled?"

Moshe wept and cried out and when he reached the Patriarchs, they too rent their garments and lamented until they reached the gates of the Holy Temple.

They then came before the Holy One, blessed be He. Avraham stepped forward and began, "Sovereign of the Universe, why have You exiled my children, and given them into the hands of the nations, and destroyed the Holy Temple, the very place where I brought my son Yitzchak as an offering before You?"

The Holy One, blessed be He, said to Avraham, "Your children have sinned and have violated the entire Torah and all of the twenty-eight letters within her."

Moshe stepped forward and said, "Sovereign of the Universe, was I not a trustworthy shepherd of Israel for forty years? And when the time came for them to enter the Land, You decreed upon me that in the desert my bones would fall. And now that Israel is exiled, you have sent for me to eulogize and cry over them! This is like the parable: 'From the good of my master I do not benefit, but from his troubles I suffer.' "

Then our mother Rachel stepped before the Holy One, blessed be He, and said, "Sovereign of the Universe, you know that Ya'akov your servant loved me with a great love, and served my father for seven years for me, and when the seven years were over and the time of our wedding approached, my father decided to switch my sister for me. This hurt me terribly and I told Ya'akov and gave him a sign by which he could distinguish me from my sister so that my father would not succeed.

"But I regretted what I had done, and I controlled myself, for I pitied my sister and did not want her to be shamed. In the evening, when my sister was to go instead of me to my betrothed, I told her of the sign which I had given Ya'akov so that he should think that this was indeed Rachel. And I even hid under their bed so that when he spoke with her, I answered, so that he would not recognize her voice. I was kind to her rather than jealous, and I did not send her away in shame.

"Now, if I, who am merely flesh and blood, dust and ash, was not jealous of my competitor and did not send her out to humility and shame, then how can You, the Living King, the Merciful One, be jealous of idols who have no real substance?"

Immediately the Holy One, blessed be He, said, "For your sake, Rachel, I will return Israel to their place."

"Next year in Jerusalem!" the prayer passed through the crowd of women.

"Amen," his mother said, wiping her eyes and closing the book. She looked out at the women and then noticed her son sitting among them. "Ichele! Ichele!" his mother exclaimed. "Why are you still awake at this hour of the night?"

"I was listening to your story, Mama," he said meekly, expecting to be reprimanded, but his mother looked at him approvingly and spread her arms out to him. He ran toward her as if drawn by a magnet and he gratefully buried his face in the folds of her printed frock, feeling safe and protected.

"The *Mashiach* will come and next year on this day we will rejoice," she told him. Close to his mother, he wondered how the *Mashiach* could possibly improve the tranquility of the hour.

Mrs. Adler, their tall, heavyset next-door neighbor, stood up with obvious difficulty. "My daughter learned a very appropriate passage from *Tehillim* in school," she declared. "She will recite it." She turned to face a young girl who blushed crimson upon hearing her mother's words. "Won't you, dear?" Mrs. Adler asked her proudly.

The girl rose. The air was clear and the midnight sky was illuminated with stars, giving the scene a dreamlike appearance. The little boy, who had never before been allowed to stay up at this hour, watched hypnotized. The girl, Debora, had just turned ten a fortnight ago. Her skin was snowy white beneath her blond braids. She stood there, looking pleadingly at her mother and nervously smoothing the ruffles on her blouse.

"Come on, come on, my lamb," Mrs. Adler coaxed her daughter. "This goes nicely with the *Midrash* on *Eichah* that Iche's mother was reading."

Debora cleared her throat and curtsied low. "By the Rivers of Babylon," she began. And under her mother's proud gaze she started reciting.

By the rivers of Babylon, there we sat,
And also wept, when we remembered Zion.
Upon the willows in its midst, we hung our harps.
For there, our captors asked of us words of song,
And those who had shattered us, mirth.
Sing for us, of the songs of Zion.
How can we sing the song of the Lord
In the land of the alien?

The words stabbed at his heart now. Yes, alien, foreign and hostile. Just as this land is to us, Iche thought with choking anger. The sight of the free-flowing river filled him with great yearning. "Oh, River Danube!" he cried out. "How I long to be but one tiny drop in your waters, carried away with the current, out of the boundaries of this hostile land and into freer waters!" Drenched with sweat despite the chilly night, he asked, "But where to? Tell me, which part of Europe is safe for the Jew?" He gazed at his white knuckles in the moonlight, and, filled with impotent rage, he cried, "Cursed be you, River Danube! For wherever your banks have split the earth to bed you, there is no freedom for me and for mine! Therefore, for me you are one of the rivers of Babylon, the waters at whose banks our forefathers wept in bondage." And gazing mesmerized at the rolling giant, he added, "Only the date and location have changed, but our fate is the same as of old. To me and to my people, Danube, you will represent the rivers of Babylon, Babylon forever!"

39

IT WAS CLOSE to seven P.M. the next evening when the frightened group of young men arrived at their meeting place in Margitsiget Park. They entered the cafe, bolting the door securely behind them. Iche reached for the little hot plate on the table and began to make coffee. His mother had packed the hot plate in his suitcase on March twenty-ninth — ten days after the Nazi coup — when he had escaped from Kassau to Budapest.

"Take it with you, Ichele," his mother had insisted.

"What am I going to do with it, Mother?"

Her eyes were red. "Take it for good luck. It came from America," she boasted, and a hint of a smile lit up her frightened face as she mentioned the Golden Land, whose shores she so hoped her only son would reach someday.

The men sat there silently for a long time, cradling their mugs in their frozen hands. "Any ideas, anybody?" Shmuel asked, breaking the gloomy stillness. Everyone just stared at him with sad eyes and shook their heads.

Suddenly the bone-chilling sound of approaching bombers shocked them out of their inertia. "Listen! Planes! Oh my God, they're right above us!" They dashed to the windows. Geza, his eyes wide with fright, pointed to the sky. "Look! They're right over our heads!"

"Yes, they are here!" Iche cried through chattering teeth.

"They are here! Oh my Lord, what are we to do?"

They watched, mesmerized with fear. The planes were flying overhead, in tight V-formations, their silver bodies shimmering in the sky. Then the bellies of the horrifying iron birds opened and strange objects from within them were dropped to the ground below, landing with an unearthly thud. It was as if some unseen hand had unleashed them from outer space, to destroy the earth in a fury.

Nearby, a bomb exploded with a thunderous roar, and the shock waves knocked the men to the ground.

"We are in the target zone!" Geza exclaimed, trying to out-yell the sounds of destruction as all of them lay drenched from head to toe in cold sweat.

Heavy artillery fire broke out, and then the aircraft, having relieved themselves of their deathly cargo, turned around and disappeared from the sky, leaving misery and destruction in their wake.

Nearby a large apartment building was ablaze, standing out like a giant torch in the dark night as it sent yellow-red flames toward the sky. The entrance to the house flew open and people scrambled out, carrying babies in their arms and pulling screaming, frightened children behind them. They were followed by men and women groaning under the weight of the badly injured who were unable to escape on their own.

Geza grabbed Misi's shoulder, turning him towards the Margitsiget Bridge, from where the continuous noise of running could be heard. Speechless, they watched people pouring across the bridge and heading for the flaming inferno. The red glow of the fire illuminated their emaciated features and bodies, their clothing little more than torn rags. With growing pain in their hearts, Misi and Geza realized that these were the Jewish men from the *munkatabor*, who had been called to the scene.

"This must be the Emergency Squad we heard so much about," Misi breathed, pointing to the Red Cross bands which the men wore next to their yellow stars. Following in close succession came many more men carrying pails and shovels. They all ran up to the burning building, where they quickly separated. The ones wearing the Red Cross arm bands — obviously the medics — knelt on the ground by the injured. They hastily opened their black bags and started treating and comforting them as the wounded lay there, writhing in pain. The rest of the men filled their buckets and joined the neighbors dousing the flames. And the door opened repeatedly, as more and more of the injured escaped, gasping for air. The sinister glare of the blaze highlighted their smoke-blackened faces. Soon the ground was covered with wounded victims screaming for help. While the SS men walked around arrogantly, barking orders, the Jewish doctors worked tirelessly to alleviate the suffering.

"My brothers! They are my brothers!" Misi cried out to the SS. "How dare you order my brothers about as if they were your slaves!"

But Shmuel was beyond hearing or caring anymore. He stared at the scene through glazed eyes, while an odd, self-satisfied half-grin played on his lips. He was totally immersed in his own thoughts. First aid, first aid, the phrase echoed in his thoughts. "First aid, first aid," he repeated, trembling. The expression seemed to hold a special fascination for him. Then an idea began to form. Initially it was just a vague feeling lodging at the border of his consciousness, and then it became more and more clear to him. And why not? he asked himself with mounting excitement, his mind working as never before. He stood up and began speaking rapidly to the others, his words coming with the conviction of a fanatic, and with the selflessness of a saint. As he painted his vision in vivid colors, they stared at him in a trance, interrupting only with a word here and there, and pinching themselves to reassure themselves that they were, indeed, wide awake. The very earth seemed to pulsate with their wildly beating hearts.

Iche peered into Shmuel's eyes and cried, "What are you waiting for?"

"What are you waiting for?" the rest of them repeated.

Hidden by the evergreen bushes bordering the pathway, Shmuel walked briskly, driven by an inner fire. On his way to the site of the unfolding drama, he stopped only briefly to observe the situation. The place was in utmost turmoil, the wounded lying everywhere and screaming for help. This is the perfect setting for me, he thought decidedly, and he lowered himself onto all fours. The ground was frozen stiff. With his heart beating in his throat, he set out to reach the selected spot unobserved.

He lay there moaning softly at first, and gradually more and more loudly. Then he heard someone approaching him, and he realized the seriousness of the situation. He felt an overpowering urge to run, but it was too late. The SS man stood right there, inquiring about his injuries. "It's my ribs," he wailed. "All my ribs must be shattered. Help me! Please somebody help!"

Soon one of the doctors stood over him, holding a roll of bandages. "Can you move?" he asked.

"No," he cried, feigning pain. "No, I can't."

"Then let me see," the stranger said, kneeling down next to Shmuel on the frozen ground. Not until Shmuel felt the stranger's warm breath on his own freezing face, did he realize how utterly unprepared he had jumped into this.

Tell him about your mission, Shmuel told himself. Tell him. Now is the time, for the opportunity will never come again. He opened his mouth to talk, but horror of horrors, no sound came from his parched lips. His vocal chords refused to obey his command.

The medic put his hand in Shmuel's perspiring palm and spoke. "Show me where it hurts," he said softly and with deep concern, but in his panic Shmuel just moaned. "All right, don't worry," the man muttered, and with stiff, frozen fingers, he began to unbutton Shmuel's shirt collar. A gust of frigid air hit his exposed chest, shocking him into alertness, and the finality of the moment overwhelmed him. He knew that he had to act quickly, for within minutes the ambulances would arrive and then it would be too late.

Oh, what have I done? he cried inwardly, but to his amazement he heard his own words being spoken as if they came from far away. "Are you Jewish? You are, aren't you?"

He could not see the stranger's face, but the doctor let go of his shirt as if a viper had bitten him. He pulled away in disgust. "I understand," the medic sneered, his voice filled with venom, and he slid even further away from Shmuel.

I botched it! Oh no! He's leaving me! He's going away! "Doctor, please listen. Let me explain."

"It needs no explanation. I understand."

"Then take this," he said in despair. "I found it here in the dark. It's your hypodermic needle," he lied.

The doctor stepped towards him. "Give it to me!"

This was the opportunity on which Shmuel had placed all his vanishing hope. He grabbed the man's hand and pulled him purposefully to the ground. "Brother! Brother!" Shmuel's rasping voice came in broken sobs. "I came here to offer you a way to escape." There was no answer. Only the cries of the wounded filled the air. "Of course, if you would consider it," Shmuel began anew.

"Of all the nerve," the man snarled in the dark. "The nerve of you to offer me to go against the law."

"Which law? Whose law?" Shmuel demanded urgently. Then it dawned on him that the man would never trust him without proof. He began speaking to him in Yiddish, but there was no response. Then, in desperation, he began reciting his favorite chapter of *Tehillim* in Hebrew:

> Yea, though I walk in the valley of the shadow of death,
> I will fear no evil, for Thou art with me.
> Thy rod and Thy staff comfort me.

The effect on the stranger was amazing. At once he was at Shmuel's side. "Cry! Cry out with pain," he whispered, barely able to control his excitement. "I am supposedly bandaging your broken ribs."

"Please! Please, you're killing me!" Shmuel screamed. "Stop, stop!"

"That's better. Go on. Go on moaning and talk in between." The doctor rolled out an elastic bandage and started winding it around his patient's chest. Between moans and groans, Shmuel managed to give over his message.

"I am to walk down between the evergreen bushes, right?" the medic repeated, his voice quivering.

"Yes, you will go to the end."

"To the Cigany Zene Cafe. Do I understand correctly?"

"Right, right," Shmuel replied impatiently. "Start moving, I can't stay here forever, you know."

"I say '*shalom*' upon reaching the building and '*mazal*' when I pass it?"

"One word more and I shall scream!" Shmuel cried.

"Act drowsy and make believe you are falling asleep now," the good doctor said, trying hard to act naturally.

"Ow, ow!" Shmuel yelled.

The doctor stood up. "Let me check to see if we missed anybody out there," he said, and with purposeful strides headed toward the evergreens and disappeared in the dark.

Lying there, Shmuel trembled and listened. He counted the minutes, his nerves strained to the limit of endurance. Finally satisfied that his brother was out of danger and not yet missed, he rolled toward the bushes. It seemed that an eternity passed until he was inside the brown wooden building, and hidden in the sealed-off meeting room. Here, flanked by Misi and Geza, in the flickering candlelight, he looked around and his eyes met the burning eyes of the newcomer.

Yet, as they laughed and cried on each others' shoulders, none of them had the slightest notion that on this night of October sixteenth, nineteen forty-four, Operation Shmuel was born, under the besieged skies of Budapest. Nor could they fathom the success it was to reap.

40

In the Lord have I put my trust;
Let me not be deceived forever.
Let me escape in Thy loving justice.
Psalms 31:2

I HEARD THE TANTALIZING, happy gurgles coming from the crib next to me, and I was wide awake in an instant. She laughed into my eyes and kicked her tiny, pink feet into the air in greeting. My heart flooded with joy and love. I glanced at the alarm clock next to me on the nightstand. "You have overslept, my darling," I said. "There is no time to play. We must bring Papa's *tefillin* bag to him at once."

I bent back the corner of my daughter's little mattress and felt for the spot which we had hollowed out in it. Well-hidden inside the space were Iztvan's *tefillin.* It was considered very dangerous to smuggle these items into our hideout, but my husband could not bring himself to leave them behind. "I need my *tefillin,*" he had explained simply. "I can't be without them."

Holding my baby in one arm and the *tefillin* in the other, I entered the adjoining room where the men sat in deep silence, hardly daring to breathe. I saw that they had already begun to *daven*, for their lips were moving soundlessly.

Little Zsuzsi looked at her father. She stretched out her arms, begging him to hold her. "Stay with Mama, my little one," he whispered to her gently, "and the minute Papa finishes *davening*, he will give you a bath."

I watched as my husband rolled up his shirt sleeve above his elbow, and proceeded to wrap the long leather straps around his left arm, fastening one of the boxes above his forearm and then the other above his forehead. He turned towards the wall and although I could not see his expression I noticed a tremor pass through his body. Soon his experienced fingers worked the *tefillin* loose from his arm. Then he turned and handed them to Uncle Yidel, who passed the *tefillin* to another man when he had finished, and so it went until everyone had had a turn.

I looked at my husband and saw how relaxed he was, how his eyes shone with hope and pride. "It's twenty to eight," he whispered. "If we want to bathe little Zsuzsi, we'd better hurry. You know we must give the 'ghosts' the bathroom by eight."

Iztvan and I took our baby into the bathroom and began washing her. After a while, Uncle Yidel stuck his head in the doorway. "It's five to eight," he whispered impatiently.

Quickly, I wrapped the child in a towel and we stepped out, my husband carrying the little pink bundle. "It's eight o'clock," several people in the room announced.

Rozalia turned on the radio. "Good morning, my fellow Hungarian citizens," it boomed, and the first illegal family member rose to use the bathroom, his movements muffled by the radio's loud blaring.

"I left the bathwater in the bassinet to flush the toilet with," my husband reminded him.

"Hey, slow down!" someone called out. "You have to remember to walk. When you run, you risk being detected from below."

"Slow down!" we hissed in unison, our fingers automatically pointing to the floor.

"Sh-sh-sh-shhh," everyone admonished each other angrily. And so, with the very first activity of the day, the bickering began.

It's Salasy who has made us so paranoid, I thought bitterly.

The air was charged, tempers were rising and a tremor passed through me at the prospect of another day of quarreling.

Pali's face was white as a sheet. "This can't go on," he cried, springing out of his seat. "I am going to write down the rules of this house," he announced, "in order to save us from this constant fighting."

Magda lunged for the paper bag. "Oh no, don't use this. There is no more paper in the stores. How will Anna smuggle all those extra loaves of bread into the house?"

Rozalia stood up with much effort and dragged herself to the armoire. She returned holding a box of ivory stationery with blue forget-me-nots embossed on the top. Wordlessly, she placed it on the table. Pali glanced at it and all the blood drained from his face. He looked at it again and then turned to his wife. They gazed at each other momentarily, and then Rozalia ran from the room sobbing, leaving an eerie silence in her wake.

I, only I, knew how precious and dear this stationery was to them, for Rozalia had once shown it to me in a moment of great bitterness. "My little sister Litzi gave it to me before she was deported," she explained. "'I'll write the minute we arrive,' she said, 'and please answer back promptly!'"

I watched Pali, who wrote with nervous, rapid strokes, while beads of perspiration formed on his knitted brow. Finally he rose, wiped his face and put his pen back into his pocket with great care. "I don't know if it will help or not," he said, "but the one thing I know is that peace among us is essential to our survival." Then his face darkened. "We are sitting on a tinder-box that is ready to explode at any moment!"

Uncle Yidel grabbed the paper from Pali, and he read its contents aloud.

HOUSE RULES

1. WALK ONLY WHEN YOU MUST AND DO IT VERY CAREFULLY.
2. FLUSH THE TOILET ONLY WHEN ABSOLUTELY NECESSARY, AND WITH PAILS OF WATER FROM THE SINK.

3. WHEN THE NEED ARISES TO DISAPPEAR FROM THE SCENE, TAKE FOOD, SILVERWARE AND DRINKING GLASSES ALONG WITH YOU.
4. MAKE ABSOLUTELY SURE THAT NO TELLTALE SIGNS REMAIN BEHIND.
5. YOU MUST LEAVE A WINDOW OPEN, REGARDLESS OF THE WEATHER, TO MINIMIZE STUFFINESS.
6. DO NOT RELY TOO MUCH ON THE RADIO TO COVER SOUND. KEEP CONVERSATION TO A MINIMUM.
7. USE SIGN LANGUAGE WHENEVER POSSIBLE.
8. MAKE DAILY HIDING DRILLS TO PERFECT YOUR TECHNIQUE.
9. TAKE BLANKETS ALONG TO MUFFLE COUGHS AND SNEEZES.
10. YOUR DISAPPEARANCE MUST BE ACCOMPLISHED IN LESS THAN SIXTY SECONDS.

"Hmm, pure genius! A real brainstorm!" The comments passed through the room, and the sudden venom in everyone's voice startled me. Something has to be done, I cried inwardly. Something, but what?

"Anna!" Lajos called. "Are you still here? You'd better go. It's late. You'll have a long line before you, and it's freezing outside!"

"Never mind the line," Anna responded, turning white. "What if there isn't any bread left?"

Anna hastily reached for her coat, but Lajos took off his sweater and gave it to her. "Here, put this on first." Then he handed her a sheet of newspaper. "Wrap your feet in this inside your galoshes," he instructed her. "It will keep them from freezing."

"And take this," Magda cried, pushing a hot baked potato into her hands. "Keep alternating it in your pockets to keep your hands warm."

And thus equipped, Anna left the house for her first bakery trip of the day. I stood by the window, clutching my baby nervously as I watched the petite girl walking quickly away from the house. In my relative safety I trembled with fear, as I did each time she left the house until the minute she returned home.

A brutal north wind rippled through the bare trees surrounding our house, disturbing the trembling birds and sending them flying up into the gray skies, their shrill cries echoing behind them. What a shame summer is over and winter is now in the air! I thought to myself sadly. I tried to focus my attention on the birds and on the large snowflakes being tossed back and forth in the wind — at everything and anything, just to take my mind off the frightening fact that my sister, my beautiful younger sister, was walking the streets with forged identification, her pockets filled with incriminating bogus ration books. Although she followed this same routine daily, the risk had increased. Karoly's words kept ringing in my ears: "The witch hunt is intense. Salasy has stationed policemen at every corner to check our documents!" My heart throbbed wildly, and I felt as if I were dying a little bit with each passing moment until I saw Anna coming home safely again.

"She is back! She is back!" I exclaimed joyfully. "She has just turned the corner, and guess who is with her? Geza!" I was exuberant, and all those present breathed a sigh of relief. I ran to open the door for them, but as soon as I glanced at Geza, my heart sank. It was a known fact among us that Geza's complexion was a foolproof barometer of his state of mind, and Geza's face was now covered from ear to ear with angry red blotches.

"Geza!" I cried, feeling faint with worry. "Geza, what happened?"

He considered my words for a second, and then he walked right past me into the room. I felt a chill run down my spine. "Stop!" I cried, running after him and grabbing the lapel of his despised SS uniform. "Tell me! You must tell me what's going on!"

"Well," he sighed, shrugging his shoulder, "if you insist."

By this time the whole family had gathered around him, begging him to speak.

"I already told you that ever since Salasy came to power, the SS have been assembling small groups of Jews on the city streets." His face paled. "They are taking them to an unspecified destination," he whispered. "I always suspected that our brothers would meet some horrible fate, but last night I found out for sure." He stopped and looked at the floor to avoid our eyes. The question hung silently in the air: "Where to?"

Suddenly the air-raid siren blared with terrible urgency, closely followed by the roar of approaching planes. Magda, who lived in morbid fear of the raids, darted into the room. "I can hear them," she said anxiously. "They are right here. I am so scared!" Then her gaze fell on Geza. "Please come downstairs with us. Karoly is at work at the munitions plant, and I am so horribly frightened without him!"

"I am at your disposal, madame," Geza said gallantly. He lifted up the sleeping litle Macika from her crib. "Come, Magda, I'll chase the airplanes away from here," he said with a forced smile and started to accompany her to the door.

An impatient murmur ran through the apartment. "Tell us," we all demanded. "Tell us before you leave this room!"

Tears glittered in Geza's eyes and I could see the pulse throbbing at his temple. "I found out by accident. I saw it. We were at the Margitsiget meeting and... and... and I happened to investigate a strange noise. Then I saw them, all lined up at the bank of the river, naked, stark naked, just like that." He covered his eyes, trying to blot out the picture, and his voice came in gasps. "One two three, just like that, shot right into the Danube."

Minutes later, I sat hunched over in the shelter, Geza's terrible words screaming at me, "They shoot them! They shoot them right into the river!"

41

Out of the depths have I called Thee, O Lord!
Psalms 130:1

THE SHADOWS had grown long when a freezing and weary Anna ran through the door. She flung her almost empty shopping bag onto the floor in despair. "There is nothing to be had," she moaned.

Rozalia picked up the bag, and as she peered into it her face lit up. "Why, there are potatoes!" she exclaimed, and, hugging the bag tightly to her body, she hurried into the kitchen to begin cooking.

"Listen!" Anna said, her face turning ashen. "Listen to what's on the radio!"

"*Peer Gynt,*" I whispered the name of the song with sudden awareness, my legs feeling weak.

Tears glistened in my sister's eyes. "Tzivia," she sobbed. "Our sister Tzivia."

"Yes," I muttered, heartbroken, as Solveg's haunting melody penetrated the room. "Oh, how she adored this song."

Magda tapped me on the shoulder. "There is no use getting sentimental," she said quietly, pointing to the blanket-covered mound in the middle of the room.

"Oh, I completely forgot!" I cried in response, and immediately both Anna and I ran to take up our regular posts. The room was still suffused with the tantalizing melody, but I no longer heard it. All I could think of was, What is the announcer of the "Voice of America" whispering into the ears of the men hidden under the blankets?

Despite the great tension, the atmosphere in the room was optimistic, as it always became whenever the "Voice of America" entered into our desperate existence. Reminding us that there existed a faraway Shangri-la, the broadcast filled us with yearning and hope. After each program, we would sit for hours and analyze every word that was spoken, interpreting them according to our wishes. The reports were fantastic morale boosters which kept us going until the next broadcast.

On that particular day, we were so engrossed in discussion about what had been aired that we failed to notice that the program on our "legal" radio had changed, until the wild applause indicated to us that Salasy was about to speak. Suddenly, the picture of that faraway land, where there was religious freedom and peace, was obscured by the harsh realities of war and our hopefulness turned to panic and despair. Weak and drained, we stared at the radio. The ovation seemed endless. Finally we heard Salasy's voice, as cold as steel and as sharp and deadly as a sword.

"It has come to my attention and has been confirmed," he boomed, "that there are still numerous undesirable elements hiding out. And let it be known, that it is not only your privilege, my Aryan comrades, but your sacred and patriotic duty to track them down and turn them in!"

We looked at each other with glazed eyes, the fear that everyone felt almost tangible.

"And let it be heard and known by all, that whoever fails to perform this sacred duty for his homeland must be ready to accept the dire consequences!" Salasy paused for breath. "This would amount to treason," he continued, "and the severe punishment will fit the crime! Let me bring it to your attention, my Aryan brothers and sisters, that this is my last warning. So repent, fellow Hungarians!" He paused to let the effect of his words register. There was more thunderous applause, and after it died down Salasy proceeded to describe in grisly detail how one who was found guilty of this crime would be forced to watch his own family being tortured before he would finally be released from his misery.

"Cannibals!" Rozalia spat in response to the endless clapping. "Blood-thirsty cannibals!"

Panic engulfed me, as terrifying pictures of our beloved saviors filled my mind. Baby Macika, sweet and smiling, as I had just seen her, snatched from her mother's arms... and... and Magda's and Karoly's heartrending cries...

"No!" I cried out, hiding my face in my hands.

I knew that Iztvan was experiencing the same guilt and concern for their lives when I heard him cry out to Karoly, who was just stepping in through the front door, "Karoly, you must find an apartment. You must move away from us."

"I see that you have been frightened by our esteemed leader," he said contemptuously. "My answer is: No, I will not move away!"

"Of course not," his wife echoed through pale lips.

"But you must! You have no choice! Didn't you hear? Don't you understand?" Karoly just stood there and shook his head. Sweat poured down Iztvan's ashen face and his voice ebbed to a whisper. "Now, because of your extraordinary selflessness, you are as hunted as we are, and as we were when you, as a perfect stranger, took us under your wing. Now it's my turn, as your most indebted and closest friend, to make sure that you and yours are safe."

"You are wasting your time," Karoly said. Then he turned to his wife. "Isn't he, my dear?"

Iztvan's face turned fiery red and his eyes filled with fear. "Then I must beg you, beseech you, implore you. Please move away from here!" But his words fell on deaf ears. "Then our only alternative, the only thing we must do, is to move away from you," Iztvan declared. "Iche," he called out, "Iche, please find us an apartment!"

Iche's eyebrows arched with surprise. "An apartment? You know there is no such thing!"

"An apartment?" Geza asked. "I don't know about an apartment, but I did hear about a condominium."

"How did you find out about it?" we asked eagerly.

"We have heard," Geza began, a shadow darkening his features, "that all men in the *munkatabor*s will be liquidated."

The information came as a terrible blow to us. We were hoping and praying that this remnant of the *munkatabor* — these thousands of Jewish men — would survive the war.

"We have also learned," Geza continued, "that these men will pass through Budapest on their way."

"Where are they going to be taken?" I asked, dazed by the news.

"Camp Strasshof."

A heartrending cry pierced the air. "Oh, no, not Camp Strasshof!"

"So we are getting ready to pluck as many men from the line as we possibly can," Geza whispered. "In our search for a place to house these men, we heard about the condominium, but it doesn't meet our needs."

"Why exactly did you pass it up?" Iztvan asked.

"It's not for just one reason, it's for many. Although the location is excellent, the place is too small for our purposes and a house in such a quiet, middle-class neighborhood is too obvious. What we need is a large, run-down house, deep in the poorer section of Budapest, where we won't be noticed."

"In what part of the city is the condominium located?" Iztvan asked anxiously.

"It's in the Zuglo."

"The Zuglo!" Uncle Yidel exclaimed. We all shared his

enthusiasm, because the Zuglo was in the eastern part of Budapest, closer to the Russian forces, and would likely be liberated first.

"The first transport might show up tonight!" Geza cried, and he and Iche reached for their overcoats and flew out of the room.

Iztvan ran after them, catching up to them before they opened the door. "My friends," he begged them, "please get the condominium for me, whatever the cost." (Fortunately for us, my husband had managed to save up a considerable sum of money while working for Mr. Stern in Budapest before the occupation of Hungary.)

42

> But God is the Judge:
> He casts down one and lifts up another.
> *Psalms 75:8*

TWO THOUSAND MEN lay sleeping on the bare floor in an abandoned building. The building had been shelled, with not one window or door left intact, nothing to keep the bitter cold at bay. But the men had collapsed, having traveled a long distance by foot the previous day. Huddled together for warmth, they had fallen asleep the moment their bodies hit the floorboards.

The other wing of the building, as it so often happens, bore no evidence of the explosion which had damaged the first part. It was here that the SS soldiers who had escorted these two thousand Jewish men were housed.

Dawn had not yet broken when the SS men came marching noisily into the room. "Up, Jews! Come on. Get up!" The men pulled themselves up with great difficulty, their emaciated bodies shivering, as they stood there in dread of the coming day.

"For the next few hours, they are yours," the SS man who had been in charge of the men until now said to his replacement.

"What a sinister sight!" the young new leader whispered, taken aback by their frightful appearance.

"Well," the older leader chuckled, "they are all yours. You may as well enjoy them!"

"Not that I am fainthearted," he said as he gazed straight ahead at the mummy-like creatures, "but... but it seems so unearthly, so uncomfortable. It makes me feel like I am in command of an army of dead men."

"Well, soon they will be," the elder leader replied, without a twinge of emotion in his voice.

Terror was mirrored in the face of the young SS officer. "I heard rumors, but I never expected this."

"You will find there are a lot of things you never expected," his superior responded, pointing to the revolver on the young soldier's side.

"Yes, I have my orders," the soldier said, paling.

Judging from the expression on the older man's face, it was obvious that he enjoyed every second of the Jews' misery. He jabbed the younger man in the ribs. "What's all the fuss about?" he exclaimed. "They're only Jews!"

The sun rose, and the sun set, and the SS changed their guard twice. Now, driven by the third escort, the Jewish men still walked on without rest or food, and more and more of them fell.

When the man who was walking near Shia collapsed onto the pavement, Shia ran horror-stricken toward the edge of the line. "The SS is coming at him with his sword!" he cried out through trembling lips.

"Don't cry. Don't mourn him, my boy," someone said in the dark, reaching out and taking the hand of the terrified youth in his own. "Don't feel sorry for him," he repeated soothingly. "If anything, envy him. He is at peace, while we don't know what price we will have to pay to earn that privilege."

The man had a deep, rich voice, and the boy sensed his warmth instantly. "Where are they taking us?" Shia asked.

"Why ask where to, when right now I don't believe I can take another step?" the man murmured in the dark.

But Shia was persistent. "Have you any idea where we are now?"

"Why are you interested? We have nowhere to escape to. There is nowhere to hide."

But Shia chattered on, asking question after question. He just wanted to be near the man. He was much too frightened and felt the need to talk. They conversed in whispers as they stiffly marched ahead.

Suddenly the older man slowed his pace. "Did I hear you right? Are you talking about what will happen when the war is over? Do you mean to say that you hope to live to see it?" he asked, incredulous. "Well, you are young," he added quickly. "You may."

"And you will, too," Shia whispered, but his words did not sound convincing, and the man shrugged him off without comment.

They walked along silently for a while, as neither could think of anything more to say. Then the man sighed and pulled the boy close. He opened his mouth, but no words escaped his lips.

"Are you all right?" Shia gasped, fear gnawing at his heart as he remembered what happened to the men once they became sick and fell.

"It's just that lately I've had time to think," the man said, "and now, in hindsight, I see it all clearly. I see now how it all happened, how we got here."

"People are greedy. It's as simple as that," the boy answered.

"Let's not discuss psychology now. That won't help us. All I want to talk about is the message I find in our existence. The age-old practice of persecuting the Jewish people must stop!" he said urgently. "Your youthful, hopeful attitude that there may be life for some Jews after the war has caused me to reconsider, and I have come to the conclusion that for some, it may be true. Now listen, and remember my words, and promise me that you will spread them among the young. Leave this country! Leave this continent!" he cried, his voice choked with emotion. "It is soaked through and through with our innocently shed blood. Run, my boy, run and never look back!"

"You will come with us. You will be our leader!" the boy whispered.

"Now listen, and don't interrupt," the old man ordered him sternly. "When you do go, leave your naive disposition, your unconditional belief in the good of mankind, behind. Leave it here, buried with the dead. Forget about the gullible Jewish boy you were. He is dead. Think strong and you will find strength. Trust only in a brother. Pool your resources and rely on them alone."

"You will be our leader. You will teach us," Shia breathed in horror.

"What I am telling you, what I want you to understand, is that you must fight for your rights. Fight for your God-given niche on this earth. Fight for *Eretz Yisrael*!"

"*Yerushalayim. Mashiach,*" Shia stammered, choking with tears.

"Shush, my boy, shush! Let me talk. Shock the world! Assert yourself. Fight back though it will be hard, very hard. And it will be harder for the rest of the world to accept your strength..." A pitiful sound rose from the older man's throat. It was a cross between laughter and crying and it made the boy shudder with fright. "...just as it was for my older brother to accept that I, the passive little baby, was able to pull myself up in the crib and stand up on my own. As the story goes, he promptly pushed me down, flat on my back, to the position he thought I would remain in forever. Understand? Do you understand what I mean to say?"

"Yes I do," the boy murmured. "The inability to assert ourselves. It haunts me."

"At least I had some relatively good times in my life, but you, you've experienced nothing but pain." There was no answer. "Your childhood, your youth, there was none. It was stolen from you, wasn't it?" Suddenly he grew impatient. "Why don't you answer?" he asked, reaching out to touch the boy.

But there was no boy to touch. His hand fell helplessly back to his side.

43

THE SIEGE OVER the city grew worse each day, and by mid-November we found that we were hiding in the air-raid shelter more often than not. The sounds of destruction terrified us, and we passed the time with nonstop chatter in order to block them out.

Today's topic, however, made me uneasy. It revolved around pigs, or, more specifically, how to prepare and cook them. It was a subject I knew next to nothing about, but I had to conceal my ignorance, for it was an open secret among Gentiles that Jews are forbidden to eat pork. As they were busily exchanging recipes, I racked my brain, thinking of how to change the subject before I, too, would be interrogated.

Suddenly the old lady turned to me. "Zsuzsi, aren't you a native of Dunantul?" she asked. "Tell us a good recipe."

"Zsuzsi will never share her recipes. She is too selfish," Magda announced in a desperate effort to bail me out.

"It's not that. It's just that everything has already been said. There is really nothing for me to add. But if you like, I could tell you about something I experienced as a child. It still stands out in my mind as vividly as when it happened."

"Let's hear, let's hear!" everyone shouted.

"Did any of you ever participate in the actual slaughtering of a pig the way it's done in a small village?"

They looked at me, puzzled. "What do you mean?" they asked in a chorus, while Anna and Magda sat there with forced smiles on their faces.

"Then I'll tell you how it was done. I was about six years old at the time, but I will never forget the excitement, nor will I forget the holiday-like atmosphere. Let me start at the beginning. My uncle arrived bright and early that day to take us to Grandmama's. Guess how we went? In a horse-drawn carriage! He was a very funny man, my uncle, and he joked with us the whole way there. It was right before Christmas, and I remember how bitterly cold it was outside, and I also remember how nice and warm it was in my grandmother's house when we arrived. Oh, and the house smelled so good from her freshly baked bread. It was a small, well-kept farmhouse with two rooms — a spacious kitchen and what Grandmama called her 'good room.' The good room, which was a parlor that doubled as a bedroom and dining room, and which we were never allowed to enter, was filled with strangers. To my surprise, Grandpapa took me and my sister Celia by the hand and led us into this room to introduce us. 'These are my granddaughters,' he said proudly. 'They are fine city girls.' All eyes were upon us, but my attention was diverted by the sight of the meticulously made up beds. I wondered how many feather quilts and pillows were under each bedspread. My sister must have wondered, too, because she whispered in my ear, 'She must use a ladder to heap them up!' and, holding back our laughter, we ran from the room.

"'I've never seen these people before. Are they related to us?' I asked my grandmother later, as I ate my buttered bread at the kitchen table. 'No,' she replied, laughing good-naturedly, 'they are our friends and neighbors who came here to help us slaughter the hog. They will also assist us in curing the meat so it will last through the winter.'

"'It's time,' Grandpapa announced after a while, and he picked up a knife and started toward the door. Everybody stood up, and, carrying bowls, chopping boards and cutting implements, went out single file from the room. 'It looks like a church procession,' my sister whispered.

"Suddenly a terrifying cry pierced the night, a cry so agonizing that, disregarding Grandfather's strict orders that I stay put in the kitchen, I went flying outside to discover its source. There, in the middle of the crowd, I spotted the pig. It seemed to me that every single person was hanging on to the poor animal. My uncle held its head, his great muscles bulging under the strain of the struggling animal. I shuddered, almost fainting at the sight."

"And then?" Maria asked with great excitement.

"And... and my aunt held a giant bowl to collect the blood, while a woman called Bozsi kept stirring it at a dizzying speed."

Just as I finished my story, the raid came to an end, and we all went back upstairs. We had hardly closed the door, when Magda and Anna looked at each other and burst out laughing. "Zsuzsi... the pig... her grandparents..." They fell on each other's shoulders, shaking with laughter.

"What's going on?" the others asked.

"Our grandparents slaughtered a pig!" Anna and I answered, choking with giggles.

Our levity was contagious. Before long, everyone in the room was holding his sides with laughter, and a long time passed until we had composed ourselves sufficiently to relate the entire story.

"But tell me, Zsuzsi," Magda persisted, "how did you have the gall to talk about something you never experienced?"

"Terus *neni*?" Anna guessed, repeating a name from the past.

"Yes," I answered. "You remember how Mama never let a morsel of leftovers go to waste."

"Sure," Anna replied. "All the uneaten food was thrown into a large pail and Terus *neni* would come each night to collect it. Poor old lady — with those scraps she fattened her pig."

"I used to help her carry it," I continued, "and on the way to her house she would tell me stories."

"In any case, it was a great story!" Magda said. Abruptly, she looked up. "Goodness!" she cried out. "It's almost Christmas! It's almost Christmas!" she repeated, trembling. "There are a million and one different traditions and customs you have to know about. Come, let's go to my room and we'll talk about some of them. And from now on, let us use every minute, every spare minute to teach you about the holiday."

We sat on Magda's bed and sang Christmas carols. "You learn fast!" she commented in surprised satisfaction, and we sang our hearts out. "This is my favorite," she remarked as we sang "Silent Night" over and over again. We were so absorbed in our caroling that we didn't notice the sound of movement in the hall, nor did we hear someone stopping outside our apartment.

Unexpectedly, there was a tap at the door. We all froze with fright, except for Magda, who kept her wits about her. "Go on singing. Loud, loud, louder!" Then she pulled me out of my seat. "Go fast. Fast!" she ordered me. "Warn them." I threw off my shoes and tiptoed into the next room, trembling so badly that I couldn't speak. I just motioned wildly.

"Is someone at the door?" Rozalia asked, turning white as a ghost.

"Yes," I whispered, finally finding my voice. "That's how reliable you all are," I said angrily. "That's how well you watch the path."

The taps on the door grew louder and more insistent.

"You can open the door," Rozalia murmured, walking toward her hiding place in the armoire. "Everybody is out of sight."

Clutching my baby desperately, I walked into the foyer. "Who is it?" I asked. "Who is there?"

"Is someone knocking?" Anna asked casually.

There was a moment of silence. "It's me."

"Who?" I repeated faintly.

"What is the matter with you, sister dear? Don't you recognize my voice?"

"It's Shia! It's Shia!" both Anna and I cried, grabbing for the doorknob. The door flew open and Shia, our lost brother, came inside and fell into our outstretched arms.

A tear escaped from Shia's half-closed lids. "I can't believe that I am here," he murmured. "I can't believe it's true. But then, if the Lord wants it so, then nothing is impossible!" He took my baby from my arms and suddenly his tears started gushing out. "My only niece," he cried. "The only one left."

"They are all still hiding," Anna reminded me, pointing to the beds.

"It's all clear," I whispered under the bed and into the closets.

"What took so long?" my husband exclaimed, looking annoyed as he crawled out from under the bed. Then he saw Shia. "Oh my God! It's you! It's you!" and he ran to embrace his brother-in-law. Shia just stood there, mesmerized, as everyone emerged from their hiding places. He came out of his trance only after Uncle Yidel appeared.

A glimmer appeared in Shia's blue eyes."Yidel, your sister Bracha and her husband Meir are on their way, too. They should be here very soon."

"Bracha?" Uncle Yidel exclaimed joyfully. "You really mean my little sister Bracha?"

"They are here!" Pali, who was watching the path, cried. "They just turned the corner." We all ran to the window to see.

"Don't make such a fuss," someone said, and we automatically pointed toward the despised wall.

In the midst of all this excitement, Aunt Bracha and Uncle Meir stepped through the door. Tears of joy flowed again and the room was buzzing with excitement once more.

Pali stood in the middle of the room, his face drawn. "Where will these three hide?" he asked, looking around wildly.

Aunt Bracha's eyes opened wide. "What do you mean, 'hide'?"

"Shhh," we breathed in horror. "There are Nazis living on the other side of that wall."

Shia turned to Bracha. "This you have to see!" he said. "Oh, you ought to see them hide!"

"Hide?" Aunt Bracha repeated in horrified confusion. "What do you mean?"

"Listen, Aunt Bracha," Iztvan tried, "you aren't familiar with our situation. Only my wife, her sister, and my daughter live here legally. Only they get ration books. Only they can be seen in the air-raid shelter. The rest of us stay up here, air raid or not. If a stranger approaches the house, we must hide."

An angry glint appeared in Aunt Bracha's eyes. "I should stay up here when we are under attack? No! There is no way you can make me."

Everyone responded with angry comments. "Who do you think you are? You can't make up new rules. If you don't like it, you can go back where you came from."

"Shhh, let me talk," Uncle Yidel said. He walked over to his fuming sister. "Calm yourself, Bracha," he said soothingly. "Bracha dear, please calm yourself. Let us talk reasonably and see what can be done."

"You don't know what I've been through," Bracha sobbed. "Losing the baby, finding Meir so ill in the hospital — it has left me a bundle of raw nerves. I can never go through with this. Never!"

"You have papers, I understand," my husband said. "Let's see them."

Bracha rummaged through her bag. "Here," she said angrily, slapping the documents on the tabletop. "You didn't know this, but I lived in an institution for weeks using these false papers and no one ever suspected me. In fact, when a Jewish girl was suspected of hiding out there, a Gentile girl told me about her suspicions before she told anyone else."

If only she hadn't bleached her hair blond! I thought,

feeling panicky. That's what all Jewish women did to alter their looks. As I kept looking at her my heart sank, for the formerly apple-cheeked, Jewish beauty's appearance had indeed greatly changed. She had lost a lot of weight, which emphasized her generous Jewish nose, and with the blond hair, she was the living image of the caricatures circulating in the newspapers depicting the Jewess trying to pass for an Aryan.

After a lengthy debate, we decided that if our mentors agreed, Bracha would register legally at our address.

This being settled and everyone now calmed down, Iztvan asked worriedly, "Where is Uncle Meir?"

We found Uncle Meir standing at the same spot near the door where he had entered. "Why don't you come in?" we asked, puzzled.

"Because," he moaned pitifully, "because I am sick."

He is acting strangely, I thought to myself. Then I really looked at him and I realized how wasted away he was.

"You don't have to punish yourself for that," my husband said, still confused. "You don't have to stand in the corner."

"All the more reason for you to come in and make yourself comfortable," Rozalia added tearfully. "We will do our best to nurse you back to health."

Horror electrified Uncle Meir's expression. "But you don't know, you don't understand! I have tuberculosis! And you know how contagious that is, and in such close quarters, it may be doubly so."

Iztvan faced him, and spoke slowly, emphasizing each word. "If I understand you correctly, you are trying to tell us that you pose a definite health hazard to all of us."

Tears filled Uncle Meir's eyes, and he nodded his head mutely.

"Then let me tell you," Iztvan continued, "that our hearts are constantly pumping our Jewish blood into our veins, a far more certain hazard to our health. If we are fainthearted, if we are afraid to take chances, then the only alternative is to tear our hearts out."

"Then it's alright if I stay?" he asked hopefully. "You don't mind?"

"Of course we don't mind," Iztvan declared. "Besides, what's the difference which sickness threatens our lives? I want you to know that we are all sick here, very, very sick. Afflicted by the deadliest parasite raging the continent — anti-Semitism."

"Now, what about me?" Shia demanded, thrusting his documents under my nose.

"What's this?" I asked as I stared at a document, signed and stamped with official seals and all. Yet, where his name should have been filled in, there was a blank space.

That familiar, mischievous expression appeared on Shia's face. "I am suffering from amnesia," he moaned in a pitiful tone. "Maybe you can help me out. Maybe you know who I am and what my alias is."

The room was filled with laughter. "What a clever idea!" I exclaimed. Then I paused for a moment. "Shia, who told you where we were hiding? And who told you how to get here?"

Shia's face darkened. He closed his mouth tightly and his eyes clouded over. "I beg of you," he whispered. "Do not ask where I came from, what I went through or what I saw. If only you could understand the agonizing guilt I feel, sitting here warm and dry, knowing what my unit is going through. And to think that the man will never know that I didn't leave on purpose, that I was whisked off my feet before I could so much as cry out. He probably feels betrayed by me. And I will never be able to explain the truth to him. He has probably given up already."

My brother's face was etched with pain so deep that I couldn't bear to see it. "Hush, brother, hush!" I told him. "Don't talk about it. Don't think about it. Just tell us who directed you here. Who knows about our hiding place? Who is behind this all? We absolutely must know."

A tremor passed through his body. "Shmuel Porgesz," he breathed. "Shmuel Porgesz and his friends."

Our tension turned into relief and a great silence fell upon the room.

After a while Anna walked over to Shia, who was still trembling. "I'm Anna Shipoc," she said. "I like the name Joska. It has an authentic Hungarian sound to it."

Shia extended his hand to my brother-in-law Pali, who happened to be standing next to him. "Joska Shipoc," he introduced himself.

"A pleasure to meet you," Pali answered with a smile.

"Here, Pali," Iztvan said, handing him Joska's documents. "This is a job for our resident scribe."

"Wait a moment!" Joska said. "Here is the pen which I was told to use."

Anna's eyes lit up. "Now that he has been baptized Joska Shipoc and he is legally our brother, can he accompany me on my shopping trips and help carry home the food?"

"Surely," Iztvan replied. Then he turned to my brother. "Just don't forget your new identity," he added.

"Oh, I am so happy for Anna," I cried. "It's hard enough for her as it is, all skin and bones, to be burdened with carrying all of the food. And now with three more mouths to feed, the journeys would kill her."

A murmur of approval passed through the room. My slightly-built brother, with his sky-blue eyes and light blond hair, fit the description of a thirteen-year-old Aryan boy very well. Although he was really seventeen, we made him four years younger, because thirteen was the blessed age at which no military or party responsibility was imposed on him.

Shmuel, Joska's heroic rescuer, came to visit us in the afternoon, dressed in his purloined SS officer's uniform. We were wild with excitement, almost crushing him in our attempts to congratulate and thank him. "We know how you waited, night after night, under the cover of darkness, hoping to save some condemned soul from death," Anna said. "We always talk about you and pray for your success. But to see my brother here..." Anna's voice caught in her throat, but she managed to cry, "May God bless you and reward you for what you have done."

"How did you boys find Shia?" Lajos asked in a tone of euphoria mingled with wonder. "How did you know where he was? How did you find him in the dark? And how did you know whom to choose?"

"Choose?" Shmuel murmured. "Why, you must be out of your mind! We haven't the faintest idea who it is we grab, or where he comes from. All we care about is saving a Jewish soul from the murderers' grasp. It was *Hashgachah*," Shmuel said modestly. "Because it was destined for Shia to come here, he was the one we happened to choose. It's as simple as that!"

"'And He rebuked the Sea of Reeds, and it was dried up. And he lead them through the depths as through a wilderness,'" Lajos whispered through his tears.

44

MACIKA MUST HAVE been crying for a long time, but with all the commotion we hadn't heard her. Now she was screaming at the top of her lungs, "Mama, mama!"

"Oh, no!" Magda cried, turning white. "I hope she didn't fall from her crib and hurt herself! Mama is coming, Mama is here!" she said, running toward the room.

Frightened, I started to run after her, but Iche, who had arrived at our apartment several minutes before, extended his arm to restrain me. "Stay here. I have something that is of utmost importance to you." He placed a large, manila envelope in my hand.

I turned the envelope over absentmindedly, my thoughts still with Macika. Iche looked at me inquisitively. "Aren't you even curious to see what this envelope contains?"

"Oh, yes," I murmured, and I began to open it. "It's a document!" I whispered. I quickly glanced at the paper and my heart skipped a beat. "The lease!" I cried. "Iche, you've gotten us the lease to the house in the Zuglo!"

Meanwhile, everyone else had gathered around Iche, who was giving them a detailed account of the miraculous rescue of my brother Joska by Shmuel, Geza and himself. When he heard my shouts, Iche turned to me.

"Shh, Zsuzsi, don't get carried away," he reminded me, pointing to the wall. "By the way, I think you're mistaken," he added with a wink. "It is not a lease. It is the deed for the property. The house will be ready for Karoly and his family to move into on December first."

"In just four days!" I exclaimed, and I ran to the Bitters' "residence," as we playfully called their one-room lodgings. "Magda, Magda, where are you?"

"Shh. Don't disturb her," she said softly, crouching on the floor and looking at me, radiant. My gaze fell on Macika, her face bright red and her almond-shaped, dark eyes shining like black diamonds under strands of her golden hair. She was standing all by herself!

"Oh," I whispered with wonder, as I stood against the opposite wall. I spread my arms wide open. "Come to me, darling," I called out to her. "Please come to Zsuzsi *neni.*" She looked at her mother, then back to me, and with sudden determination, she put one tiny foot in front of the other and took her first step toward me.

"Oh, Magda, what a lucky day for us!" I said excitedly, remembering my reason for coming. "Iche just brought us the deed for the house, and it will be ready for occupancy in four days. I'll help you pack. We all will!"

Magda did not seem to share my excitement. "Don't you understand what this means for us?" I asked her. "Have you the slightest notion of the agony we've been going through since Salasy's speech? We worry about you day and night!"

Still Magda did not answer. She just sat there, cradling her baby. The serenity in her face overwhelmed me, and then it occurred to me that none of my words had penetrated yet. All Magda could think about was that her daughter had taken her first step.

"Let me call her again," I offered. "Macika, my dear, come to me." Anna, who had been watching from the entranceway, hurried into the room, wild with excitement. She picked Macika up and hugged her. "You are walking! You are walking! You took your first step!" Then she became thoughtful. "What's today's date?" she asked, and without waiting for an answer, she said, "It's the twenty-seventh of November! Happy birthday, my dear Macika! Happy first birthday to you!"

"Finally!" Magda exclaimed indignantly. "I thought nobody here would remember." But Anna was already walking out of the room with Macika in her arms to show her off to everyone.

With a beatific smile, Magda turned her radiant face towards me. "Even though I knew she would eventually walk," she said blushing, "I never expected my reaction to be like this! I'm ashamed to tell you. I'm afraid you will laugh at me, but to me, seeing her let go and walk to us was like a miracle, the greatest miracle on earth!"

"Also the greatest turning point in her young life," I added, carried away with the big event. Suddenly my words turned sour in my mouth. Everyone is expected to learn how to walk, I thought to myself, and my heart filled with secret tears for the many Jewish children who would never take more than their first steps, who had been forced to start life by taking their very last steps. Suddenly a great longing for my little nieces and nephews overwhelmed me — the joy, the family, the excitement. A bitter cry rose in my soul: How dare the world view those little, innocent Jewish children as if they mattered to none, as if they were born from a stone?

At that moment a sad truth was revealed to me. I knew then that all future joyful occasions in my life would be marred by the vision of my lost family. I tried hard to compose myself in order not to spoil Magda's joy. "When will the world learn that people of all creeds, colors and races have the same basic human needs?" I asked aloud.

Then Joska's mocking answer came, as if from far away, "Why not worry instead about whether we will have the chance to find the answer? Will we live to see this war end?"

"Bracha!" my husband shouted above the blare of the air-raid siren. "Bracha, remember: Stick to your guns!"

Fear stabbed at me as I descended the steps, clinging to my baby for comfort. How will those in the shelter react to our newly arrived guests? I fretted. Oh, my God, what will they say?

Bracha's appearance did not please me, and with a pounding heart, I watched Mr. Horvat looking her over. His gaze wandered to my brother, Joska, and back again to Bracha. Say something, I prodded myself. Introduce them. But my throat tightened up and I was unable to utter a sound.

From the corner of my eye, I saw Iche entering the bunker. With the sure and arrogant stride of an SS man, he walked over to the superintendent and, to my great relief, said, "May I have the pleasure of introducing my distant cousin, Monika Halas."

"Monika" extended her hand to Mr. Horvat, ignoring the rest of them, and without further ado, she sank into the nearest chair and focused all her attention on her knitting needles.

"Stockings?" the elder Mrs. Nagy asked, trying to be friendly. "Are you knitting stockings?" Monika played her role very well. She regarded the woman with a cold stare, and, without stopping her knitting, she turned her head away.

She will be alright, I thought with relief. I never would have believed that Iztvan's aunt could be so cold and aloof. But then again, this was the price she had to pay for being allowed to join us in the shelter.

Uncle Yidel's warning echoed in my mind: "Monika, there is one thing that you must always remember. Not a word. Not a sound to anyone. There is no telling what lies Zsuzsi and Anna have told them. You have no idea what lies we are living here."

"She won't talk to anybody," I whispered to old Mrs. Nagy. "She is very hurt, mourning her whole family. I mean her immediate family. They are lost, and, poor soul, she is all alone." Mrs. Nagy's eyebrows arched up, and she looked at me with a strange expression. All eyes were now riveted on me. I realized with horror that I had just given the description of a Jew. Who else would have lost all of her family? A cold sweat enveloped me from head to toe.

Then Iche, dear Iche, came to my rescue again.

"Remember the constant bombing of the city of Szeged, before the Allied forces occupied it and wrested it from our hands?" Iche whispered solemnly. "She was out shopping then, and when she came home, she found that all seven members of her family had been killed in the raid."

Monika whimpered in her seat and looked at Iche blankly. Then she turned to face the wall.

"She was found wandering on the highways, and someone mercifully recognized her and brought her to the city."

"Oh, heavens!" the old lady sighed, a tear escaping from her puffy eyes. "Poor lamb, poor lamb. Who does she stay with?"

"She lives with me," Iche replied, "but I have my party obligations and, given her state of mind, I am afraid to leave her home alone, even for a second. She is so bitter, she might kill herself."

"Why don't you leave her with us?" Magda suggested.

"With you?" Iche asked, feigning surprise.

"Of course, with us," Magda answered, and then, turning to Mr. Horvat, she added, "with your permission, of course."

"Helping out a fellow Hungarian in her hour of need," Mr. Horvat repled proudly, "is our Christian duty."

Then I noticed everyone staring at my brother. "This is my baby brother, Joska Shipoc," I said.

"My mother sent him to us so that we would have a man in the house," Anna added with a grin.

Joska straightened himself up to his full height. "Girls need a man in the house. Girls have to be protected."

"How old are you?" Lasi asked him, and I became aware that he had been eyeing Joska the entire time.

"I am thirteen. How old are you?"

"I am fourteen, just a year older than you, and by the way, my name is Lasi Nagy and I hope we'll be friends."

"Fourteen?" Joska asked, incredulous. He stood next to him and measured himself against Lasi's six-foot frame. "I never realized what a runt I am!"

Somewhere in the distance a bomb exploded with a terrible roar, its impact shaking the very earth under our feet. The laughter on the boys' faces turned to fear, and they huddled close to each other for protection.

From time to time I shot a furtive glance toward the two boys, wondering what they were talking about. I didn't dare move closer to listen, but my heart skipped a beat as I wondered, What does a Jewish boy with a strict Jewish education, who is a veteran of a forced-labor camp, have in common with a rich, anti-Semitic, Aryan, Hungarian boy? How much time will it take for Lasi to sense the strangeness in my brother?

No, I told myself, No. This can't go on. We cannot allow this. Joska will have to become one of the ghosts upstairs, out of the sight of these inquisitive eyes.

Suddenly my train of thought was interrupted by a strange sound followed by pitiful moans. I turned my head toward their source and saw Lasi doubled over in pain, clutching at his side. Ersabet jumped up as if she had been shot from a cannon."Lasi," she shrieked, frantic. "Lasi, my baby, what's the matter with you?"

Lasi covered his mouth and ran toward the lavatory, making retching sounds. His frightened mother and grandmother followed closely behind him. Lasi and his mother disappeared inside, while the old lady leaned heavily on the door and cried, "If only my son were here!"

45

I COULD NOT FATHOM how baby Macika always knew the exact time of her father's return from work each night, but the fact remained that she did, and without fail she would sit and wait for him by the door, teddy bear in hand, listening for his footsteps. It fascinated me no end to observe her reaction when she heard her father turn the doorknob. Her two little hands would shoot up to cover her face as she tried to make herself invisible.

How simple her world is, I would think to myself with envy.

Karoly would walk around her, lamenting, "Where is my precious little girl? Why isn't she here to greet Papa today?"

Then she would throw her hands up and cry joyfully, "Pa-pa-pa-pa!"

I loved to watch her, and I never ceased to marvel at the difference the six months between her and little Zsuzsi made. Today, however, something was wrong. Karoly completely disregarded his little one.

"Darling," Magda mouthed, gesturing toward the trembling little girl as she went to greet her husband.

But Karoly seemed too upset to heed her advice. He simply buried his face on Magda's shoulder. "I never expected it to come to this," he sobbed. "Oh, oh, what is this world coming to?"

By this time we had all crowded around them. "What's going on?" we asked in unison. "What happened?"

Karoly finally found his voice. "Even the gutters are congested. Hoards of Jewish men are being driven through the streets, and what a miserable condition they are in! What a pitiful sight for the eyes to behold! My first impulse was to run away from the scene, but first I had to know where these men were being taken, so I walked over to an SS man and asked him.

"'Our orders are to escort them to the frontier of the Reich,' he replied, and, poking me good-naturedly in the ribs, he gloated, 'What an easy, economical solution! What do you say, brother?'

"His answer confirmed my most terrible fears, and, fighting the urge to tear him to pieces, I made myself ask him, 'How about the ghetto, my Aryan brother? When will they finally get rid of all the Jews in the ghetto?'

"He looked at me in surprise. 'The ghetto? Why are you asking about the ghetto? Don't you know that the entire ghetto is wired to explosives? All we have to do is push a button, and those Jews will go flying up to the sky!' "

As he recounted the story, Karoly's fists were clenched in anger, and tears rolled down his face — tears, the humiliating, useless tool of helpless rage.

Suddenly and unexpectedly, Meir appeared in the doorway. Seeing him for the first time, Karoly gazed at him and the color drained from his face. His eyes had a look I had never seen before. "That's one of them," he shrieked. "That's one of them! Help, help! Please, Magda, help me! I am going mad!"

It took us a long time to convince Karoly that Meir was, indeed, "one of them," and that he and his wife and my brother had found their way to our house that day, while Karoly was at work.

Because of the nature of Meir's illness, Rozalia and Pali had offered him their somewhat private sleeping chamber, the narrow little foyer between the bathroom and dining room.

This meant that from now on, four more people would be forced to sleep on the already overcrowded floor in the dining room, bringing the total number of occupants in the apartment to nine.

In light of these conditions, we again approached the Bitters with the offer of the house in the Zuglo, in the hope that they would agree to make the move — not for their benefit, but for our own. This time, to our great relief, Karoly and Magda graciously, albeit reluctantly, accepted. Immediately, the tremendous responsibility and fear for their lives that I had felt for so long left me. Right then and there, we decided that they would move on the first of December, as soon as the house became ours.

Between air raids we helped Magda wash, iron and pack their things, talking all the while. There seemed to be in each of us an unquenchable thirst to learn about the other's innermost thoughts. And I yearned for the time when I would be able to bring to the attention of the whole world who they were and what they stood for. I longed for the day when I would be able to shout to the world: "Karoly and Magda Bitter saved us!"

"I can't believe that in three days we will be moving," Magda remarked on the way up from the shelter.

"Oh, how I will miss you," I said with a sigh.

"And I'll miss you," she said as we stepped into the foyer. "I hate having to leave you."

"How will life be for us, not knowing what is happening to one another?"

Then Magda's face lit up. "I have an idea. Maybe we can communicate through mental telepathy."

"What's that?" Anna asked, her eyes opening wide with wonder.

"Well, I really don't understand exactly how it works," Magda answered, "but I've heard that people who really care for each other can use it successfully." She stopped for a moment and thought. "I'll tell you what we'll do. Each night at exactly ten o'clock we will shut out everything from our minds and concentrate deeply on each other's message."

"It's agreed," we promised. "At ten each night."

Anna, who had to clarify every detail, asked, "What if there's an air raid at that time?"

Magda paled at the mention of the words "air raid," and I immediately regretted that the subject had been brought up. Visibly agitated, she turned toward me. "How can you and your sister always stay so calm and unruffled amidst the rain of bombs during the air raids, while at the first sound of the siren, I fall apart?" she asked, her tone bordering on hysterical. "Zsuzsi, Zsuzsi," she pleaded, "let me in on your secret. Please tell me how you do it. Give it to me as a farewell present."

"I wish I could tell you," I began, clearing my throat nervously. "How I would love to share it with you. Perhaps it is because we live our lives constantly engulfed in fear. Perhaps there is no more fear left in us for that."

Magda looked at me reproachfully. "Don't try to convince yourself or me that you don't care any more and that you have given up. I see to what lengths you go to conceal your true identities. Why fear discovery by the Nazis and yet have no fear of the bombs?"

"Well, I suppose it must be our ancient dread of being given over into the hands of our enemies and seeing them rejoice in our pain."

"But in either case," Magda argued, "you have only one life to lose."

"Oh, Magda," Anna exclaimed, "you can call it the 'survival instinct.' But whatever you call it, I am telling you right now that there is an awfully big difference between our being hit by a random bomb and our being singled out, annihilated as a race, having all we love systematically destroyed, and being torn from our roots." Her voice began to quiver as she spoke. "The torch, Magda, the torch passed down by our ancestors through thousands of years would be extinguished in our hands."

"But I still say, you have only one life to lose," Magda repeated.

A tremor passed through Anna's body. "Oh, Magda, I never want you to understand this. To do so, you would have to pay a tremendous price."

A heavy silence came between us. Magda fidgeted nervously with the strings of her apron. "So how can you explain this?" she demanded. "How could you, the People of the Book, have been so ignorant and not seen what Hitler had in mind until it was too late?"

The shadow of uncertainty lifted from my sister's face and I felt her heart breaking with every syllable that she uttered. "If only we hadn't seen anti-Semitism with our own eyes all our lives; if only we hadn't suffered its consequences from early childhood; if only we hadn't heard with our own ears, scores of times, in many versions, how our parents and their parents had to cope with prejudice; if only we hadn't witnessed how anti-Semitism abated, and then flared up again..." Her words slurred as she gasped for breath. "And Magda, if only we hadn't learned, despite all this, to live such beautiful, richly rewarding lives, based on love and trust!" Trembling and exhausted, Anna threw herself on a stack of sheets that were piled up on the unmade bed.

"The siren!" Magda cried. "Oh no, not again! If only you could stay home more often and come with me to the shelter most of the time."

As soon as we entered the shelter, Julia Horvat greeted us with the news. "Lasi is in the hospital," she said solemnly.

We were shocked by her announcement. At once, everyone began bombarding her with questions. My brother's blue eyes widened in surprise. "But moments before the attack he was talking to me and he looked perfectly fine!"

Julia's eyes narrowed and, giving Joska an icy stare, she spat angrily, "You should have seen him writhing in pain and begging for help!" We stared at her in astonishment. "My husband had to accompany them to the hospital, for his mother and grandmother were in shock."

A day passed, followed by a restless night, and many times we made our way back and forth from the shelter, but there was still no sign of our superintendent, nor had word reached us about Lasi's condition or his whereabouts. The air in the shelter was heavy with fear. In spite of ourselves, we were genuinely concerned about this Gentile youth whose fate was intimately linked to our own.

What if the ambulance was bombed? I thought. Oh, my God, what then? We hid our fears behind a facade of affected cheerfulness. "No news is good news," we tried consoling Julia, but behind her back we grimaced with worry.

"Oh, not knowing what has happened to them is driving me insane," Julia wailed. "It will be my death."

The air raid must have been very near to us, for the sounds of destruction were terrifying.

"Shh, I think someone is at the door," Erika cried, incredulous.

"Who would be out during this raid?" Julia said as she counted heads. "I don't understand. We are all here!"

Then the knocking and kicking at the door became louder. "Open the door!" the voice shouted.

Cries of joy rang through the air. "Janos Horvat! Janos Horvat! He's here! He's here!"

Julia opened the door and Janos Horvat, half-frozen, staggered inside.

"Where have you been? Why have you been out so long? Tell us, how is Lasi?"

"Well," Mr. Horvat replied, "until the doctors said that Lasi would survive, I couldn't leave the two women alone."

"Why? What is wrong with him?"

"Lasi is very lucky that his mother took him to the hospital. It was an emergency and they operated on him almost instantly. They call it acute appendicitis. Have you ever heard of that? The doctors said that his appendix was full of pus and already perforated. They also said it's a miracle that he is alive. Thanks to his youth and otherwise good health, he was able to survive the infection."

"Janos, dear," Julia sobbed, "your hands are like icicles. How long have you been outside?"

A guilty look appeared on Janos's face. "The raid caught me right by the highway."

"And you didn't seek shelter? You walked home in the midst of the bombing?"

Janos stared at the floor. "I couldn't bear torturing you, knowing how worried all of you were, so I walked home," he explained.

"Will Lasi really be alright?" Erika asked, her eyes brimming with tears.

"He seems to be out of danger, but the doctors are watching him very carefully."

Erika fell to her knees. "Come, everyone, follow me in prayer."

And overwhelmed with pity for Lasi's great suffereing and the suffering of his mother and grandmother, I, too, began to pray. "Please Lord, heal this boy Lasi. He is all his mother has."

But the words turned sour in my mouth. Something stirred in my soul, and the text of my prayer changed entirely. "Almighty Lord in Heaven, you know each and every single secret in my heart. Who am I and who am I trying to fool? Please, my Lord, accept my heartfelt thanks for removing Lasi from the scene, for removing him before he had time to reflect upon my brother Joska's strange ways. Before he could have discovered who we are, before he could have destroyed us all."

46

"IT SEEMS that an entire squadron of bombers dumped its payload on us tonight," Karoly sighed as he and Magda wearily made their way upstairs from the shelter and into the apartment at four o'clock in the morning. "We haven't seen a night as frightening as this."

"And at six, the alarm clock will wake you," Magda said with compassion. "Poor dear. And to think that this is our last night here. Some night to remember," she whispered, her gaze riveted on the shadowy creatures sprawled out across the floor, already fast asleep. "I have learned to love you all. I will miss you."

All too soon, the alarm sounded, shattering Karoly's fitful sleep. "Blasted clock!" he muttered groggily, reaching out to shut off the alarm. He turned toward the wall in a gesture of defiance and told himself, I am not going to work today. I am going back to sleep. Then he remembered the words of his foreman: "Your work is as dear to our motherland as are the actions of the brave men in the army. It is only because of your work manufacturing ammunition that they can fight the enemy. Staying away without good reason is treason and will be dealt with accordingly."

It's no use, Karoly, and you know it, he chastised himself, rolling onto his back. He lay there perfectly still for a few moments, and watched his breath turn into vapor in the frigid air. Then, with sudden determination, he jumped up, threw his old flannel robe over his shoulders and slid his feet into the slippers on the floor by his bed. The insides of his slippers were cold as ice, causing him to shiver all the way to the kitchen.

He walked over to the gas range to light the flame under the baby's bottle, which Magda had left immersed in a pot of water the night before. He lit the gas under the little percolator and measured out some mudlike grain that passed for coffee.

At ten to seven, fully dressed and buttoned up tightly against the cold, Karoly removed the baby's bottle from the pot. He checked and double-checked the temperature of its contents, making sure it was just right, and he tiptoed noiselessly back into the main room. Stopping next to the little crib which he had so lovingly built with his own hands, he gently placed the nipple of the bottle between his daughter's lips, and stood there, spellbound, as she began to drink the liquid with eyes closed, fast asleep. A loving glow illuminated his tired features. He bent down and kissed the sweet little child. "Sleep my darling, sleep," he murmured softly. "Enjoy your warm, cozy bed." The clock on the mantle in the next room chimed seven o'clock. "It's time for Papa to be on his way to work."

As he stepped outside, a gust of cold air struck him in the face, simultaneously rousing him from his drowsy state and reminding him that today was moving day. The freshly fallen snow crunched beneath his heels, but Karoly was too absorbed in his thoughts to notice his surroundings. When he boarded his regular trolley, the conductor greeted him amicably, while Karoly thought to himself with detachment, Will you miss me tomorrow? He headed straight for his usual window seat and made himself comfortable, his elbow resting on the windowsill. He leaned his head on his hand and closed his eyes.

His father was standing by his bed, pulling at his covers. "Wake up, sleepyhead, come and get dressed. I have a surprise for you."

"A surprise?" Karoly cried. "What is it?"

His father put his finger to his lips. "Shh, you'll wake up the whole house."

Quickly, he dressed himself. "What's the surprise? What is it, Papa?"

His father revealed nothing, but his face wore a grin that stretched from ear to ear. "Come, I'll help you put on your boots. It's cold outside."

"Oh, Papa, look at all that snow!" Karoly shouted with excitement. "When did it fall?"

"Look," his father said, pointing to the majestic Tatra mountains in the distance.

"They're very beautiful," the young Karoly said softly, awed by the sight.

"And now for the surprise," his father announced with a mysterious smile. Taking the boy's small hands into his own large, work-roughened ones, he guided him gently toward the bend.

"Can this be real?" Karoly squealed with delight as his eyes fell upon Babushka, his pet pony, who was harnessed to a brand-new sled. Karoly half ran, half stumbled through the knee-high snow to see this special gift. He hugged and kissed Babushka, and the pony nudged his hands and face with her warm, wet muzzle.

Karoly sat next to his father, the two of them covered with a thick, woolen blanket. His father let him hold the reins with him, which filled his heart with pride. They looked at each other, sensing that a new, close bond had formed between them. Without speaking, they understood each other, father and son. They started singing at the top of their lungs as the sled glided gracefully into the enchanted night.

Then suddenly, without warning, the song died on his father's lips and turned into a heartrending cry. Terror-stricken and too frightened for words, the young boy began screaming into the night.

"Wake up, brother," a deep, masculine voice urged him, as someone tapped him on the shoulder. The trolley had stopped moving. Red-faced and still very much under the influence of his dream, Karoly rushed toward the door and down the steps, away from the staring faces. He stood on the sidewalk trembling, wondering how far he was from his regular stop. For an indeterminate length of time he remained there, unable to will himself to board another trolley, despite the nagging voice inside him telling him that he was late for work.

All at once a car halted at the curb. The door swung wide open. "Hey, Karoly, old friend! Hop in. We're going to the same plant, you know."

"Good morning, Mr. Barany," he greeted his foreman, concealing his hatred for this Nazi with a respectful tone.

Barany stared at Karoly, his eyes narrowing. "Are you sick?"

"Something came over me. It never happened before. I just felt very faint, so I got off the trolley."

"Feeling better now?" Barany asked absentmindedly. Not waiting for an answer, he turned to face the man at the wheel, the director of the factory where they worked.

"Don't make a problem out of it, Oscar," the director was saying. "My daughter Katy will pick it up on her way home from school tomorrow."

"Sometimes it irks me that I have to be the one to find the means of transportation for Theresa's gifts to her sister," Barany muttered. "I'm always on the spot, having to ask favors of people."

"Don't mention it, friend. Just give me your address and we'll take care of it."

"Thank you very much," Barany said. "The address is 15-15 Amerikas Utca."

"Oh, yes, I remember now. It's in the Zuglo, isn't it?"

"15-15 Amerikas Utca!" Karoly exclaimed. "Oh, Mr. Barany, what a coincidence. What an interesting coincidence."

There was no response from the others. His comment was lost in their cries of horror and the sound of brakes screeching. The smell of fear hit Karoly in the pit of his stomach. All three of them leaped from the car to stare at the sight that lay ahead. The munitions plant, where all three of them had worked and spent the better part of their waking hours, had been reduced to a heap of broken stones and bricks during the previous night's air raid.

The director was the first to find his voice. "I know about the horrors of war. I have seen plenty of suffering in my days at the front. But this... all those men on the night shift, buried alive! It's too awful to imagine! And to think that we ourselves left the building only a few hours before!" He shuddered. "It could just as easily have happened to us!"

"There, but for the grace of God, go I," Oscar Barany said, letting out his breath.

"Are my eyes playing tricks on me?" Karoly muttered, rubbing his eyes and gazing at the exposed beams among the ruins. "It looks as if giant, black arms are reaching to the sky, begging for the shelling to stop, pleading for mercy." Mercy, he repeated to himself. But mercy and war do not mix. He watched, terrified, as rescue workers combed the ruins for bodies. What a grisly job, he thought, his compassion stirred for the men who performed such a gruesome task.

"Someone is coming!" the director cried. His shout brought Karoly out of his daze.

"What rotten luck," Barany said. "Here he comes and we're standing in the middle of a strictly off-limits zone. We should have known better than to let ourselves be caught in this restricted area."

Then a sigh of relief escaped from the director's lips. "Oh, it's only Colonel Elmy."

"Colonel Elmy," Barany echoed, and with brisk strides the two men went off to meet him. Karoly fell in step behind them.

The director threw him a dark look. "Stay there until you are summoned," he barked. Taken aback, Karoly stopped in mid-stride.

There was handshaking and backslapping, and Karoly had no doubt that the three were old friends. He couldn't hear what they were saying, but he felt the eyes of the colonel on him. The wind carried Barany's words in his direction. "He is just one of my workers. Karoly," Barany called out, "the colonel wants to see you." Then he and the director walked away.

The colonel looked at Karoly wordlessly and held out his hand. Immediately, Karoly understood, and he handed the colonel his documents for examination. He stood there, watching Elmy's every move.

The colonel had a large, doughy face splotched bluish-red and purple by the merciless, freezing wind. He appeared to be inspecting the papers, but Karoly could see that his mind was elsewhere. He is debating my fate, Karoly realized. It stopped his heart.

After a while, the frozen lips parted. "Which section? What assignment?"

Karoly looked at him bewildered, his pulse throbbing at his throat. "Colonel Elmy, sir, I report humbly. I am forbidden to give out information regarding my job."

Elmy regarded him coolly. "And what makes you think you can't answer a colonel?" the man asked, suppressing a smile.

"We were ordered to keep everything secret concerning the plant," Karoly explained with a zealous air. "It's for the protection of our Homeland!"

"Oh, yes, of course," the colonel replied derisively. Then his voice assumed the ring of authority. "I am sending you to a new assignment."

"Yes, Colonel Elmy, sir."

All Karoly noticed was an official-looking letterhead which the colonel signed with stiff, frozen fingers.

"The Number Seven-H streetcar will take you there, and remember, talking about what you have seen here is forbidden under penalty of death!"

"Yes, Colonel Elmy, sir!" With the ingrained obedience of a military officer, Karoly folded the paper quickly, stuffed it in his pocket and ran to board the trolley.

The trolley had already begun moving when he remembered to check the letter to find out what office he was headed for. No, oh no, not this! he cried inwardly as he stared at the address in the letter. Blinded by rage, he saw the thirteen Jews in his mind's eye, those thirteen Jews he had been hiding in his home at the very risk of his own and his family's life. The irony of it. Oh, the irony of it, he thought to himself in anger. I, Karoly Bitter, am to report to the recruiting committee. He almost laughed out loud. I am to fight against the liberating forces! I will go there, he told himself heatedly, and walk up to the bloody officer in charge. I will tell him, I will tell that Nazi, "I will gladly give my life for my Homeland, but not to lengthen its misery. Here, put the bullet through my heart, right here. My body will find rest in my beloved Hungarian soil."

Suddenly he was struck by an idea, an idea exquisite in its simplicity. Karoly, you are an idiot, he chided himself. It is so obvious. How could you not have seen it until now? This is just what Iztvan is always talking about. Those were his father's parting words: "Next to every door, locked by virtue of tyranny, will appear, sooner or later, invisible doors of escape!" Of course they will, they're bound to, he told himself with determination. He signaled the conductor to let him off.

A hymn of thanksgiving rose in his heart, a hymn of thanksgiving to the Lord Who showed him the way before it was too late for escape. With remarkable calm, he alighted from the Seven-H and headed for the trolley that would take him home.

Only when he began walking down the familiar little path leading to his house, did it dawn on him. "Today is moving day. 15-15 Amerikas Utca, 15-15 Amerikas Utca," he chanted as he walked. He was alone on the path, his only witness the windy skies, and he let down his guard and gave vent to his raging anger. Tears came to his eyes as he shook his fists at the heavens. "Traitors! Nazis!" he cried. "Your day of reckoning will come!"

47

There are many devices in a man's heart;
But the counsel of the Lord, that shall stand.
Proverbs 19:21

"KAROLY IS COMING!" Rozalia whispered with surprise.

Magda leaped to the window. "He is coming," she cried. "What a wonderful husband I have! I wonder how he got his foreman to give him the day off," she said, laughing.

"I'm sure he knows how you dislike the thought of moving at night," Anna said.

Happiness flooded Magda's childlike features. "Let me put on a freshly laundered blouse," she sang, while her slender fingers nimbly removed the curlers from her golden blond hair. She ran to the vestibule to greet her husband just as he opened the front door. "Oh, Karoly, you're home! How on earth did you manage to get away? Everything is ready and packed. Shall we wake the baby?" She pulled Karoly by the hand into their room, showing him off to everyone. "You see," she exclaimed, "true love knows no obstacles!"

To my surprise, Karoly's face did not reflect any of Magda's enthusiasm. If anything, he appeared downcast. I sensed that something was terribly wrong, even before I heard him say in a low voice, "It's not that, Magda." His face was ghostly white.

"I... I don't understand," Magda stammered, as if she were seeing him now for the first time, and her happy, little-girl expression changed to one of maternal concern and love. "Are you all right, dear? You're not sick, are you?"

We all crowded around Karoly. The air was charged, and the urgency in his voice as he spoke made me tremble with fear. We listened raptly to Karoly's story, occasionally interrupting with the horrified comment, "Karoly was almost drafted into the Nazi Army!"

Suddenly Magda's eyes widened, and her expression became trancelike. "It was a miracle!" she whispered. "Oh, Karoly, falling asleep on the trolley saved you. It's as if your father came to warn you to get off the streetcar so that you wouldn't arrive at the plant with all the other workers. If you had taken your regular route, you would have been shipped off to the recruiting office with all of them and there would have been no way for you to escape!"

"And with my patriotic performance, the colonel felt he could trust me well enough to send me without an escort!" Karoly added.

I gaped at them in wonder. "Karoly," I murmured, "your wife is right. You have experienced a great miracle today, a frightfully beautiful miracle."

"Of course. I see it now," Pali remarked. "They must have met the workers at the bus stop and immediately recruited them. With the building in ruins and all the names and addresses of the workers lost, they never would have located everyone otherwise. They certainly worked very cleverly," he added with contempt.

"And never again would I have seen my little family and my friends," Karoly said, weeping.

With frightened eyes, Magda regarded the little girl resting in her father's arms. "Bad people tried to take our Papa away," she told her tearfully. "They tried to tear him from us and send him to a faraway land to fight their miserable war for them. They wanted to throw him into the crossfire, to use him as cannon fodder," she sobbed. "Our Papa! The nerve of them!"

All of us were awe-struck by the enormity of this incident and its possible consequences. Iztvan was the first to compose himself. "Our friend Feri will make new identification papers for you, Karoly, and tomorrow you can proceed with moving just as you had planned, without fear of discovery by the Nazis."

Karoly shook his head vigorously. "That's what I thought too, and was even getting excited at the prospect of moving day, when I remembered about Barany." By another stroke of luck, he explained, he had learned that his foreman, Oscar Barany, lived in the same building where he was supposed to move. "He'll report me to his friend, Colonel Elmy, for sure."

"A miracle! A true miracle!" we all murmured at once, thinking how horrid it would have been to arrive at the new address and only then discover the foreman right next door!

"Now, Karoly," Iztvan said lightly, patting him on the shoulder, "no reason to fret. You can stay right here and join our ranks. You can become a ghost like us. How about it, brother? Can I welcome you?"

"No," Karoly declared decisively. "I cannot do that, for it would kill Magda. Not one day has passed that she hasn't told me how she could never bear the tension of our being separated during a raid. She would rather kill herself than endure what Zsuzsi goes through."

Joska stood up, his face aglow with excitement, his eyes as clear and blue as a May sky after a spring shower. The room was buzzing like a beehive, and it was impossible to make out a word that anyone was saying. "I think I have the answer for Karoly. Please hear me out," he implored us.

"Let's hear what Joska has to say," Karoly said, more in a tone of mockery over the hopelessness of his situation than in anticipation of a constructive suggestion.

"It's so simple," Joska exclaimed. "I believe the Red Cross can help you. Shmuel told me about it. I think this is the perfect solution to your problem."

The room became silent and everyone turned to him. "How can the Red Cross help Karoly?" we asked.

"Well, hundreds of people flock to the city daily. They are running from the Red Army. Karoly and Magda could pose as refugees, too, and no one will be the wiser. The Red Cross helps these people out with all their domestic needs. Most of them arrive with only the clothes on their backs. According to Shmuel, many of them don't even have their papers with them."

Karoly considered this for a moment. "Sounds interesting," he said.

"Very much so," Iztvan agreed.

"Wait," Joska said. "This is the most important part. Not only does the Red Cross provide the refugees with new documents and a place to live, but they give them ration books as well!"

In the commotion we hadn't realized that Geza had entered our apartment. "Geza!" Karoly cried, as he ran to greet him. "Geza, my friend, God has sent you here today to help us decide what to do."

As Karoly repeated his story to him, Geza's face paled. He pursed his lips and stroked his chin as he contemplated the latest developments, and a brief silence descended on the room. Then, choosing his words with great care, Geza declared, "Joska is right. This might be the only way out. But remember," he continued, looking at Karoly's worried face, "it's a risk, and as long as we take risks, we have to be ready to deal with the consequences. Life is one long, continuous risk and no one can be one hundred percent sure of anything. Now, don't get me wrong — I'm not telling you what to do. Only you and Magda can decide. But whatever course you choose, I'll do my utmost to help you, and you'll have the wholehearted support of my friends as well."

"Needless to say," Iztvan added, "we will also help you in every way we can." Everyone nodded his agreement.

"How, may I ask, can you help us?"

"Well, we can offer you some sound advice," Uncle Yidel interjected heatedly. "In my opinion, you have legal grounds for staying here. After all, the plant where you worked was destroyed, so at least for a few days you can safely explain staying home until you are relocated. I hate having to see you make such an important decision under so much pressure."

"You want him to stay here and become an easy target for the Nazis?" Anna asked in disbelief. "Is that what you are suggesting, Yidel?"

"Anna, you don't understand. The plant is gone, and so are the records of all the workers. So who is going to miss him?" Yidel explained.

"Your reasoning has merits, Yidel," Geza said, "but considering that the plant was a municipal project, the government probably has duplicates stashed away at some other office. You know how this bureaucracy works! I shudder to think what they would do to Karoly if they found him."

Yidel tried again. "They have more pressing problems on their hands," he said with conviction.

"Well, yes and no," Geza said. "There is a great food shortage in the city and the people resent seeing German-made trucks rumbling through the city at all hours of the day and night, carrying our produce out of the land. Even the promise of Aryan supremacy looks quite different on an empty stomach. And the worst of it," he added in such a low voice that it seemed as if he were talking to himself, "is that there is hardly a house that is not in mourning over a father or husband or son."

We stared at him through worried eyes. "What does that have to do with our problem?" I asked.

"I can't see the connection either," Karoly said. "All I know is that I am in desperate need of direction and I don't have much time."

"It's just that I'm frightened," Geza explained quickly, beads of perspiration appearing on his forehead. "You must excuse me. I was one step ahead of myself. I was simply wondering how valuable you might be to the authorities. They could make a public example of your escape to teach the populace a lesson, to show them what happens to those who rebel and take the law into their own hands." The truth of his words was undeniable.

"I want to get away from here!" Magda cried, her face a ghostly white. "And as fast as we can!"

Guilt flooded Karoly's features. "The truth of the matter is that I am now a deserter." His face was ashen under the weight of his self-accusation.

A terrible scream burst from Magda's lips. "I never thought of it that way! I never saw it as it really is! Karoly, the punishment! The punishment for this crime! The firing squad!"

"What are we waiting for?" Geza interrupted. "Come on, let's get down to work. If we all cooperate, you can be out of here in no time." Then he turned to Pali. "First, let's choose new identities. You write down the names and towns," he instructed him. "Karoly and Magda, let me see your overcoats and the baby's snowsuit. They have to be fixed up to fit the occasion."

Obediently, they followed his orders. Geza glanced at Magda's good tweed coat. "Don't you have an old one? I would hate to dirty this."

Magda brought out a faded navy-blue coat. "It's from my school days," she explained.

"This will do," he said, "but Karoly's coat needs doctoring. I hope you don't mind." Without waiting for an answer, he threw Karoly's treasured overcoat on the floor. It landed at Uncle Yidel's feet. "Trample on it, mess it up, make it look like it was worn on a harrowing journey for three days straight and slept in for three nights," Geza instructed him. Then, reaching for the baby's bottle, he promptly overturned it and sprinkled some drops of milk onto the baby's freshly laundered snowsuit. "It will dry white," he told Magda, who looked as if she might faint at the mere thought of taking her little girl out in public in a soiled outfit. "Now each of you take a pillowcase from the hamper and stuff it with your essential clothing, some of it dirty and some of it clean. Make up a similar bundle for the baby."

Within minutes, the Bitters had packed their things as Geza had instructed them. Magda stood there with a forlorn look on her face, holding the small bundles. It tore at our hearts to see her like this. "Magda," Geza said soothingly, "I promise you that my friends and I will slowly smuggle all of your belongings to your new place. Now, get something very warm to wrap the baby in. All mothers do that — it will make you appear more realistic."

Karoly brought a black crocheted shawl from the closet, the kind peasant wives wore as winter coats. "It once belonged to my grandmother."

"Perfect," Geza said approvingly. "Just what we needed."

"What am I going to tell them in the shelter?" I agonized.

"That's no problem," Geza replied with a deadpan expression on his face. "Tell them that Magda's grandmother gave birth to twins and they went to the christening."

Everyone burst out laughing, breaking the tension.

"Rozalia, if your offer still stands," Geza said, "we are all as hungry as wolves and ready to eat. Come, Karoly and Magda, you must eat before you go. You don't know when your next meal will be."

The table was set for three. We always ate in groups of three to give a legal appearance to all our meals in case any uninvited strangers appeared at our door.

My husband brought out another chair for me, and, pointing to Geza, explained, "Now there are four legals here. Sit down and eat. You haven't put a thing in your mouth the whole day."

Magda, Karoly, Geza and I sat around the dining-room table, which was covered with a red-and-white-checked tablecloth. The aroma of freshly boiled potato soup wafted into the room.

"Where did you get potatoes?" I asked, incredulous.

"We found them when we went shopping this morning," Anna replied. Turning to me with laughter in her eyes, she added, "This should teach you a lesson, Zsuzsi. Now you know that we can go out of the house and return safely, just as we did today, even without your standing at the window and trembling."

"So the food came to me easily today," I remarked dryly, as I dipped my spoon into the steaming hot soup.

"Nothing came easily today, not to you or to any of us," my husband added with a shudder.

Pali brought a sheet of paper to the table. "We have chosen the names and addresses."

"Fine," Geza said. "I will get you 'Feri's Special!' No one but the boys in our own gang has this fabulous forgery. It is the most important paper there is, false or genuine. Your 'mission,' as indicated in your papers, will be so sensitive that you will not be allowed to reveal even the name of the person you are to answer to. This means, my dear friend, that no police officer will have the right to interrogate you. The superintendent of your new house will cringe in fear before you. I think you understand. You are your own boss and can come and go at will."

"I think that's pretty good for a fugitive," Karoly said, grinning.

The word fugitive lingered in my mind and stabbed at my heart. Fugitives. Karoly and Magda, the protectors of fugitives, now fugitives themselves.

Geza put on his overcoat and signaled for the Bitters to follow.

"Magda," I cried, "if anything, *anything* goes wrong, please don't hesitate to come right back — today, tomorrow or any other day. I figured out what to tell them in the shelter in order to leave the door open for you to return at any time without arousing suspicion."

Magda's eyes opened wide. "That's impossible," she sobbed.

"Just listen. I am going to tell them that while you were out, an old friend of your family came with the bad news that your mother had a stroke, and you went to find out how serious the situation really was. From there we will improvise according to our needs. Either you heard reassuring news and you will come right back, or you received such a frightening report that you went straight to the train station and rushed home. Oh, Magda, if you only knew how it hurts me to make your mother sick even in words," I said through my tears.

"Zsuzsi," Magda interrupted, "Zsuzsi, it just struck me this second!"

I looked at her with worried eyes. "Of course, if you object, I can say something else to the superintendent."

She dismissed my words with a wave of her hand. "I have no objection. Whatever you say is all right with me." There was urgency in her voice now. "But it just occurred to me that this house in the Zuglo is empty and all paid for."

"What a shame, Magda," I replied sadly. "What a terrible shame that you and Karoly can't occupy it."

"You're missing the point," she replied anxiously. "Zsuzsi, it's you and yours I'm thinking about now."

"You mean to say that we should move there?"

"That's what I've been trying to tell you!" she exclaimed excitedly. "Who knows when the announcer of the 'Voice of America' will declare: 'The Red Army is speedily advancing toward the capital city of Hungary from the East!'" Her tone became more insistent. "It's only a ninety-minute ride from here to the Zuglo." She looked at me pleadingly. "Don't let yourselves get stuck here."

"I have an idea," Anna cried, beaming. "Let us open a door for ourselves, too. Let's tell the group in the shelter that we, too, are contemplating going home to our parents for the holidays. This will lend legitimacy to our comings and goings," she added triumphantly. "It's only one more story for them to swallow. I assure you they won't choke on it," she giggled.

"Lies and more lies," I muttered. "God in Heaven, what

liars we have become!"

Karoly gathered up his bundles. "Let's go, Magda."

Trembling, Magda turned to me. "Zsuzsi," she sobbed, "is this really happening to us, or is it only a bad dream?"

Geza leaped to his feet. "No farewells, no tears," he ordered us. "This day has been taxing enough. Save your energies for the challenge ahead. Let's go."

Anna closed the door behind them softly, her eyes brimming. "There they go," she murmured. "The last of the unsung heroes in whose merit the world might prevail."

Immeasurable weariness overcame me. The oppressiveness of the day was taking its toll. Being separated from Magda and Karoly, not knowing their fate, filled me with terror. Come now, I prodded myself, stop this. Your head must be clear, for at any minute the siren may sound and then you'll have quite a story to tell in the shelter! But looking at all the pale and drawn faces around me did not help lift my spirits at all, nor did hearing Rozalia's sobs from behind the closed doors.

Then, amidst the sadness, came Iztvan's voice, clear and strong, like a ray of sunshine: "'From the depths of my heart, have I called thee, O Lord....'"

It was followed by silence. No other sound disrupted the stillness of the dimly-lit room. The downcast faces brightened as their pale lips moved in silent prayer, and the expression of gloom on their haggard faces slowly changed to one of hope.

48

THE GRANDFATHER CLOCK chimed eight A.M. in Karoly and Magda's empty room. Iche walked through the doorway, smiling. We all assailed him with questions at once, hoping he would know of the fate of our dear friends. "Yes, the Bitters were given a spacious apartment," he assured us. "According to the janitor, it belonged to a Jewish family with a bunch of grown kids."

"Which floor?"

"As luck would have it, it's on the ground floor, apartment number one."

Murmurs of approval spread through the room. Then Iche began to laugh. "No one seems to be interested in the name of the street and the section of the city the house is in."

"Oh yes, tell us!"

I held my breath. "Vilmos Császár Utca 91," Iche replied. I let out a sigh of relief. I had been sick with worry that Magda, who was a native of Budapest, might be recognized. But Wilmos Chasar Utca was in a neighborhood quite far from where she grew up, and so it presented little danger for her.

"It's a six-family house," Iche continued, "but please don't ask me about the superintendent or what kind of people live there. I myself am dying of curiosity." He picked up the packages of clothing that he was to take to Karoly and Magda. "I'll keep you posted, but now I must go," he said. Anna and I walked him to the door, shouting "Heil Hitler" as he left.

At the sound of the siren, Monika reached for her shopping bag of yarn and needles. "No matter how many times that siren blares, its sound is just as horrifying as it was the first time I heard it!" she said.

Once everyone was in the shelter, Magda was immediately missed, for she always used to be the first one there. "Where is Magda?" everyone asked in a chorus.

"Yes, where is Magda?" Mr. Horvat repeated. "I hope she didn't get stuck outside in the middle of the air raid. She is terrified enough when she is down here in the shelter."

I proceeded to relate my story in as few words as I could manage.

An awkward silence followed, and then came their shocked comments. "A stroke? What a shame. She must still be a young woman."

"Magda is beside herself, the poor thing," I sobbed.

Maria was agitated to no end. Her face was a ghostly white, her round, dark eyes filled with fear. "It's frightening to think about these unexpected calamities. First Lasi was stricken so suddenly, and now Magda's mother, who, according to Magda, was the picture of health. "So much bad luck lately," she whined, holding her son protectively. "It's almost... almost as if this place were jinxed!"

"Maybe," I blurted out, still staring at her, "maybe we should take up Mother's offer and go home for the holidays. What do you say, Anna?"

Anna turned to consult with Joska. "Shall I change my mind and go home, too?" she asked him.

"Why not? It's a woman's perogative to change her mind, you know. As for myself, I will definitely go home. I already told you so."

Maria's eyes were luminous with fear. "I, too, would escape from here if I only had a place to go to."

Later, when I was upstairs again, I told the family what had happened. "It was easy. They swallowed the story, hook, line and sinker! I'll give you the details later." And with that I turned to finish the baby's laundry.

Anna took the wet, clean laundry from my hands. "I am taking it outside to dry on the line. We seldom have such sunny days in December."

She began walking down the stairs. "Wait for me," I heard Erika shout. "I'm just grabbing my sweater. I will come help you."

Soon their laughter filled the backyard. It was only much later that I realized how long they had been out. I opened the window and called down, "Anna, come in. You'll catch a cold."

"Can you please come here?" she asked in a small voice.

Then Mr. Horvat called to me gruffly, "I have to talk to you. Come down right now!"

Mr. Horvat's stern, unfriendly voice shocked me, and Joska and I flew down the steps anxiously. Julyanna Kerekes was standing by her daughter's side in the yard when we arrived. The hostile atmosphere and all the nervous glances struck me like a bolt of lightning. Before I could find my voice to ask for an explanation, Maria cried out, "I am cold. Let's go inside and summon the police." Her eyes were filled with contempt as she spoke.

We all gathered downstairs in the shelter. "Would someone please tell me what is going on?" I asked, finally finding my voice.

"I don't know, Zsuzsi," Anna replied. "I don't understand what Maria wants from us."

"You don't understand? Or do you!" she spat her words at the girls. Utterly confused, I found myself unable to form the words to ask her what she meant.

"Maria thinks," Janos Horvat said bleakly, "that the girls mirror-signaled information to the enemy planes!"

"To the enemy?" I asked, taken aback. "Which enemy? And how?"

"I don't know what Maria wants to make out of this," my

sister sobbed hysterically. "All I know is that I accidentally hit Erika in the eye with a wet diaper, and she took her mirror from her apron pocket to inspect her eye. The mirror reflected a ray of sun into my eyes, blinding me for a moment, and so I took out my mirror and reflected the sun into her eyes. We were just having a little fun!"

"Fun!" Maria shouted derisively from the opposite end of the shelter. "I saw what they did with my own eyes. I wasn't born yesterday, you know."

"Neither was I," I retorted, "and I don't see anything wrong with two bored, frustrated teenagers letting themselves go and having a good time once in a while."

"Mr. Horvat just spelled it out for you," Maria exploded, her words dripping with venom, "but you don't want to believe it!"

I felt the blood rushing to my head. "Maria," I cried. "Maria! I hope you aren't suggesting that they...that they are..."

"I am only telling you what I saw with my own two eyes, and I happen to read a lot of spy stories, so I know what I saw. It's fascinating, the things spies will think of doing. For your information, I just read a story in which spies communicated with the enemy through mirror signals."

Suddenly I became aware that an awkward silence had come over the room. Everyone looked around wildly, avoiding eye contact with one another. All of a sudden Maria's strange accusation hit me full force. I turned to Erika's mother to see how she was reacting, and the very earth trembled under my feet. She is frightened. Oh, my Lord, she is frightened. She believes it. Almighty God! She is her mother. She must know that it is true. Can it be that Erika is a spy, and she used my unsuspecting sister as part of her conspiracy?

Fear gripped my heart. I must do something. I must hide Anna. I cannot let my sister fall into the hands of those cold-blooded interrogators. They will torture her. They will never believe that she is innocent and that Erika alone is a spy. Oh, what's the difference anyway? What difference will it make to the Nazis whether or not Anna is a spy, when she has committed a far worse sin: she is a Jew!

The train of my nightmarish thoughts was interrupted by Julia Horvat. "I do believe we have a problem," she said, turning to Maria. "The question is, should we involve the police or should we try to settle it with our highly esteemed block overseer, Mr. Eperjesy, the senior SS officer, who himself represents the law ?"

Maria swung around to face Julia. "What do you think we should do?"

Julia looked up at her husband. "What's your opinion, dear?"

"Well, there are only six more days until the fifteenth of the month, when Mr. Eperjesy makes his monthly visit. I would say, let's wait until then for him to take care of it. It's not necessary to put such young and quite possibly innocent teenagers through a harsh police interrogation."

"You will be responsible, Janos," Julia warned him. "Remember it, my dear."

"This is disgusting!" I exclaimed. "It's sheer madness!"

Anna peered at me through downcast eyes. "I don't even know what to deny, for I have done no wrong."

"Don't disturb us, please!" Mr. Horvat said with an air of authority. Then, turning to Maria, he asked point-blank, "What do you say?"

"I trust you, Janos, and now it's your responsibility."

"Then it's settled. We'll wait for the overseer."

Panic seized me anew as I recalled th sword-wielding anti-Semite. Then the irony of the situation ...t me. What's the difference if it's the police or him? I cried inwardly. In either case we are lost.

Upstairs, my words were met with an uproar. "What? Anna and Erika signaling to enemy planes?" Iztvan asked, his face pale.

"Is this woman mad?!" Rozalia exclaimed, wringing her hands.

Joska faced me. "Am I imagining things," he said, "or were Erika and her mother really as frightened as I thought they were?"

My husband gazed at me questioningly. Joska's eyes were wide, and he stared at me and said in a low voice, "It's incredible, but why should they be so frightened? Why should Erika and her mother — pure-blooded Aryans — panic, if it's not true?"

His words were met with shocked silence. Tears brimmed in Anna's eyes. "I brought this upon you. It's all my fault."

All at once, Iztvan's haggard face brightened. "You know what? Maybe in our fright we are blowing this whole thing up out of proportion. Maybe we are disregarding the possibility that right now, Maria, feeling ashamed, may be racking her brain, trying to get out of this mess with dignity. Zsuzsi, why don't you strike up a conversation with her? Give her a chance to wash her face in public. Forgive and forget."

Iztvan's suggestion was met with vehement opposition. "It's too late," Pali said. "It's out of Maria's hands now. Now that the Horvats know, they must report to the block overseer, Eperjesy. He will bring it up at the next meeting of the Nazi Party. After all, isn't that why Salasy appointed him in the first place? We all know what will happen the moment Eperjesy looks at Anna's false papers."

Everybody began talking at once. Someone turned up the volume on the radio, and all I could discern amidst the chaos was "Zuglo, Zuglo." The desperation and urgency in everyone's voices shocked me into the awareness that the situation was even worse than I had thought, and with this terrible knowledge, I could only whisper, "My God, my God!"

Before I had a chance to regain my composure, I heard them making plans for us to move to the Zuglo. "The best thing for us is to get out early in the morning," my husband proposed, "so that there will be plenty of time left for us to see the neighborhood."

"Oh no, not again," I cried. "Yesterday Magda, and now us.

I can't take this pressure any more!" I threw myself on my bed and closed my eyes. Sleep. Sleep and forget. God in Heaven, I can't afford to go mad! But sleep evaded me. I tossed and turned, and in my disturbed frame of mind I could almost hear the minutes ticking by, bringing me closer with dizzying speed to December fifteenth and the dreaded confrontation with the Nazi overseer.

My nightmarish thoughts were abruptly interrupted by the blaring of the siren again, and I automatically reached for my baby. "In any case," my husband whispered, his voice urgent and insistent, "try to get Mr. Horvat's permission for you to leave."

"Yes, yes," my brother Lajos hissed, "tell him how miserable your parents would be if, after accepting their invitation for Christmas, you would be unable to come."

Uncle Yidel's eyes widened. "Yes, yes. Play on the holiday spirit," he urged me.

As soon as I stepped inside the air-raid shelter, I scanned the room for Maria. I found her sitting in her usual place with her baby in her lap. I greeted her and pulled up a chair by her side. She acknowledged my greeting with a curt nod of her head and then she turned her attention to her baby, completely ignoring my presence. I searched for the right words to engage her in conversation, hoping it would draw in everyone. In this way, I would be able to feel out the Horvats on our planned trip.

To my great disappointment, the all-clear alarm rang out. People breathed a sigh of relief, and I, feeling like an utter failure, stood up to follow everyone out.

Janos Horvat tapped me on the shoulder by the door. Panic surged through me. This is it, I told myself, avoiding my sister's gaze.

With remarkable outward calm Anna said, "How do you do, Mr. Horvat?"

"What a beautiful little girl this sister of yours has," he remarked. A warm smile played on his lips and spread slowly to his eyes, illuminating his weather-beaten face. "My, how this one has grown," he exclaimed, taking her from my arms. "How old is she now?"

Mr. Horvat's unexpected kindness brought tears to my eyes. "She will be seven months old on the thirteenth of December," I answered in a melancholy tone, "and to think that my parents have not yet seen her. Maria spoiled it," I sobbed. "I must be going now," I murmured, reaching for my child. He placed the baby gently back into my arms. Furtively, he looked around the room.

"We are alone. You can talk," Julia whispered to him.

"Anna, I just want you to know..." he began haltingly. "I want you to know that Maria upset me very much today. I can't tell you how shocked I am." I didn't know what to make of this. Then, from the corner of my eye, I glanced at my sister. I saw Anna's lips moving and then Mr. Horvat said, "Shush, Anna, shush. I know how you feel. I even told my wife that I thought it was absurd."

"It is," Julia confirmed, nodding her agreement.

"And I said to her, 'I won't let the poor darlings' holiday be spoiled. So why wait another week for Mr. Eperjesy's visit when it may be too late, with all the trains full of servicemen going home for the holiday at the last minute?' So I went to see the overseer immediately, just before the raid."

Wanting to hide my anxiety, I commented, "What a considerate thing to do."

Mr. Horvat ignored my remark. "How much would we give for our son Janos Junior to come home for Christmas!" he said to his wife.

Finally, I couldn't stand the suspense any longer. "And what does our highly esteemed Aryan brother think about this farce?" I asked, sucking in my breath.

Janos Horvat smiled and I exhaled softly, eager to hear the verdict. "'Well, well,' he quoted. 'This is ridiculous!' That's what he said. And because he is so smart and educated and knows so much, he laughed it off. 'Tell the girls that they can pack up right this minute and go home. If Erika's explanation doesn't suit me, I know where to find Anna. After all, how many Anna Shipocs live at the respectable address of Szel Kalman Utca 40 in Szombathely?' Good news, isn't it?" he concluded.

"Oh, you will never be sorry for this, Mr. Horvat," I cried. "You know we have connections in the Nazi Party and access to many powerful people."

"And our folks are waiting for us to help them slaughter the pig," Anna said excitedly.

"A pig as big as an elephant," I added. "And I'm sure Mama will remember you and Mr. Eperjesy as well." Without blinking an eye, I turned to Anna. "We won't be back when the rent is due," I said. "Please get me three hundred and fifty pengo. Let me pay next month's rent in advance."

Horvat's eyebrows shot up in surprise. "Why, won't Monika be able to see to the rent, or is she going too?"

"Monika?" Anna snapped, the contempt in her voice evident. "That's all we would need. She would probably forget where she placed the money, let alone when to pay the rent. Besides, she's not our responsibility. Let her friends take care of her."

Anna started to leave the room, but Janos blocked her way. "What's your hurry? You can pay when you know exactly when you are going to leave."

"We were planning to take the early morning train tomorrow, if that's all right with you," Anna said. "Our folks will be waiting for us at the station bright and early Wednesday morning."

"In that case," said Janos beaming, "get the money."

Anna turned to face me and said in a voice loud enough for everyone to hear, "Lucky I didn't listen to you, Sis. I haven't yet sent the telegram saying that we can't come home."

A few minutes later, we brought the rent money to his office, and he indicated to us to sit down. He strode toward his desk and made himself comfortable in his old, beaten-up chair. With slow, deliberate motions he made out a receipt and handed it to Anna. As she examined it, her face registered shock and surprise. "Goodness! Handwriting like this is fitting for the director of the Hungarian National Bank!"

Julia wrinkled her nose. "Maybe he could have been one," she said wistfully, "if he had had more education in that head of his, if he had been born to a different family."

Then, in a very cordial manner, they ushered us to the door, all the while wishing us a safe journey, a merry Christmas and a happy New Year, as if we were their best friends. Then Janos inclined his six-foot frame toward me and whispered into my ear, "Remember, not a peep about what has transpired between us here tonight. We certainly don't want to put any ideas into Maria's pretty little head." We murmured our farewells, and headed upstairs, anxious to begin packing.

A short while later, the air-raid siren went off once again, sending us back to the shelter. There was a big surprise waiting for us there. The old lady and Ersabet had come back. They were sitting in their regular chairs, as if they had never been away. "Ersabet!" I called out, as I ran to her. "Oh, Ersabet, how is your son?"

A smile warmed her face. "The doctors say it's a miracle that he is alive," she answered me. "Thank God, he is on the mend," she added, telling the beads of her rosary. The old lady's lips moved in silent prayer.

"How lucky for us to be leaving here," Anna whispered to me once we were out of the shelter and out of earshot.

"I hate them and fear them," I said. "But at the same time, I still feel sorry for Ersabet. A mother is a mother."

"Did you see how terrible she looks?" asked Anna.

"Of course," I nodded, thinking of how I constantly fretted over my own child, and, with an involuntary movement, I squeezed little Zsuzsi to my heart, holding her as close as possible.

We stepped into the room, and I quickly looked around to see how the packing had progressed. "Have you forgotten that we are moving early in the morning?" I asked them angrily. "Why haven't you packed yet?"

"We have," Lajos said. "Do you want to see?" He immediately fell to the ground and rolled under the bed, and soon three little bundles appeared on the carpet, followed by my brother. "We will wear as much of our clothing as we can so as not to call attention to ourselves," he explained.

"I packed the baby's things in this shopping bag," Rozalia added, "along with some silverware, drinking cups and cooking utensils. And this," she lifted up a little red pot, "contains a fried batter for soup. All it needs is a little boiling water, and you'll have a delicious, hot meal in no time. A rounded spoonful of batter will make enough soup for all of you. Use it sparingly. Make it last until you find some other source of food."

"And here, take this," my husband said, handing me a manila envelope. "Hide it under your clothes before we go."

A shudder passed through my body. "The emergency kit," I cried. "Lord in Heaven, the emergency kit." I gazed at it, remembering every single item we put in there, preparing smugly for an emergency we never expected to come. The words uttered in relative safety so long ago by my smiling husband raced through my mind, bringing home the sad truth: "In case we have to flee, we must take this with us," he had said then. "It contains everything we could possibly need." Then he had shown us the duplicates of our falsified documents, the forged ration books, and both the large and small pengo bills. Taking a bunch of small change from his pocket and juggling it between his hands, he had added sternly, "This is for carfare. Keep a lot of change in your pocket when you are out on the street, and constantly hold some of it in your hand. Who knows?" he had said. "It might give you an edge over your pursuers if it ever comes to that, God forbid!"

A frightening picture sprang into my mind: me, trying to fade into the crowd with a baby in my arms. Blinded by tears, I gazed at my daughter. "Sorry, my dear," I whispered. "Your father's warning wasn't uttered with you and me in mind."

The tension in the room was so thick that I could almost touch it. "I am talking to you, Zsuzsi," my husband said nervously. He pointed to the set of new keys in his hands. "Each envelope contains a set like this," he explained. "Whoever gets to the house first will be able to let himself inside."

Why can't you spell it out? I thought to myself. Why don't you simply say, Whoever will be lucky enough to make it?

Pali approached us, holding documents of change of address. "They are ready. They are all filled out, and each of them is stamped with the official seal, bearing tomorrow's date. So rest easy, you have done your patriotic duty," he added cynically. "You have reported your change of address to the local precinct within the twenty-four-hour time period, as all law-abiding Hungarian citizens are compelled to do."

So it's really happening, I thought, as I watched my husband and my brother pull socks over their boots to muffle the sounds of their footsteps. Iztvan switched on his flashlight and covered it with a dark cloth to dim its brightness. "Please see if it's clear," he told me.

I opened the door and peered out, listening for sounds in the empty stairwell. I pulled my head back in. "The timing of the latest alert couldn't have been better if we had planned it ourselves," I whispered. "Who would be awake now, after sitting in the shelter half the night?"

"God be with you," we chanted as my husband and my brother walked out the door. When their steps died away, I picked up the baby and one bag, and Anna took two shopping bags. "I hope they won't be awakened by the sound of my pounding heart," Anna muttered.

Monika began to weep uncontrollably. "Oh, no!" she sobbed. "I am to stay here without you and sit alone in the shelter among those vile anti-Semites!"

"Just stick to your act, Monika," I whispered to her before we left. "Every one of them thinks you are mad. There's no need for you to worry. You are playing your part very well."

And when I thought this was the end,
This was the end and there would be no more,
Faith seized me and whispered:
Where there is life, there is still hope.
Put forth your right foot, and never mind the odds,
For the Lord walks with all who tread this road,
This road called hope against all hope of hopes.

Book Four

49

> My tears have been my bread day and night,
> While they say to me all the day, "Where is your God?"
>
> *Psalms 42:4*

THERE WAS MUCH more to Number Five Dombalya Utca than met the eye. Each and every tenant who had recently moved into the beautiful building which was hidden behind the colorful lilac bushes had a secret reason for being there. In the apartment directly below that of Zsuzsi Kovacs and Anna Shipoc, lived Dr. Endre Kerekes, formerly a much sought-after dentist and oral surgeon from the city of Gyor. This lanky, blue-eyed six-footer, with the look of a pure-blooded Aryan, was actually a Jew who was also hiding out under false identification papers with his wife Julyanna and daughter Erika.

Dr. Kerekes restlessly paced the floor in the heavily curtained living room. It was still early, and his wife and daughter lay fast asleep in the adjoining rooms. "I wish that I too could sleep longer in the morning," he thought wistfully. He dreaded the early morning hours, for the entire day still lay ahead of him with nothing to do, and boredom and idleness reduced him to panic. But he was an early riser, partly by nature and partly from habit, a result of the busy schedule he'd always had. He missed the hustle and bustle of his office, and he hated his new life within these confining walls. "I love to work!" he declared to himself, and all who knew him could testify that his work was, indeed, his life. "How I wish that what I've told everybody was true: that I've come to Budapest to offer my services to the heroic boys whose teeth have been damaged in battle, since I am too old to serve my homeland as a soldier myself."

Then, as he usually did during this time of total quiet, he relived the events leading up to the abandonment of his home and the town of his boyhood and all he had established there. Recollections of the last days in his office came back to haunt him. The awful memories still reduced him to tears, and the same tension which he had felt then, gripped him anew.

Evelin Green, the last patient he treated the afternoon before his disappearance, was sitting in his office. She had no idea what was happening to the soul of her father's best friend. Only Dr. Kerekes knew how much this play-acting was costing him, for Evelin Green was almost a family member in the Kerekes household.

Now his memories raced, and in his mind he was standing with Evelin's father, Tamas, on the corner of Petofy Iztvan Utca on March 19, 1944, the day Hitler occupied Hungary. Both men were shaken and forlorn. "What are we to do?" they asked each other in bewilderment.

"There is only one thing we can do," Endre said, "and that may or may not save us. We must hide out with forged Gentile documents." Endre knew this could be done because his own brother, Mendel, a construction engineer, had almost finished a building where his entire family would hide out. He tried to describe what was awaiting the Jewish population. "Tamas," he urged, "on no account are we to move into the ghetto. It has been created for only one reason: to herd us together. But there is a direct line from there to hell, where Hitler's people are burning Jews alive."

Tamas moved away. His eyes were burning and wild, but when his voice came, there was a forced calmness in it, and he sounded almost paternal. "Look, Endre. You are sick. You are hallucinating. Try to go home and take something to calm yourself." Then he stared ahead, at the faraway horizon, to avoid looking Endre in the eye. "I advise you to see my friend Morris, Dr. Morris Stark."

But since the yellow stars were already pinned on their lapels and the air was full of rumors about the ghetto, Endre made another attempt.

"Try to move to Budapest, my friend, where at least, among so many people, you may have a chance."

"To hide as a criminal?" Tamas exclaimed, pulling himself up to his full height. "Why, they can't make me resort to that!" he cried. "They can't — not while I'm still carrying the bullet in my body from the First World War," and he pointed to his left hand which hung at his side, lame and useless. "And you know what," he raved, his eyes aflame, "if you really want to know what I think about all your stupid stories, I will tell you: they are the imagined horrors created by a very sick mind and I never want to hear them again!"

Tamas's words still rang in Endre's head, and he covered his ears with his hands and closed his eyes to block out the episode. But it would not go away. The scene merely changed: "I'm so afraid of your drill," came Evelin's small voice from the past, and then his own reaction to it: Oh, Evelin, he thought to himself, if only you knew the terrors which are awaiting you, you would laugh at the insignificance of this momentary discomfort. He felt the earth trembling beneath him, but outwardly, he was the calm, reassuring dentist, not giving Evelin even the slightest hint of the tumult raging inside his soul. Only he knew how much this charade was costing him, how guilty he felt. He and Julyanna would gladly have taken the girl along with them, provided her parents had consented. But he had never extended the offer because he was too scared to reveal the secret even to his best friend. Evelin, sweet child, he thought now, did they sentence you to immediate death, or were you thrown into a slave-labor camp so that they could extract the last remaining strength from your small body?

As he recalled all the hardships they had endured, even with his brother's help, in order to move to their present address, it became clear to him that he never would have been able to succeed on his own. And with this realization he knew that the gnawing sense of guilt would remain with him forever. Tamas, he cried inwardly, forgive me for telling you all the grisly details without giving you any alternatives! How hard I made it for you. I know, my friend, that you believed it. You did! Each and every word. But you felt powerless to do anything, so you denied it vehemently.

Then he recalled his feelings of rebellion before taking leave of his beloved office. Who will sit in this chair of mine? Whom will the Nazis proclaim the lawful owner of my dental surgery after I am gone? Upon whom will the Nazi government bestow all my belongings as a gift — all that I worked for, for almost a lifetime, never taking even one vacation? Yes, he thought, I kept pushing myself to work, work, work all those years. Although Julyanna and Erika would beg me to vacation with them on the sunny beaches of the Balaton, I could never spare the time. First I would plead that I had to pay off the mortgage on our home. Then I had to pay for the more modern equipment I bought for my office, and so it went. And now that everything was paid for, should someone else enjoy it? No! Burn it! Don't let it be offered on a silver platter to some freeloader who will incite hatred and spread lies about you in order to grab your hard-earned assets! They are cunning, those Nazi robbers, and they succeed by using a well-tested strategy: Give the Jews a few relatively good, peaceful years, and they will work and build and make the land prosper. Then, cast them aside and steal the trusting fools blind!

His rage over his helplessness was mounting, but he knew perfectly well that if he succeeded in arranging to have his office set on fire after his disappearance, the Nazis would take revenge on his suffering brethren.

Suddenly, feelings of shame overtook him. His body was drenched in cold sweat. How can I grieve over my material losses when all I should do now is sing hymns of praise and thanksgiving for being here with my wife and child, with my entire immediate family living in comfort and relative safety?!

He was so lost in thought that he didn't hear the knocking on the door, nor did he hear it open, but soon he heard Erika cry, "Grandmama, what's the matter?"

"How many more times will I have to tell you not to call me grandmother!" His mother rebuked her angrily. "My name, for the time being, is Mrs. Nagy! You mustn't forget that, even when we are alone."

Endre turned abruptly and saw his mother standing in the middle of the room, with his wife and daughter facing her. His mother's face was as pale as her starched white blouse and her snow-white hair, which she wore pulled back from her face in a tight knot at the nape of her neck. Her black eyes, which stood out in sharp contrast, were now filled with animal-like, unrestrained fear.

"Mother, speak! What happened?"

But she was unable to respond. She just stood there, gasping for air as three pairs of eyes stared at her expectantly. Finally, her voice came, weak and subdued. "It's Ersabet. I'm so worried about her. She's been acting strangely ever since the day those two SS officers first came to visit Zsuzsi and Anna." She paused, nervously studying her hands. "I'm afraid that now, after months of seeing them come and go, the tension has become too much for her to bear. I think she's on the verge of a nervous collapse!"

"Calm yourself, Mother. Please sit down," Endre said, realizing that his mother hadn't moved an inch since she had entered.

"I must go now," she answered. "I can't leave Ersabet alone in the house. I only wanted you to be aware of what is happening to her. I really must go now," the old lady repeated in a weak voice. "I want to be with Ersabet when she wakes up. Laslo had to give her an injection; that's how distraught she was." Then the old woman clenched her fists, and her dark eyes burned with anger. "I hope we all live to see the day when I will make those girls pay for the constant fear their associations have caused us." With those words, she turned and left.

When she returned to her own apartment, she brought a chair over to the couch where her daughter-in-law was sleeping. She sat there patiently, holding and patting Ersabet's hands. Her heart ached for Ersabet, because the younger woman had had a frightful experience with the Gestapo that had left her crippled with terror, a terror that gnawed away at her, never subsiding, because she was unable to speak about the incident. She bore her burden alone, refusing to discuss it no matter how much her family begged her to talk about it. Her lips were sealed, at least during her waking hours. But at night, in her sleep, it was another story altogether.

When, in her nightmares, her awful memories returned to haunt her, she was unable to control herself. She often awoke to find her husband holding her, reassuring her and begging her to talk about that fateful morning when two SS men had dragged her parents away in a black limousine, never to be seen again.

Poor Ersabet, the old lady thought as she sat there motionless so as not to wake her. The woman's tears began to flow, running into the countless wrinkles that crisscrossed her cheeks. She watched her tears fall with a feeling of detachment, as if they had no connection with her. She was accustomed to crying. It wasn't new to her at all.

She felt a tug on her hand. Ersabet was stirring. "It must have been so hard on you," the old lady said quietly. "Poor child!" She bent over to kiss her, and, to her great surprise, Ersabet began to speak.

"I remember it clearly," she said haltingly. Her mother-in-law sat perfectly still, listening intently. "It was on the twenty-fifth of March when my next-door neighbor, Rachel Adler, whose husband headed the *Judencouncil*, appeared in my doorway holding an empty cup in her hands. Looking at her, I knew instantly that something was awfully wrong.

"'Can you please lend me a cup of sugar?' she asked with a stiff smile on her face, her eyes enormous with fright. She pointed to my son, who happened to be in the kitchen just then. 'Send him out,' she whispered through clenched teeth. Just then I looked out the window and saw Laslo coming down the path. 'Look, Father is coming,' I said, and before I knew it, he was running out to meet his papa.

"'It's your parents,' Rachel said breathlessly. 'My husband overheard that they are on the Gestapo's blacklist.'

"'Why?' I asked, horrified.

"'In their case, because they are rich and powerful,' she whispered. Then she looked around. 'Are you sure that we are alone?'

"'Yes! Go on! What do the Nazis want from them?'

"'I suppose they want to find out if they have any hidden money.' Then she said softly, 'Don't waste time. If Elkanah heard correctly, they could be picked up at any time, even today.'

"'What shall I do?' I asked, panic-stricken.

"'Go tell them to leave the house so that the SS men don't find them at home when they come for them.'

"'Where can they go?' I asked, fighting the hysteria that kept choking me with iron fingers.

"'The first and most important thing is to get them out of the house,' she repeated, 'even if they have to walk the streets until you can come up with something better.'

"'Yes,' I agreed. 'I think that the street is pretty safe. After all, the Gestapo officers do not know them, so they wouldn't be able to recognize them.' I reached for my coat, but before I got to the door, Rachel grabbed my arm.

"'Remember — if you make one wrong move, we will all be dead! You, your parents, your husband and your child. And so will we — Elkanah, the children and I. It won't be difficult to guess who your informers were.'

"I dashed for the back door as my husband and son came in leisurely through the front entrance. 'Tell Laslo,' I told

Rachel breathlessly, 'that I have no time and I also don't want to have to explain the situation to my son.'

"I ran outside thinking to myself that this whole thing was like a horror film. I tried to restrain myself from running through the streets to reach my parents' house faster. Rachel's terrifying warning echoed in my mind: 'One wrong move and we'll all be dead!'

"When I finally reached my parents' house, I looked around for a black limousine, the official car of the Gestapo. I didn't see one, and as I neared their building, I spotted my father through the window of his store, which occupied the ground floor of the house. Gratitude rose in my heart. Thank God I had come in time! I took a deep breath and entered the store. My father was alone. 'Where is Mother?' I asked him anxiously. Then I grabbed hold of his hand. 'Papa, go find her while I get your coats.'

"'Why?' he asked with a puzzled expression on his face.

"'Father! You two must get out of here quickly, before the Gestapo arrives.'

"'The Gestapo! Why would they come for us?'

"'Because they think that you have lots of money stashed away someplace.'

"'But we haven't!'

"'That is why you must run from them: because no matter what you tell them, they won't believe you.' Mother had joined us by this time. After I repeated the news for her, we all just stood there, speechless. Thinking of all the stories we had heard, we shivered with horror. The Gestapo inquisitors had a way of making their unlucky victims speak, and we knew that it was woe to the ones who had nothing to tell them and nothing to give!

"'Where shall we go?' my parents asked me in bewilderment.

"'Out. Away from here. Walk around in the vicinity of the marketplace. I will come for you as soon as Laslo and I find a place for you to hide.'"

Ersabet tried desperately to fight the effects of the sedative Laslo had given her, which made her dizzy beyond words. But she was determined to talk, and the old lady was anxious to listen. This was the first time anybody had heard about that fateful day when Ersabet's parents had disappeared, leaving her with her frightful nightmares.

Ersabet pulled herself up to a half-sitting position, covered her shivering body with the colorful afghan — a gift from her mother — and continued her recitation. "My mind was working feverishly. I kept telling myself that the wisest thing to do would be to go home and consult Laslo, but for some inexplicable reason, I couldn't abandon them, not even for a second. I had to be able to see them all the time, and so I started to walk behind them at a distance as they made their way to the marketplace.

"As I followed them, I tried to devise a plan. I knew that this house would be ready for occupancy in a few weeks and that my parents already had aliases which would enable them to come and live here with us. I simply had to think of a non-Jewish friend who would give them shelter until then. Suddenly, I knew what to do. I almost cried out with excitement. Why hadn't I thought of it before? I quickened my pace in order to catch up with them.

"'Papa,' I whispered as I neared them, 'I think I have a solution. Go to Ferenc's house.' Ferenc Koves was their faithful employee and friend of twenty-five years. 'Maybe he and his wife will let you stay with them. Even if it is only for tonight, there is no need to worry. We will come up with something else tomorrow.' And on impulse, I took the engagement ring which Laslo had given me and which I had never taken off my finger in twenty years, and I slipped it into my mother's hand. 'Here. Give it to them as a token of my gratitude. I will stand outside for a few minutes to see if the Koveses let you in, and then I will go home and consult Laslo. And Mother dear, if everything is alright and if it is safe for me to enter their house later, please pull up the shade of the middle window and I will come in and discuss the next steps we must take.' They both nodded approvingly and turned the corner to resume their course.

"The Koveses lived — how shall I describe it — on the outskirts of the city, or, rather, at the beginning of a little town called Olad. In any case, it was a very long walk, and to make matters even worse, my mother had a bad heart condition, so I decided that, for my own peace of mind, I would follow them without their knowing, to see them there safely. The snow was melting, and even though a snowflower could be seen here and there, the blossoms did little to cheer up the two forlorn figures who were making their way through the hills with obvious difficulty, but without stopping. I sensed their anxiety, but all I could do was to let them continue.

"Finally, they came to the crossroads, and from there they turned into the little village. All at once, I heard the command ring out loud and clear: 'Halt!' There, right in front of my parents, stood the formidable black limousine. Two men emerged from the car. One was wearing the despised black uniform of the Gestapo and the other was none other than our trusted and well-liked employee, Ferenc Koves. I saw my own terror and surprise mirrored on my parents' faces. My heart froze as I heard Ferenc's chilling words: 'Here are your pigeons!' And as I stood by watching helplessly, I saw my dear parents climb into the waiting car. That was the last time I ever saw them."

Ersabet covered her eyes the way she always did when her cries rang out in the dark of the night, but this time she was silent. Only after a little while did she begin to cry softly.

The old woman sat very still for a long time without uttering a sound. When she was certain that Ersabet had said all she had to say, she began to speak. Her words came quietly, hardly above a whisper. "God loves you, my child." The only response she received was a painful, questioning look in Ersabet's eyes. "Yes, He does," she repeated tenderly, "because not only did He allow you to do all that was humanly possible for your parents, but He also demonstrated to you that it was His will,

His decree that your parents be given over to the Gestapo by this 'Judas,' and not merely the result of your advice to them. Did you ever give yourself credit for your extraordinary bravery in going to your parents' house even though you knew that the SS men could be there at any minute?" Ersabet didn't answer.

"I am proud of you, my daughter!" And with those words the old woman stood up to leave. She didn't want to give her daughter-in-law a chance to answer. Better to let my words sink in, she thought. And please, dear God, she prayed, please help her accept what I have said and ease her suffering. She tiptoed out of the room as quickly as her tired legs could carry her.

Worn-out and dazed, the old lady dragged herself to the kitchen. Her energies were taxed to the limit. All she wanted to do was lie down in her bed, to sleep, to forget. Instead, she did what she had done so many times in the past few months. She simply reminded herself that if life must go on, there must be food prepared and, still immersed in her troubles, she automatically began cooking the evening meal.

When she heard the door to the adjoining apartment open, she ran to her door and peered through the tiny peephole. There stood another one of the despised SS boys again, accompanied by the two girls, who were bidding farewell to them with a loud "Heil Hitler." In response, the boy jumped to attention, his black boots shimmering, and he raised his right hand high in the customary Nazi salutation. Then he turned and left, his stride arrogant and self-assured. The old woman leaned her aching head against the door, listening to his footsteps fade as the "Heil Hitler"s reverberated through the hallway.

She stood there motionless for a short while until she heard a sound from the kitchen which told her that a pot was boiling over. That brought her to her senses, and she returned to the stove. Without thinking, she readjusted the flame and wiped the gas range clean. She felt totally exhausted, like an oversized rag doll. How wrong we were, she thought bitterly, to have once, so long ago, called those two girls "nice and harmless," but who could have foreseen this? Who would have ever dreamed such a thing possible? She felt betrayed and lost.

What shall we do? She kept asking herself this question over and over again, but in vain. Then, as she always did when she needed comfort, she began to recite her favorite verse from *Tehillim:* "Some speak of their horses/ Others boast of the mighty numbers of their chariots/ But my strength comes from You, my Lord."

50

THE HORVATS STOOD at the office door for a while listening closely, and only after they heard the girls' door slam upstairs did they dare to speak. "How did you like Anna's remark about my handwriting?" Janos whispered, wiping beads of sweat from his face with the back of his hand.

"Don't worry, dear. They seem to have big eyes but short memories. Remember how worried we were when Zsuzsi made that remark about my portrait? But then she never mentioned it again. They're busy with their own lives."

"I hope you're right. And Julia, my dear, do you believe what they say? Can we be so lucky? Will they really be leaving?"

"Of course they will," she assured him. "And I hope they are hit by a bomb on the way! Then they'll never come back. But let's not discuss them any more. Right now the table is set and the soup is boiling. I'm starved. Let's go upstairs before another air raid sends us back to the shelter."

When they stepped into the neat little kitchen in their apartment, Janos cried out, "With such good news in the offing, I don't think it's fair not to tell the others. Please keep the soup hot. I'll be right back."

Janos half-walked, half-ran to their bedroom, then into the spacious walk-in closet. Nervously, he searched for the light switch hidden behind a shelf. That was the signal to the occupants of the bunker that he wished to gain entry. He stood there motionless, waiting for the trapdoor to open. Impatient and quivering with joy, the urgency of the moment overwhelmed him, and it seemed as if hours were passing as he waited for them to let him in. Finally, after what seemed an eternity, the trapdoor slid open and he stepped down. It immediately closed tightly behind him, and he found himself standing in the darkness. "It's me," he said softly, and a second door opened noiselessly from the inside. He stepped into the secret chamber, the existence of which was known only to himself, his wife and the Davidsons.

The room he entered was large and inviting, and decorated in tasteful, expensive style. One corner was used as a dining area where a large, mahogany table stood surrounded by matching Sheraton chairs, each upholstered with hand-stitched petit-point fabric. The other end of the room, which functioned as a bedroom, was sealed off by a black, hand-painted Chinese screen. The middle area contained the parlor suite, upholstered in warm hues of beige and wine. The room was flooded with light, and heavy, tightly drawn, wine-colored drapes hung on the walls, giving the impression of high, wide windows. But in actuality, there were none: this chamber was located entirely underground, with no indication whatsoever from the outside that it existed at all.

When Janos entered the secret room, the three men who sat around the table were listening so intently to the forbidden "Voice of America" that they didn't even notice him. But he found Erika and her companion sitting on easy chairs, apparently in a very good mood. The woman was in her late thirties or early forties. She had platinum-blond hair, flawless skin and dark eyes that sparkled with laughter.

"Oh, how funny," the woman chuckled. "We just heard the news on the radio that Mendel and I were washed ashore from the Danube."

"Yes. You supposedly drowned yourselves to avoid being relocated to the ghetto," Erika laughed.

"How stupid can they be? Just yesterday we were supposed to have died from swallowing poison. Somebody ought to tell them to make up their minds about where we were found and how we ended our lives," she joked.

The tall, lanky man so engrossed in listening to reports of the latest events in the outside world was the man known as Dr. Kerekes. In reality, he was Dr. Nagy's brother, and both of them were living under assumed names. They were the sons of the old woman, known as Mrs. Nagy, who lived across the hall from Zsuzsi and Anna. The third man, Mendel Davidson, was also their brother. He needed no alias because he and his wife hadn't set foot out of the bunker (and they had no intention of doing so) from the day they had moved in — June 14, 1944, one day before the Jews had to move to the ghetto.

Aniko, Mendel's wife, was a former opera singer with the National Hungarian Opera House. She had been known as *Pacsirta*, "songbird." The Gestapo had sought her out because she was very successful, both professionally and financially, and she therefore made an ideal target for their hatred. Naturally, what the Nazis really wanted was Aniko's considerable wealth. But luckily, her parents, who lived in Poland, had convinced her to hide out under an alias only a few days before they themselves had been deported and killed in the gas chambers.

It had happened in the spring of 1941. While the Hungarian Jews had virtually no knowledge of what was going on within the borders of Poland, Hitler's extermination plan was already in full swing. The Nazis managed to conceal this information from the Jews of Europe even after they had conquered the land. That was the secret of their success in rounding up all the continent's Jews without protest. The Jews were promised work in Germany after they were left without any other means or opportunity to support themselves and their families. Only the Polish Jews knew the truth, because the gas chambers were built on Polish soil.

One dark night that same year, Mendel and Aniko Davidson were awakened by the doorbell. "Let's ignore it," Aniko suggested, trembling, but the ringing grew louder and more insisent. Mendel started toward the door. "No, no!" Aniko cried. Her fears were well-founded: a nocturnal visitor at a Jew's door often meant the police with arrest warrants for crimes never committed. But in this case, it could have also been the police coming for Aniko, who was born in Poland and later became a naturalized Hungarian citizen. The naturalized citizens were harassed and sometimes stripped of their citizenship and deported back to their countries of origin. In Hungary, the only thing worse than being a Jew, in the eyes of the authorities, was being a Polish Jew.

The bell rang incessantly and someone began to kick at the door. When Mendel finally opened it a crack to peek out, he was surprised to find that the hall was not only pitch dark but seemed to be completely deserted. Before he had time to close the door, someone reached out in the dark and thrust an envelope into his hands. Then he heard a click and the hall light came on. He stood there, stunned, holding an envelope that bore no name or address and gazing at the back of a man who was running down the steps.

Mendel stumbled back inside. He broke the seal of the envelope, and with Aniko looking over his shoulder, he read the letter. They stood there in their nightclothes, shivering, and their horror grew with each syllable they read:

My dearest children:

Terrible things are happening here in Poland. Hitler is earnestly bent upon our destruction. Heed my words! The only way a Jew can stay alive is if he hides far beyond the reach of Hitler and his bloodthirsty collaborators. Prepare for that time now, for sooner or later Hitler will overrun Hungary too, just as he did Poland. But by that time, it will be too late, much too late. I won't elaborate upon the methods that the Nazis are using to annihilate us because if I did, you would attribute this warning to a sick old man's fantasies. But heed my words! The death they inflict upon us is extremely brutal! My advice to you, my children, is to build a house and move there with Aryan identities as soon as possible. I can't advise you how to go about it.

You will find a way if you seek it.

Mendel, I entreat you! Look immediately for a site upon which you can build!

Mother and I send you all our prayers and kisses!

Two days later, the same thing was repeated: the buzzing in the night and the envelope thrust into Mendel's hands, but this time the envelope contained a large bundle of American dollars with this little note attached to it:

We are sending this money to you as we and our friends no longer need it. We will be deported on Monday. Our only advice is to build the house and buy documents attesting to your pure Aryan blood. Don't make any mistakes! Know that the Nazis demand that you have not only your own identification papers, but also your parents' papers. Don't delay! We love you. Don't waste time worrying about us. Act!

That is how Mendel Davidson conceived of the idea to build the house in which they were hiding out. Approximately two years later it was completed, thanks to Aniko's parents' last desperate warning.

As Janos stood waiting at the entrance of the bunker, all three brothers and other members of the Davidson family were now gathering to have their supper. Because of the genius of Mendel, the construction engineer, it was impossible to detect the bunker's existence from the outside, no matter from which angle the building was viewed.

Lasi was the first one to greet Janos. Without delay, Janos blurted out the news as quickly as he could. There was a shocked silence. Then Lasi let out a roar of joy. "Bulletin!" he cried. "Bulletin! The Nazi boy and his sisters will leave tomorrow night, to go home for the holidays!"

"If this is true, Janos, oh my God, if this is true," Dr. Nagy cried at the top of his lungs, trying to overshout the others, "then this boy by the name of Lasi Nagy, whom you admitted into this emergency room with a ruptured appendix, an infection that my distinguished colleagues and I had expected to be long and lingering..."

"...will now heal fast!" everyone completed his sentence, and began laughing. Overcome with joy, the old lady hugged Aniko. "I feel like dancing, Aniko," she said."

After several minutes of celebration, Aniko went into the kitchen to bring out the meal and they all sat down to eat. The atmosphere in the bunker turned calm and quiet, with all its occupants lost in thought. "Let's talk about something," Lasi finally said.

"What's there to talk about?" his father asked.

"Talk about your boyhood years. I would like to know if your generation knew anti-Semitism, too."

A pained expression appeared on his father's face while his uncle, Dr. Kerekes, cried out, "They say that history always repeats itself. Remember how we asked our father the same things, Mendel, and in a similar setting, too?"

"Yes," Mendel said softly. "Papa was sitting as we are now, with his three brothers, at the dining-room table at Grandmama's house after supper. But then we were the younger generation. Ah, where have the years gone?"

"Here I am now with a grown son of my own, a boy who is much worse off than we were in our generation," Lasi's father said, "because even though anti-Semitism existed everywhere then too, our lives weren't threatened by it as his life is."

"And how we laughed behind our parents' and grandparents' backs," Mendel continued. "'They are ignorant,' we said. 'They are uneducated, those old folks, and that's why they can't eliminate the senseless anti-Semitism in their world. But we are smart, we are college-educated. We will do our utmost to see that anti-Semitism will never again rear its ugly head. We will chase it away forever!' And we were true to our vow, as we earnestly began to look for a clue as to what causes it."

"And what happened?" Lasi asked. "Did you find out?"

"We certainly did, but when we confronted Papa with our findings, he laughed in our faces. 'I didn't need to send you to the university for that,' he said. 'My generation learned it for free, and our parents did too, even though they never saw the inside of a university classroom!'"

"But what is it that you learned?" Lasi persisted.

"We learned what our elders had known all along, that we were used by our fellow Hungarian citizens whenever misfortune befell them. We were the eternal scapegoat for all their woes, real and imaginary!"

"But in our arrogance, we still felt that we could find a way to fight it," Lasi's father added.

"Yes," Mendel murmured, "until we were faced with it, with nothing on earth to do but acknowledge it. How helpless we are! How very helpless!"

"You should have pointed it out to the non-Jews. Maybe they blame us without even realizing it! Maybe they aren't aware of the suffering they inflict upon us," Lasi cried.

"No, don't fool yourself," his father replied. "It is done consciously. We learned that at the university. 'Richárd Berkesy got mail today,' we would warn one another. We avoided this student on the days he received mail from home, because at those times he treated us very unpleasantly. We could never understand why until Mendel discovered the connection. Richárd Berkesy was the last male member, the last hope of an impoverished, aristocratic family. His family had scrimped and saved in order to provide him with a good education. Now Richárd was many things: he was good-looking, lively and fun to be around, but there was one thing he most definitely was not — diligent and successful in his studies. Every postcard he received from home reminded him of his family's expectations of him, and it flooded him with self-hatred. But because Richard preferred pursuing the good life to pursuing his studies, he learned to get rid of his guilt feelings quickly. He transferred to us all of his self-hatred and attained a safe target for his scorn.

"When we told Papa about it at the end of the year, he merely nodded in acknowledgment. 'Now that you have come so far, now that you are so smart and educated, I hope you will come up with something constructive to counteract it,' he said."

Suddenly, Julyanna Kerekes interrupted the brothers' story. "Now I understand what my grandmother said about 'blood libels!'" she exclaimed. "And it was so long ago. Isn't it funny how episodes from our childhood have a way of surfacing without warning, after they seemed to be completely erased from our memories?" She sighed. "But why talk about it?"

"Mother, is it something from *your* childhood?"

"Yes," she whispered.

"Then tell us about it," Erika begged her, her eyes large and luminous like two bright torches.

Julyanna stood up. Beads of perspiration formed on her face as she spoke, and she seemed to be in a kind of trance. "At the mere suggestion that our landlord's crop would not be successful, my parents' faces would pale. They prayed for rain, they prayed for sunshine, they prayed for whatever seemed to be lacking. And strangely enough, they never let us children know the real reason they were so concerned with the land's yield. But now it's so clear: they were afraid of the baron's wrath. They knew how defenseless they were in the face of his anger." She began to speak faster and faster as the frightful memories came back to her for the first time. "It's like a dream. My mother came running into the room one day, too upset to notice me. She ran straight to my father who was reading the newspaper. 'Itzig, listen!' she said.

"Father's eyebrows shot up in surprise. He put down the newspaper. 'What is bothering you, Rachel?'

"'Maria told me that there is trouble up there,' Mother said, pointing in the direction of the hill where the baron's castle overlooked the valley.

"'I know,' Father answered. 'I heard that today he lost some of his best milking cows to a disease among his herd.'

"Despair was etched on Mother's face and she whispered as though she were afraid to bring the words out into the open. 'And our neighbor Ella just told me that the crop will come out badly this season, too.'

"There was a lot of whispering in our house that year, and the most terrible accusations were hurled at us in school. 'Mother,' I cried one day as I came home, 'is it true that we use blood to bake our matzos? All the children said so today, and they even told me that their parents forbade them to play with me. They can't be my friends anymore! They can't because the Jews kill little Christian children every year just before Passover, and use their blood to make matzos.' My mother's face turned chalk-white and she turned to her mother, who, by this time, was standing up, holding on to the back of her chair. Her face was also completely ashen. She is dead, I thought, and I started to tremble as I recalled what my friend Ruthy had told me just a few days before when she lost her grandmother.

"'You know how my grandmother died?' she whispered in my ear.

"'How?' I asked respectfully, for she was very knowledgeable.

"'First, she had a lot of wrinkles on her face and even on her hands,' she said knowingly, 'and then she became very white. And that's all.'

"But now my own grandmother started screaming hysterically, 'Oh no, Rachel, not again! Not another blood libel!' Then she pulled me to her. 'Tell them,' she cried, 'tell those fools that we are not even allowed to cook our meat and poultry without salting and soaking them first, in order to draw out any blood which remained in the slaughtered animal.'

"And as I stood there trembling and dazed, my mother threw her arms up toward heaven. 'A Jew kill another mother's child?' she cried. 'My God, such a lie! Such an impossibility! Who could have thought of this insane idea?'

"Then my father came running into the room. 'Rachel, don't you see the child?' he asked. He swept me up in his arms and carried me outside into the garden. He lowered himself onto the bench, still holding me very tightly. I fell asleep peacefully, feeling secure in his arms. The incident was never mentioned again, and it slipped my mind completely until now." Julyanna collapsed wearily onto her chair as she finished her tale.

Aniko, visibly distressed by the turn the conversation had taken, quietly cleared the table and disappeared into the kitchen.

"And here we stand now," Lasi said sadly, "no better off than the generations preceding us. You know, I know, and all our ancestors knew, yet we didn't do a thing about it. If only you knew how much I despise myself for following you here to this bunker to hide, as though we were criminals, instead of standing up to the whole bunch of them. Why did you hide here? And why did I follow you when every drop of my blood cried out to me to fight those murderers, not just sit and rot here." Then he turned to the occupants of the bunker. "Why, Father? Why, uncles?" he cried. "Why did you spend all this time, energy and money building this bunker? You, who were a step ahead of the rest of the Jews, who knew what was in store for us — why didn't you organize, arm yourselves? Why didn't you stage an uprising the day you were ordered to move into the ghetto? How could you run away as you did, and let the other poor, unsuspecting Jews go of their own free will into the slaughterhouse? Did you still believe in the goodwill of your fellow Hungarian citizens? Or was it that you forgot how many times in the past we were driven from the nations of Europe? Well, let me remind you how the story goes: we gratefully settle in a new land. We build and work and dream that this time we have found a permanent homeland where our children will be able to raise our grandchildren in peace, where they will reap the fruits of our backbreaking labor..."

"Nonsense!" Erika screamed. "Look at our history and all you will see is how we were driven from our host countries as soon as we acquired a financially secure position in the land. Raise children and grandchildren in peace? Ridiculous. Wherever Jews settled, wherever we dared to begin to feel secure, anti-Semitism grew along with us. The same lies are always used to incite the people against us. Then there were the pogroms, and before we knew what was happening to us, the poor children were left to inherit the dark roads, driven, penniless, to start the vicious circle anew in another land."

"Let me explain," Laslo interrupted, trying to put an end to Lasi's accusations.

But he was not to be stopped now. "Just answer this," Lasi demanded. "How long will it take for us to learn that we can't fight hate with love, and certainly not with trust?! We should be armed! We should have been prepared!"

"And just imagine," Erika said derisively, "we were brought up to be such patriots, our hearts imbued with love and loyalty toward this land. What our parents should have done was talk to us honestly and tell us how uncertain our existence here really is!"

Lasi turned his fury on her now. "How can you expect this of them," he shouted, "when their entire lives have been based on self-deception? Can't you see it, Erika? And all this time they impressed upon us the virtue of honesty, and told us time and again that the gravest sin on earth is self-deception." Then he turned to his father. "Tell me, Father," he yelled, "tell me, if you can, how you like having your own words come back to mock you?" Lasi stopped and wiped his perspiring brow. He was suddenly astonished at the angry tone he was using toward his elders. His face turned crimson. "Father!" he cried. "Forgive me, please! I was carried away."

"Never mind, my son. This is a very timely question indeed — yes, very timely," Laslo stammered. "But the best way I can explain it to you is to say that what you call self-deception is, in my language, hope — a strong belief that things will take a turn for the better. And let me remind you, my son, that this very ability, this very gift from God, to be able to hope against hope even in the most adverse situations, is the secret of our survival.

"And to answer your question, my son, as to why we didn't warn our fellow Jews and tell them what we knew — it was because we felt that as long as we couldn't help them to escape the horrors of the ghetto and what it represented, it would be not only pointless to tell them, but extremely cruel as well. Do you think that just because your uncle is an architect and had the means and the know-how to prepare this hideout, that everybody could have done so?"

"You have to be aware," Mendel added heatedly, "that a bunker like this needs to be built with the utmost secrecy. Whom else could I have trusted besides my dear friend, Janos Horvat? Yes, you two, this bunker and the entire foundation of this house was built, stone by stone, by Janos and me with our own hands."

"And before we could let the workers finish up the house," Mr. Horvat laughed, "we had to build a wall to camouflage it, which we later had to tear down to ensure its secrecy. What a job that was!"

"And to answer your question about why we didn't stage an uprising," Dr. Kerekes interjected, "that was done already, in Poland." His voice cracked, and to Erika's and Lasi's astonishment, he began to cry. Not knowing how to respond to this display of emotion, they began to weep as well. That helped Dr. Kerekes to compose himself quickly. He put his finger to his mouth. "I don't want Aniko to hear what we are discussing," he said, "because she lost her only sister in the Warsaw ghetto uprising."

"Tell us about the uprising, please!" they begged.

"What shall I say? It was a bloodbath which will forever testify that, although man is surrounded with the trappings of civilization, he is still the same savage animal he has been since the beginning of time."

"But please," Lasi persisted, "tell us what happened before Aniko comes back."

"All right," he began wearily. "Shortly before they were herded into the ghetto, the Polish Jews learned what it was all about. In a last, desperate effort, a number of Warsaw Jews tried to arm themselves, quickly learning a few things about ammunition. In secret, they manufactured some homemade bombs to greet their captors with when the wagons came to take them to the gas chambers. Time was very limited and so were their meager supplies, but the group managed to smuggle a few of their members over the border in order to tell the world about their plight and to ask for ammunition so that they would have a fighting chance."

Lasi's eyes shone, his whole face a question mark. "Father, and...?"

"Don't get your hopes up, my son. What happened is what usually happens when Jewish blood is shed: the world chose to be deaf and blind! But we reaped the rewards of the efforts of those selfless Jewish youths. We have since learned that it was they who brought us the letter of warning and the money from Aniko's parents."

"Please go on, Father," Lasi urged.

"And the world's silence, of course, confirmed to Hitler that he could do whatever he pleased with the Jews, and he didn't waste any time. It wasn't long before the Jewish rebels in Warsaw — children, boys and girls about your age — were overpowered. Some were killed on the spot while the rest were marched to an open field where they were ordered, at gunpoint, to dig their own graves and then lie in them waiting to be shot. The hate-crazed Nazis shoveled back the earth onto their still-living bodies."

Dr. Kerekes hid his face in his hands. "And we learned from reliable sources," he wept, "that the earth on the field was seen to move for days!"

"I have never heard anything so horrible!" Janos Horvat cried. "It makes me, the only Aryan present, hang my head in shame!"

"But you are not the only one to be ashamed," the old woman cried, her dark eyes aglow as she groped for the right words to express her feelings. "We are all ashamed. Each and every person who is alive today or who was ever living on this earth is ashamed! Can't you see that horrors like this, and in fact all cold-blooded murders, be they committed by an individual or by a group, be they in the name of Hitler, Mussolini, or Stalin, are carried out by men willingly? Yes, you heard me right — willingly! Otherwise they would have no power. We, civilized mankind, cultured, educated and well-mannered, have learned to manufacture deadlier and deadlier weapons with which to destroy our enemies." She paused for a moment, and then continued, her voice lower now. "But we have failed to realize that our only enemy is Cain, the murderer who lurks in our hearts and who has been there since the beginning of time. He waits quietly for a leader to arise, a real, flesh-and-blood Cain, who will let his chained brother within us run amok on earth. This is the root of all human tragedies. So let us pray for a release from this age-old curse!"

Dr. Kerekes wiped his perspiring brow with the back of his hand. For a moment he lost his balance, but then he steadied himself and turned to Lasi and Erika. "This was not a subject one talks about lightly," he said softly. "But I felt that you deserved some honest answers. Now it is up to you to decide if you could have done otherwise!" And he hastily left the room.

After Janos returned to his apartment, he told Julia about the reactions of their friends to the good news. "You know," he said between spoonfuls of soup, "you wouldn't believe how Lasi has changed. Remember how even as a child he was so full of compassion? Remember how, in the park, he would avoid stepping on even one tiny ant? Now all he dreams about is revenge, sweet revenge."

A sigh escaped from Julia's lips. "I don't know," she said

thoughtfully, turning toward her husband. "I really don't know how to say this. I always had the feeling that the Almighty Lord endowed the Jewish people with an overabundance of kindness. This is the root of all their suffering. Otherwise, how can you explain this calculated cruelty of the Gentiles toward them? It must be temporary and it will surely disappear after the Jews learn to stand up for themselves and strike back. Am I right, my dear?"

"Let's call it a day," Janos said, stifling a yawn. "I'm tired, and I'm not too fond of philosophizing in the middle of the night."

51

When I weep, it is to the Lord that I cry;
When I weep, it is toward the Lord that I
struggle to become worthy of favor.
Psalms 142:2

FEAR GRIPPED ME as the front door closed softly behind us. "I never believed it could be as dark as this," I sighed, trembling with fright. But my eyes gradually grew accustomed to the dark as we slowly made our way down the path. We stopped briefly next to an unfinished building, where my husband and Lajos were waiting for us. There was a quick exchange of words between the men. Iztvan took Joska's place at my side, while my brothers walked briskly to the end of the path and soon disappeared around the bend. I walked between my husband and Anna, holding my baby close to my heart.

The meadow lay ahead of us, shrouded in darkness. Not one ray of light escaped from behind the blackout curtains of the distant buildings of the Kor Ut to cheer us, nor could we detect a single star to light up the pitch-black night and help ease our feelings of fear and despair.

We walked in silence, and I remembered the bright June day on which I first set foot on this very path. Then it was late spring and the meadow was ablaze with sunshine, and amidst the carpet of lush grass, wildflowers greeted us, bringing the promise of life. But now, stealing away in this predawn hour of darkness, our dream of walking away from this merciless persecution as free men seemed to be nothing more than a fantasy.

The wind raced through the barren meadow, screaming at me, "What do you think you are doing, bringing a baby out on such a bitter, cold night!"

"What a change the passage of summer and autumn has made on this place," I said quietly.

"Yes," my husband agreed absentmindedly. Then he added in a more forceful tone, "But nothing has changed, where our hope, our great determination and will to survive are concerned!"

I stopped at the end of the path before we turned, wanting to take a last, parting glance at the whitewashed house where we had spent the past several months of our lives. I could not see it in the dark, but I knew it was there and I felt as if it was beckoning to me. I could almost hear it whisper, "Why go? It's safe and warm in here. Don't be a fool! Come back!"

Thus, standing there in the bitter cold, a terrible yearning overtook my soul, and all at once, the house of terror from which we were fleeing, with all its sinister occupants spying on us from the other side of the wall, lost its suffocating hold of terror on me. Despite even the frightening prospect of a confrontation with Mr. Eperjesy at the request of Maria and all our Nazi neighbors, I still wondered about the wisdom of our decision. Was our hasty judgment sound? Did events really warrant our taking this drastic step? All of the horrible recollections paled in contrast to the dark, unknown road ahead, with all its faceless dangers lurking before us.

It was only then that I fully grasped the finality of the hour, and every atom in my body cried out: It's too late. You can never go back!

As if from a distance, I heard Iztvan and Anna urging me, "We'll lose the boys. Let's hurry."

The frozen ground at the Kor Ut echoed in response to the impact of our heels, loudly protesting the intrusion on its domain of silence at this dim hour of quietude.

We strained our eyes, frantically searching for the boys. Suddenly I noticed two shadows moving on the far side of the road. "There they are," I sighed with relief.

"Thank the good Lord," the others murmured softly.

We all tried hard not to stumble in the dark as we kept our boys in sight. We moved on numb, frozen legs for what seemed an eternity, and then, in the near distance we heard the sound of vehicles.

"Just a little more patience," my husband urged. "We're almost there."

A faint ray of light, as if a sign of hope, appeared then on the horizon. It was at that moment that I first caught a glimpse of the magnificent Horthy Miklos Bridge, almost hidden in the predawn light, spanning the dark river over to Pest, and my emotions lurched between relief and panic. "I can see the bridge," I gasped. "We're almost there."

Anna stepped forward. "Now I am going to board the bus as if I were one of the citizens who lives the good life in the hills of Buda and commutes into the modern city of Pest to make a living," she declared firmly. Her voice carried a forced cheerfulness which did little to lift my spirits. She squeezed my hand hard. "I'll see you soon," she whispered, and walked briskly ahead of us.

"I hope so," I said softly. "I hope to God that we haven't walked so far in vain."

"Of course not," Iztvan replied emphatically. "With all the vehicles dumping all these commuters at the bus stop by the bridge where we will soon board, who will notice us?"

After a few minutes we reached the bus stop, and it wasn't long before the bus arrived. As I entered the bus, I was relieved to see that Anna and the two boys were sitting far apart from one another. Each had also managed to grab a window seat. I could not see their faces since they were looking out the windows, watching the sunrise, but I sighed with relief knowing that the other passengers could not see them either.

I sat down next to my husband. Iztvan, with remarkable outward calm, seemed completely absorbed in reading his newspaper. Slowly I relaxed.

All of a sudden, the silence in the bus was shattered by the terrifying sound of bullets whizzing by at close range. There was a moment of quiet horror after which all the passengers hurled themselves to the floor for cover.

"It's all right, Aryan sisters and brothers," the driver called. "The Swedish Consulate around the corner was harboring some Jews. The SS must have come to finish them off!"

"Let's see! Let's see!" came the excited response of the passengers. People ran toward the exit door. "Open up! Open the door!" they demanded loudly.

And amidst the chaos I saw my sister and brothers alighting from the bus with the mob. As I watched them disappear around the corner I noticed a street sign: Vadas Utca.

The driver is right, I thought to myself. Sweden has remained neutral in the war. There is indeed an "immune house" on Vadas Utca. The realization that what the driver had said was true stabbed at my heart like a knife. Panicking, I pinched my husband and pointed to the door, begging him silently: Run, run while you can!

Iztvan gazed at our sleeping baby. "It fascinates me," he said with a smile, "how she manages to sleep through all this noise." Then he bent over her. "Avrumele's daughter!" he whispered into her blanket.

"Avrumele's daughter! Avrumele's daughter!" I stared at him open-mouthed as his words rang in my ears. All at once a tremor passed through me, and a picture quickly flashed through my mind, a picture of a beloved face, so fragile, so thin, almost lost in a long, snow-white beard. The Rebbe. The Rebbe's words rushed into my consciousness from the past, and, awed and trembling, I clung to his promise: "Avrumele's daughter! The Almighty Lord will grant your wish. You will survive with your husband and with your child!"

"Thank you, Rebbe," I whispered, exhaling softly, and my feelings of panic left me.

"The passengers are returning," my husband said quietly.

We heard them laughing as they casually discussed the tragic massacre. "I heard she was a young girl with a baby." I bit my finger until it bled to choke back my pain and outrage over the shedding of innocent Jewish blood. "She was very pretty and young."

Then a woman with such an unpleasant, nasal voice that was reason enough for me to want to tear her to shreds, cried out, "I heard it from an eyewitness, that the girl saw the Gestapo the second she stepped outside. She immediately realized what it meant and she ran back and began to kick at the door, but of course, I don't have to tell you, the door was locked!" She spoke breathlessly, like one not accustomed to holding people's attention for very long.

"We missed the show by a minute," a whining voice came from the back of the bus.

"I don't understand," a young boy exclaimed. "If my sources are correct, then the police have no jurisdiction over the Swedish immune houses. I wonder how they got them."

"That's what I call Hungarian resourcefulness — rather, Hungarian brains — at work," the driver cried, a wide grin spreading across his round, hateful face. "Let me put it this way," he said laughing. "As the saying goes, if the Gestapo can't go to get the Jew, then the Jew will come to the Gestapo. Ha, ha, ha! Especially," he continued, gloating, "if the flow of food into the building is interrupted. Isn't that clever!"

A sickly looking young man shot out of a seat to my left. "It serves them right," he sneered. His Adam's apple bobbed up and down in his thin, white neck as he spoke. "Let me ask you all this question: By what right does this madman, Raoul Wallenberg, come here from Sweden to distribute Swedish citizenship papers among the Jews?"

"And to buy the best building in town and give it the

respectable name of 'Swedish Consulate.' Whoever heard of diplomatic immunity for Jews?"

"And I ask," a thin voice cried from behind me, "what right does he have to interfere with how we Aryan Hungarians are treating our own Jews? Believe me," he added with contempt, "we could have made much better use of this building for our own purposes."

"Shhh!" An excited cry came from the passengers who were sitting near the windows. "Somebody must be coming out again. I see the Gestapo aiming their guns."

"Kill! Kill! Kill!" they yelled, stamping their feet.

I sat there, chilled to my bones. They would no doubt tear us to pieces with their bare hands if they knew who we were. Lord in Heaven, please don't let it happen again! I cried inwardly.

Suddenly my husband jerked my hand, and I looked up to see the driver walking down the aisle. There was no mistake: he was coming straight toward us. I hunched over the baby, quivering with terror that our true identity would be discovered. I was utterly at a loss for words to deny my terrible sin.

Wearing a satisfied smirk on his face as he searched my eyes, the driver stopped next to us. I thought with great envy about the girl lying dead in the snow in front of the Swedish Consulate. In a daze I watched his hand shoot up in the Nazi salute. "Heil Hitler!" he cried.

Too astonished to think, I responded automatically, "Heil Hitler! Heil!"

"Aryan sister," he boomed, so that everyone could hear. "I feel it is my duty to ask you to disembark from this bus. With all the shooting going on, I would rather not drive with a baby on board."

Murmurs of approval were heard. "Thank you, Aryan brother," my husband said, taking my arm as I stood up.

No, you are not fainting, I told myself. Just put one foot in front of the other...

As my husband led me off the bus and across the street, I

could still hear the driver's voice. "Yes, we must protect the Aryan children, the Aryan children who are to inherit the earth!"

"Here we are," Iztvan said softly as we turned the corner. "This is the block."

"Finally," I sighed, my legs so weak they could barely support me. Then I caught a glimpse of something which sent new strength surging back into my weary limbs. "Look, look!" I cried breathlessly. "Look at the first house from the corner. They're signaling with the venetian blind!"

"Yes," Iztvan whispered, and purposely slowing our pace, we crossed the avenue.

My heart was racing. "I do hope all three of them are in there," I said. I glanced at the address: Amerikas Utca 15-15. My husband held the door open for me and we recited the age-old Yiddish blessing as we entered the vestibule: "*Zoll zein mit mazel.*"

Within moments, the inside door opened, and my sister and brothers were standing before us. "Why didn't you follow us?" Joska exclaimed.

"We were so frightened for you!" Anna cried. "Why did you stay there, with the mob thirsting for blood?"

"What's the point of rattling on about it?" Lajos said, grinning from ear to ear. "They're here, thank the Almighty."

"We came here by the long route in order to check out all the transportation stops against our homemade map, and," he added proudly, "it's perfectly accurate."

After I fed the baby, Anna took her from my lap. "How hungry you must have been, how very hungry, but not a peep out of your sweet little mouth," she crooned to her between hugs and kisses. "May the Almighty reward you for being such a good little girl!" Tears formed in her green eyes beneath her thick, dark lashes. "Never in my life will I forget the agony we lived through until we saw you and your Mama and Papa here, safe and sound," she sobbed.

"Nor will I ever forget what I witnessed, Anna," I said,

trembling at the mere thought of our recent experience on the bus. "Anna, it was so terrifying. I feel I've glimpsed their naked souls."

"Please, Zsuzsi, let's not waste time while our neighbors, the Baranys, are out. I must unpack, and you must get to work exploring the neighborhood."

"Alright," I replied, wrapping up the baby once more and reaching for my overcoat.

"You're taking the baby?" my husband exclaimed, flabbergasted. "Have you lost your mind?"

"I can't leave the house without her. Please," I begged him, "please understand."

"You'll stand out like a sore thumb, parading up and down the block with her," he snapped angrily, taking her out of my arms.

I had no choice but to comply. Fear engulfed me as the door closed behind me, my empty arms dropping to my sides. Will I ever come back here? And if I do, will I find her here? Oh, my dear Lord, will I ever see her again? But then, the still forms of mother and child lying lifeless in the snow screamed at me louder than words. How useless the Jewish mother's loving, protective arms proved to be. Shocked into this new awareness, I stepped outside with iron determination, alert, searching for clues, clues which might aid or hinder our escape if, God forbid, the need ever arose.

First I walked to the bus stop in order to familiarize myself with the neighborhood and to check out every single means of public transportation in the vicinity. Nothing will escape my attention, I vowed, as I looked around, calculating every angle from which we could approach each and every bus stop. Every street name and the layout of each block was registered in my mind with perfect accuracy. I traveled up and down the streets, looking furtively into every backyard and alley, my mind racing, making mental notes, all the while trying to find a connecting path to our house.

This alley leads to the backyard of the property with the

open well in the middle, I concluded. And from there it is only a few steps to the house with the large patio. That will lead us straight to the number 36 bus, a good alternate route, I noted with satisfaction. Then, if we turn to the right, we will end up at the number 71 streetcar.

With my mission accomplished, I realized how cold I felt, and so I decided to take the shortcut home through the alleys, all the while rehearsing silently everything that I had learned. When I reached our house, I noticed something, and my heart skipped a beat. Can this be true? I asked myself, rubbing my eyes. I burst into the house, hardly able to contain my excitement. "Anna," I cried, "please run into the bedroom and pull up the venetian blind from the window that opens onto the alley, and wait for me!"

"Why?"

"Just do as I ask you, please," I begged. "I'll explain later." I ran outside for a moment, and then I hurried back into the house to tell the others. "I was right!" I shouted with excitement. "I knew I was right! I just had to make sure!"

"Stop talking in riddles!" Lajos demanded. "We are not mind readers."

"Now listen to this," I said regaining my composure. "We all know that every house on this block is identical." My husband's face fell in disappointment. "But there is one priceless difference. You see," I explained with triumph, "the corner house, unlike ours and the others on the block, has no windows facing onto the alley! And the alleys are all surrounded with tall, thick evergreen bushes from each entrance."

My outburst was followed by silence. The unasked question, "So what's so special about that?" hung in the air.

"Don't you see? Since we are at street level and hemmed in at both ends with all those shrubs, we can just step out of the window and no one will see us!"

"And we're only one house away from the corner," my husband added, finally catching on.

"How much easier that makes a getaway!" Joska commented breathlessly.

"And I found two more routes through the back alleys that lead to the buses. What more can we ask for!"

"For starters," Lajos replied, casting his bright, blue eyes skyward, "I would ask that this war end right now and that innocent Jewish blood never again be shed."

"*Amen, amen,*" we all said in unison.

"*Amen,*" I whispered, dabbing my eyes as I stepped out into the hall with Anna, the two of us determined to find out everything we could about the layout of the house.

We crossed the hall, stopped before the door bearing the placard "Oscar Barany," and listened for some signs of life, but there were none. I pulled the bell cord once, then twice, so nervously that I almost tore it. "Thank God they're not home," I said softly.

We went outside again and I tried the knob on the back door. It was locked. It appeared that this door leading to the alley was not used regularly.

"Look at this," Anna exclaimed as she peered through a glass pane in the door. "Look at all the space between the two houses! Thank God, these houses are separated and no one can hear us from the other side of the wall." She turned to face me. "And look at these thick walls," she whispered. "Zsuzsi, this house was built with us in mind! Please, let's go downstairs now and examine the shelter so that we can relax."

I opened the door leading to the shelter and stared at the narrow staircase, which was illuminated by a single light bulb dangling from the ceiling. Then I remembered something. "Go back and tell them to walk the length and breadth of the house with their shoes on, so that we'll know whether their movements can be detected from here," I instructed my sister.

I descended the steps to the shelter and listened carefully for sounds from above, but there were none. I waited several minutes, and then, satisfied that the floors and ceilings were indeed soundproof, I went upstairs to join my family.

"Anna was right," I told my husband while I warmed my hands over the black iron stove. "This house was built with our needs in mind."

"Is there firewood in the bin?" Iztvan asked me anxiously.

"It's filled to the top," I answered, "as stipulated in the contract."

"Fine," my husband said, breathing a sigh of relief. "What else have you discovered?"

"I stumbled onto the Baranys' larder. What a spectacle! Chunks and chunks of smoked hams dangling from the ceiling beams. I could hardly squeeze myself in. It was filled with every kind of food imaginable, not to mention the countless jars of canned fruits stacked on the top shelves."

A shadow of sadness passed over Iztvan's face. "Now go and tell this to all the deprived, starving masses. Go tell them that all their sacrifices are beneficial only to their manipulative leaders and not for the 'salvation of their beloved homeland,' as they are reminded day and night." Then, with a dismissive wave of his hand, he added, "They are so brainwashed, so blinded by empty promises and inciting slogans against the Jews that it is virtually impossible for them to perceive the truth."

Lajos's face became distorted with anger. "Oh, the awesome power of slogans!" he cried. "Oh, how they tyrannize!"

Our discussion was interrupted by the blare of the air-raid siren. The sound was just as unwelcome and startling here as it was back in Buda. I quickly picked up the baby, and then it dawned on me that no one besides ourselves was in the building; there were no prying eyes to see whether we hurried to the shelter or not. I put her back in her crib, sighing with relief. "There's no reason for us to be banished to the shelter without our papa," I whispered to her, smiling. "We're as much at risk up here as down there. Just for today, we'll stay upstairs." Little Zsuzsi smiled at me as if she understood, and turned over to go to sleep.

"I wish I were free to go to the shelter like I was in Buda,"

Joska said. "But here I'm a ghost, and I must stay upstairs." Then he added with a shrug, "I suppose it's not for me to make up the rules of the house."

We were fortunate. The siege was far away from the Zuglo, and we were able to catch up on our sleep. This blessed state of freedom lasted until midday, when Joska began to wave his arms as he stood at his observation post behind the window. "They are here," he said sadly.

"Please remember," Iztvan cried, "don't encourage their friendship. Give them the cold shoulder right from the start."

"If Monika, the most extroverted and vivacious of all of us, can do it," Anna said with conviction, "then I'm sure we can, too."

She had hardly completed her sentence when I heard footsteps in the hallway. The men quickly hid. My blood froze as I heard the knock on our door.

52

I OPENED THE DOOR and saw a couple in their mid-thirties standing before us. "You see, Oscar?" the woman bubbled excitedly. "I told you they'd be here already." Then she turned to us. "Oh, I am thrilled to meet you." The woman seemed to lack any affectations. Her voice was natural and it rang with true friendliness. "I am Theresa Barany," she introduced herself, "and this is my husband, Oscar."

My baby started to cry. "I am Zsuzsi Kovacs and this is my sister, Anna Shipoc. Excuse me, I have to pick up my daughter."

"A baby!" she cried with excitement. "Zsuzsi, I didn't know that you had an infant! Imagine, Oscar, a baby in the house!"

Mr. Barany ignored her comment. "This place is in shipshape condition," he remarked as he looked around. "When did you unpack everything?"

"Thank you," I smiled, thinking how lucky it was for us that he wasn't around when we'd arrived with hardly more packages than we could carry on our backs.

Theresa was enchanted by our baby. She took her from my arms and kissed her tenderly. Then she carried her over to the large mirror hanging over the buffet. "Now this is funny," she said, holding the baby's face against her cheek. "Come here, dear," she called to her husband. "Now look and tell me if this baby does not resemble me more than her mother."

"Hm-m," said Oscar, looking clearly uncomfortable. He glanced from me to the baby, to his wife, and then back to the baby. "Her mother seems to have the same fair complexion, except that her hair is dark."

Under their scrutinizing gaze, I thought to myself, How lucky I am that I don't have to wear the incriminating wig! (My long, dark hair, which I had cut when I first got married, had now grown back in.) Despite the awkwardness of the situation, I managed an easy reply. "With her blond hair and blue eyes, she is the image of my husband," I said, my smile adding credibility to the lie: Iztvan's hair and eyes are brown and he has a Jewish nose as well!

My baby became impatient with the smothering stranger and stretched out her arms to me. Grateful for the opportunity to end the conversation, I muttered something about feeding her, and the Baranys finally left.

"So much for our plans to remain aloof," Anna remarked bitterly.

"Men plan and God laughs," Iztvan said, emerging from his hiding place. "Now tell me. How in Heaven's name are we going to be able to keep them out of the house?"

"The woman is a bit mad," Anna said, "but to tell you the truth, I can see her point. Your blond baby does look a bit like her."

"Stop it, Anna!" I exclaimed, stamping my foot in helpless rage. "Stop it, because if I hear those words again…"

I paused in mid-sentence when I realized that Anna was looking at me with round, hurt-filled eyes. "Forgive me, Anna," I said, trembling. "And please don't ask me why this upset me so much. I honestly don't know myself."

Moments later, the siren sounded loudly. "Back to the old nightmare," I cried and picked up little Zsuzsi, quickly wrapping her in a blanket. Anna and I hurried toward the door. "Oh, how I dread going to the bunker and leaving you all up here!"

We found Theresa waiting for us in the hall. "Come! I'll

take you to the shelter," she urged us breathlessly. "Hurry, run!" We followed her down the stairs and into the large room. "Here we are," she said, slamming the door and exhaling softly. "In here we're safe and sound, so let's relax." Leaning heavily against the thick, iron door she made a wide, sweeping motion with her hand. "This will come as a pleasant surprise to you, girls," she said. "We renovated this cellar into one of the most modern shelters in the city. The walls are reinforced with steel beams," she explained, pointing to the corners. "And look at all those sandbags stacked under the window. You have no idea how much work and money went into this," she added with barely concealed pride.

"Say thank you to Theresa *neni* and Oscar *bacsi* for making this place so safe and letting us share it with them," I cooed jokingly to my daughter.

"She's adorable," Theresa cried. "Look how she's smiling at me, as if she understood." Then she reached out for her.

"No, please," I stammered awkwardly, flinching away from her.

Theresa's eyebrows arched in surprise. "Is it that you don't trust me with her?" she asked indignantly.

"Don't be silly, Theresa," I replied, still holding fast to my daughter. "It's just... well, it's just that... "

"Zsuzsi never lets go of her when we're in the shelter," Anna interrupted, eyeing me disparagingly. "She even refuses to give her to me! Don't ask me why, Theresa. I could never figure it out myself."

But as it turned out, Theresa was not one to give up so easily when she really wanted something. She looked at me pleadingly. "I'm sure you heard on the radio about the sighting of enemy planes over Baja," she said. "And you know that means it will be only eight or ten minutes before those accursed bombers reach this part of Budapest. Let me hold her at least until then."

Defeated, I handed her the baby. "Then promise you'll give her back to me in exactly seven minutes," I said reluctantly, "and without my having to ask."

"It's a deal," she replied eagerly, synchronizing her wristwatch to mine.

"You're so remarkably calm, while I am so frightened of the approaching bombers," I said, just to cover my anxiety and annoyance at having to relinquish my baby, even for a few minutes.

"You can shiver in your skin, if that's what you want," Theresa said sharply, "but there's no reason to. How many times must I tell you that this bunker is one hundred percent bombproof?" Then, abruptly, she changed the subject. "You know, I really don't know how to say this without sounding presumptuous," she began. "But my Oscar... my Oscar is very valuable to the Party. He is a very important man." Then she turned to me and asked, "Where is your husband?"

"I wish I knew," I whispered, shivers running down my spine. "I haven't heard from him since September. The last letter came on September twelfth from the... from the Russian front," I stammered, and buried my face in my hands.

A shocked silence followed my revelation. Then Theresa spoke, more to herself than to me, and hardly above a whisper. "Poor dear, a baby, and so young, so young. Now I understand. That explains it. That's why you cling so to your child." She said this without making the slightest move to hand little Zsuzsi back to me, and I, thankful for the end to Theresa's questions, pretended to have forgotten our pact, while she remained completely absorbed with the baby throughout the raid.

That evening, little Zsuzsi, who had been sleeping through the night since the age of six weeks, screamed for hours. "Are you teething? Is that why you're so miserable? Please let Mama see it." I explored her little mouth with my finger but found not even the slightest suggestion of swelling. Is she coming down with a cold? I wondered, nervously pacing back and forth with her to calm her. Is she feverish? I touched her forehead to check. "Oh, no!" I cried. "She's hot!" I ran to wake my husband. "Iztvan, the baby is sick. She's burning hot!"

"The baby?" my husband exclaimed, jumping out of bed. Instantly, he was awake and alert. "Did you take her temperature? How much fever does she have?"

I ran to the bathroom to get the thermometer, and quickly took her temperature. "You read it," I said to Iztvan, holding the thermometer in front of him and averting my gaze. My hands were shaking so badly that I couldn't hold it steady. "How much?" I asked anxiously.

A puzzled expression appeared on his face. "It's normal. Let's take it again."

"How much?" I asked again after taking a second reading.

"It's normal," he replied. We looked at each other in despair, with the whole household now looking on.

"I wish there was a doctor I could call," I lamented, "or at least someone older and more experienced than us." The baby was passed from hand to hand, but no one could make her stop crying. We were numb with fear.

"Zsuzsi," my husband said. "Something just occurred to me. I think I know what she wants."

"What? What can it be?" I asked in panic.

"She might simply be hungry. With these last few days being so very hectic... I think she just hasn't been getting enough nourishment. Zsuzsi, you must find some farina for her. After all, she's seven months old already, and she is certainly ready for solid foods."

"We shall ask Theresa," Anna declared. "She will do whatever she can for little Zsuzsi."

When dawn finally broke, I stationed myself at the window and waited impatiently for Mr. Barany to leave for work. "At last," I sighed and ran across the hall to Theresa's apartment.

Theresa came to the door looking like a queen, a powder-blue, hand-embroidered dressing gown thrown hastily over a nightgown of the same color. She looked at me curiously.

"I... I'm sorry for disturbing you," I stammered. "I've been up for hours — I didn't realize how early it was, and that you would still be sleeping."

"Don't be silly," she said with a smile. "I've already given Oscar a hot breakfast and sent him off to work, so how could I still be sleeping? Come right in, dear," she said, moving away from the door, "unless you mind that the beds are not yet made and that the house is such a mess."

"Oh no, Theresa, I am not the kind who goes visiting neighbors for morning coffee. Believe me," I continued, allowing a note of melancholy to slip into my voice, "if I hadn't found myself in such a tight spot, I would have thought twice before ringing your bell. But Theresa," I said, "I need your help badly."

Her eyes widened. "What's the matter?"

"It's my baby," I cried. "She hasn't slept a wink. She screamed from hunger all night long. It almost tore my heart in two. I must buy her some farina! Maybe you can recommend a grocer."

"Well," she replied thoughtfully, "that depends. If you're asking me to recommend a regular grocer, he will honor your food ticket from A to Z, but you can forget about farina. But if you're willing to pay black-market prices, then you can get anything you want. Or almost anything," she chuckled.

"Where?" I asked excitedly.

"I can send you there," she said, closely watching my reaction.

"Oh, thanks so much! You are saving the baby's life! Please, give me the directions."

"Alright. You turn left by the exit door, and keep walking for two blocks. Then you'll see a bright green door. You can't miss it. On it is written in large black letters, 'Sandor and Lola's Family Grocery Store,' but don't be misled by the name. There's nothing folksy about the place, except to the folks who can afford to pay their prices!" She laughed good-naturedly.

"Thanks, Theresa. Thanks a million times," I repeated, hurrying off.

"Don't forget to tell Sandor the grocer that Theresa Barany sent you and that you are the new owner of the condominium across from mine," she called after me. "And, Zsuzsi, a word of caution: Be discreet! I don't have to tell you that what you are about to do is a crime with grave consequences for all involved. Remember, even the walls have ears!"

Oh, if only I had known what sharp ears Janos the grocer had, I never would have dared to go near that store!

The man at the counter was full of smiles. "I would never dream of saying no to Mrs. Barany's friend," he gushed. "There is only one problem," he continued, scratching his chin. "Did she tell you that farina is very expensive?"

"Oh, Sandor," I answered naively, "I'll pay you whatever price you ask. You see," I explained in a voice filled with emotion, "I have a seven-month-old baby, and she is virtually starving!"

"Hmm," he said, gazing straight at me. I began to feel my skin crawl. Then, without another word, he turned and disappeared into a back room. I stood there, drenched in a cold sweat, contemplating all the frightening possibilities. What if Theresa tricked me? What if he has a telephone back there and is informing the police of my crime?

But the man reappeared a short while later, holding a small brown bag in his hands. "This is a kilogram of farina. How much of it do you want?"

"Would it be very selfish of me if I asked for the whole thing? Unless, of course, I would be depriving some other babies of this essential nourishment."

"It's up to you," he said. Then he named the price, which amounted to a king's ransom.

I paid it promptly, without batting an eye, and, clutching the great treasure in my hands, walked out of the store.

"Hungarian sister!" he called after me. "Come back for a second. I want to tell you something, my Aryan sister. Every day we're supplied with a different product. Tomorrow, it will be dried peas."

"Oh, thank you," I said, hardly believing my luck. "When would be the best time for me to come?"

He seemed to be considering something, and he didn't say anything for a moment. Then he answered slowly, "Late, late in the afternoon. Let me give my supplier time to unload."

"That's fine with me," I replied gratefully.

"Then let's make it four o'clock, Mrs. Kovacs. Four o'clock sharp! And please be punctual. There's no point in having my special customers meet one another here," he said, winking his eye as a conspiring smile played on his lips.

"I shall be prompt," I answered casually, hiding my uneasiness.

The next afternoon I filled a large pot to the brim with tap water and left it on the stove to boil. "By the time I return with the goods," I explained to Anna, "the water will have boiled."

I headed for the store in a state of euphoria. Oh, what a delicious soup we will have, I thought to myself. Giddy with hunger, I could almost smell the aroma of the thick broth already.

And then, just as I was approaching my destination, I heard a voice: "Don't set foot in there! Go back! Go back!"

I stopped abruptly, and looked around for the source of the voice, but I didn't see a soul. The block was deserted and quiet. The warning had come from nowhere else but within my own soul. Astonished and quaking with fear, I gripped the iron railing by the sidewalk for support. Of course, of course, I must turn back right now!

Only it was too late. There stood the grocer, waiting for me on the doorstep, mouthing to me soundlessly, "I've got the stuff."

I had no alternative but to step inside. The inner voice still urged me, Don't go in there! Run for your life! I greeted him with a big smile, all the while digging my nails into my palms to remind myself to be natural.

"And how did the little princess enjoy the farina?" Sandor asked warmly on his way to the back room. "Excuse me a moment. I'll be right back."

I stood alone in the store, trembling while I wondered,

Would he have pity in his heart for me if he knew? And in my panic, the image of the dead bodies of the Jewish mother and child flashed into my mind. There would be no pity. There is no pity, nor is there justice. The just are dead. But then Karoly's and Magda's names rang in my ears, giving me renewed hope. There are still some good people left. You must think of them, Zsuzsi, if you and yours are to survive.

"I've got it," Sandor said, interrupting my nightmarish thoughts. I stared at him, not believing my good fortune, as he placed two kilograms of dried peas into my bag. I paid him a handsome sum, and then, stuffing my change into my coat pocket, I hastily left the store.

"Pardon me," I apologized to the woman I collided with as I rushed out.

"Never mind, it's all my fault," the woman replied, her voice as sweet as honey. Surprised, I gazed into the woman's heavily made-up face, and was immediately smitten with an intense dislike toward her.

"Oh, Lola," the proprietor exclaimed from the open door. "Lola! What a coincidence. I know how badly you wanted to meet her. Mrs. Kovacs," he said loudly, "allow me to introduce you. This is my sister, Lola."

"Of course," I said, wrestling with the sudden urge to run. I stepped back into the store and automatically shook her fleshy hand.

"I am Zsuzsi Kovacs. How do you do?"

"Lola Samos," she replied, giving my hand a lukewarm squeeze while watching me through ice-cold, blue eyes.

"You may be wondering why I wanted to meet you," she said. "Think. Lola Samos. Does the name ring a bell?" I shook my head. "Don't you remember who sold you your condominium?"

"I bought it through an agency, so I didn't know your name, but I always wanted to meet you," I lied outright. "I wanted to thank you for keeping the place in such good condition for us."

"And I have been so looking forward to getting to know you," she said with the same deplorable sweetness. "I've heard such nice things about you and your sister, but especially about your little girl. I spoke to Theresa just this morning, and I am telling you, she simply adores your little one. She is absolutely wild about her." Lola spoke without taking her eyes off me for even a moment. "Theresa and I are great friends," she added.

All at once, a new fear assailed me, followed by a strange sense of calmness, a calm which I had learned to recognize by then as an omen of horrible things to come. I struggled to keep myself steady as I walked out of the store, but my heart cried out in fear: Dear God, how many more tortures are you still hiding for us?

53

"THAT'S ALL FOR NOW," Sandor Boros said with a satisfied grin as he locked up the store. Greed burned in his dark, beady eyes. "The longer I keep the goods, the more money they will bring," he commented to his sister. His mouth quivered in his thin, ratlike face. "My customers are made of money."

"Money," Lola said slowly, with pain in her voice. "The curse of our clan, Sandor. Either we have none whatsoever, or we have much that is worthless. Brother," she pleaded, "sell our supplies only for their worth in valuables. Don't sell one gram more for cash." A wistful cry escaped from her lips. "I am left counting their worthless money, while they have my house!"

Her brother made no comment. He was busy sorting the pengo bills and stacking them into neat piles of hundreds and fifties.

"Sandor, did I tell you that I am staying for supper?" Lola asked. "Andras will pick me up late, after work. It's one of those busy days at headquarters," she added with barely concealed pride. Then she went into the kitchen to prepare the meal.

A short while later, Lola came out of the kitchen wearing a large apron over her orange-and-yellow checked dress. "The roast you gave me is in the oven. I think there is enough to last you an entire week!" Seeing that he did not respond, she repeated herself with an uneasy laugh.

"Thanks," he said absentmindedly, obviously deep in thought. Then he looked at her. "Lola, I've got it. I figured out a way to do it."

"Do what?"

"Do what you're always asking me to do. I will simply tell the customers that my suppliers have set new terms, and that they will only sell their products for their worth in valuables, and not an iota for cash."

"Finally," she responded with approval. "Did you notice those earrings Mrs. Kovacs was wearing?" They glanced at each other and their eyes locked for a fleeting moment. "We Boroses understand each other well," Lola commented.

"I guess we're made of the same stuff," Sandor added, and they both laughed.

Lola set the table with a white damask cloth of a fine thread, and the good silver and china as well. All were presents from her new husband, Andras Samos, the appointed caretaker of confiscated Jewish goods. "He is a good man, my Andras," she murmured to herself as she gazed upon the beautiful table setting. "He has a heart of gold."

She pulled out a chair and sat down, closed her eyes and recalled the events of the past twelve months. The pain she had felt, the horror, when the notice came from the army that Peter, her husband of six years, "gave his life for the good of his Homeland." My heart would have broken if not for my brother Sandor and Theresa, she thought. Theresa, my friend. Wasn't it Theresa who had dragged me to the SS-sponsored party, held in their newly renovated air-raid shelter, where I had the good fortune of meeting Andras Samos, who introduced me to the life of glamor befitting a high-ranking SS officer's wife? Yes, she chuckled to herself, reliving that night of nights when they had fallen in love. Theresa was indeed a good friend.

Oh, how happy I was then! I was on top of the world when Andras, in one of his more demonstrative moods, had swept me off my feet and whispered in my ear, "My very own wife. Oh, to have somebody on my side, the two of us against the world."

And then, shortly after the wedding, the nightmare had begun. Lola learned that the house she and Andras lived in belonged to the Kahans, Andras's former employer. "Mr. Kahan asked me to hide the family from the police," he explained. "Of course, I only played along and immediately went to report them. I don't know how it happened, but by the time the Gestapo arrived, the son had escaped. Lola," he cried, "it haunts me! What if he still lives? What if he comes back?"

And, shaken to the core by her husband's disclosure, Lola cried out, "Then we must leave this house! Oh, why did you ever make me sell my condominium in the Zuglo?"

The hurt was evident in Andras's face. "Do you think me a coward, that I should hide out from a *Jew*? "

Although the incident had never been mentioned again, our life has not been quite the same since, she thought. Never again has Andras been as trusting and truthful with me. It is as if something between us died that night.

Early that evening, Andras Samos proceeded with the ritual of grooming himself for the special occasion, which gave him great pleasure and a boost of self-confidence as well. He stood in front of the full-length mirror, cradling the little crystal dish, which was filled with a sticky solution of sugar water. He repeatedly dipped his fingers in it and then wet the whiskers above his upper lip, twisting them into a stiff, pointy mustache. He looked admiringly at his image in the glass. Oh, what an imposing figure of a man! he thought with satisfaction, while in truth, the dark, somber mustache on his soft, fleshy face presided over a receding chin, emphasizing the weakness of his character.

Well, a man is entitled to a little privacy, he rationalized. In any case, what good would it do me if Lola knew the truth: that the days I am supposedly working late, I am actually searching the ghetto and the yellow-star houses. Elchanan Kahan, that dirty Jew! After all, what right does he have to keep the great Aryan, Andras Samos, in fear? Today will be the day for you, Elchanan Kahan, to swim in the frozen Danube River, he silently vowed.

He reached for his freshly pressed Nazi uniform and put it on slowly, one arm, then the other, savoring every moment with sensuous delight. Then, after gulping down a few glasses of strong, red wine, he made one final inspection of himself in the mirror. He laughed out loud while thinking with secret delight of the Jews who huddled behind the cordoned-off ghetto walis, trembling and petrified at the sight of him. "Oh, what a cowardly lot!"

54

THE FIRST DAY passed, then the next, and slowly I relaxed. By this time, I had given in to Theresa's annoying demands to let her hold the baby in the air-raid shelter, but I found consolation in the fact that she never visited our apartment, which would have been our undoing.

On Friday morning we had an unwelcome visitor to the shelter in the person of Lola. She came to help Theresa set up a party to be held that night for their mutual friends. They were in an exuberant mood and didn't stop discussing the gathering — what they were preparing, which high-ranking and important guests would be attending. Their chatter on the subject was interrupted only once. "Don't you agree, Lola," Theresa asked, repeating the procedure of holding my baby's face to hers, "that this is how my children would look if I had any?" Her comment made me tremble all over again.

"I don't understand why it bothers you if Theresa loves our baby and thinks she looks like her," my husband commented when I described the incident to him afterwards. "Your fear of Lola and Theresa is absurd and irrational. You are working yourself into a panic for no reason."

"I agree with Zsuzsi," Anna interjected. "Theresa is nothing but trouble, and Lola fills me with terror. She is like the Angel of Death in human form," she added.

Behind the heavy blackout curtains, the Baranys' apartment was flooded with light. The two women stood back and admired the beautiful table. They moved about the room, first inspecting the bar, which was brimming with the best liquors and wines. "It's perfect," Lola said happily. The aroma of a variety of different meats roasting in the kitchen provided a festive finishing touch.

"We won't be able to eat even half of what we've made," Theresa exclaimed proudly.

"Never mind," Lola replied cheerfully. "We'll do as the ancient Romans did," she chuckled. "We'll disgorge the food to make room for more."

They laughed heartily without realizing the striking similarities between both cases: the chosen few who gorge their food, while the masses are dying of hunger.

At eight o'clock the man of the house, Oscar Barany, arrived home with Herr Walter Krull, his superior officer. As he ushered him in with great ceremony, Theresa stared at their guest of honor, stunned. "But where is Helga?" she asked.

Herr Krull did not reply. He simply strode over to the bar and poured himself a drink. Then, slamming his goblet down on the counter-top, he cried. "I'm through with Helga!"

A heavy silence descended upon the room. Lola tiptoed to the table and quietly removed the setting immediately to the right of Walter's seat. Soon afterwards, Andras arrived, followed by Sandor Boros and his fiancée, Viola.

After a few minutes, they all took their seats around the table. But their honored guest, Herr Walter Krull, remained standing by the bar, lost in a black mood.

"I've never seen him drinking so heavily," Oscar whispered to Viola, who was sitting next to him.

"Neither have I," she whispered back. "No one has seen Herr Krull drunk before."

After everyone finished the main course, the three women

cleared the dishes. They were in the kitchen when it happened, and it was so sudden that it left them all in shock. "Turn on the phonograph. I want to dance!" Herr Krull demanded in a hoarse, drunken voice. Oscar ran to obey his orders. He put on a record of the Hungarian *czardas* while the others carried the table to the window and rolled up the rug.

Lola timidly approached the soldier. "Herr Krull," she whispered, "if only you had forewarned us that you were coming alone, we would have invited one of the stunning new girls from across the hall."

Herr Krull stared at her through bloodshot eyes. "So what's holding you back? Call one over. Now."

Fear was mirrored in her little, buttonlike eyes. She checked her wristwatch nervously. "At this hour?"

"No one ever says no to Herr Krull! Go tell her to come over. Right now!" he bellowed, smashing the decanter of red wine against the wall.

"Certainly, of course. Certainly, Walter," Lola replied, and, trembling, she reluctantly started toward the door. Meanwhile, Theresa dropped to her knees and began mopping up the red liquid which had spilled between the rolled-up carpet and the wall.

I have no choice, Lola told herself with despair, as she knocked softly on the door. "It's me, Lola. Please come to the door."

In a split second we were all awake. "The window," we all mouthed silently to one another.

"Come on, Zsuzsi, open up. I need you!"

We looked at each other questioningly. I opened the door a crack. "What's the idea waking me at this hour? The baby kept me up for so long and I just fell asleep."

"Zsuzsi," she said sweetly. "It just occurred to me. We are having such a lovely party. Why not come over and join the fun?"

"Are you joking? I'm half asleep!" I said, starting to close the door. But Lola was fast, and she stuck her foot into the doorway. My eyes were now getting used to the dim light, and I was shocked to see despair etched on her face.

"I'll tell you the truth," she blurted out. "He's too important, and who would dare incur his wrath?"

"I'm confused, Lola. I don't understand what you're trying to tell me. If I'm not mistaken, and this is an invitation, then I'm sorry but I can't come now. I was here all evening and would have been delighted to come earlier. But not now!"

Tears formed in her eyes. "Zsuzsi, our friend is a very important man," she explained, "and he has had a falling-out with his girlfriend."

"Well!" I exclaimed. "I am not used to going to parties just to fill in for someone's missing lady. Now please take your foot away, Lola. I want to go back to sleep."

"I'll let you go back to sleep if that's still what you want to do after you hear his name," she retorted. "You know who he is? Herr Walter Krull!"*

"Herr Walter Krull?" I said, groping for words. I felt as if I was going to faint. This was the man whom Hitler had sent to Hungary to organize the deportation of the Jews.

"Oh, what distinguished friends you have," I commented, trying to sound natural. "Imagine, me meeting Herr Walter Krull in person!"

"I knew you'd sing a different tune if I told you. So this means you will come?" she asked in a tone that sounded more like a statement than a request.

"Wait a minute. Give me some time to get dressed. Come back in half an hour and I'll be ready."

"Bring your sister Anna, too, and the baby," she called back. "I'm sure Theresa will be delighted!"

The urgency of the moment overwhelmed me as I slammed the door after Lola left. I ran to the others with the hateful name of Walter Krull echoing back from every corner and nook of the room. My relatives regarded me with anxious

---

*Author's note: This is not his real name.

eyes. "Hurry!" Joska cried. "You are still wearing your robe, and we must go!"

It was only then that I realized that everyone was dressed, and all our worldly possessions, which we had just unpacked a week ago, were already stuffed back into our shopping bags.

"I'll help you get ready," Anna volunteered, pulling me into the other room. I was too dizzy to protest and she tugged my nightgown off. Within a few minutes, she managed to dress me. "She's ready," Anna whispered, buttoning my coat.

The window yielded noiselessly, thanks to my brother Lajos's foresight. He had oiled the hinges the minute we declared it "the escape route."

The cold air shocked me back to my senses and I realized that "first you" meant me. I stepped onto a little footstool, and carefully, so as not to make any noise, I climbed over the windowsill, landing in an alley illuminated by the milky predawn sky. Hardly aware that I had sunken knee-deep into the unbroken, white carpet of snow, I watched nervously as my husband lowered my little darling into my arms. Within seconds, he was standing next to me. We watched the rest of our gang climbing through the window. Then, as if from afar, came the sound of the window being closed. We stared at each other in a shocked stupor, too numb to move.

I can't recall how long it took for us to get there. I was only vaguely aware of having been in and out of streetcars. I also haven't the slightest idea how long I walked, my feet frozen and numb, my eyes blinded by the snow. I was oblivious to everything but our not losing sight of one another.

"Lovag Utca," I heard the conductor announce, and suddenly the house loomed before us.

"We will wait for you here," Iztvan said to me as he led us through a large hole in a wall and into a bombed-out house. For a fleeting moment we stood there shivering, bound together by a singular, unspoken fear: What if Karoly turns us away?

"First floor, first door," my husband reminded me, breaking the eerie silence.

"I won't be able to bear the suspense, Zsuzsi," Anna said, her voice quivering like a dying bird. "Please have mercy on us. Please come back quickly!"

"But...but...I can't move. Anna, I am deathly afraid!"

"Afraid?" my husband cried. "Oh, I don't ever want to hear that word again!"

"But...but...what if...?"

"If! Why! When!" he shouted. "People like us don't ask questions. Just trust in God and go."

My husband's confidence invigorated me, and I started walking toward the house, carrying my whimpering baby. "I know you are hungry," I whispered in her ear, "but just a little more patience and we'll be in Karoly *bacsi*'s house where it will be nice and warm." All the while, I imagined in vivid detail the terror I was about to inflict upon them by my nocturnal visit. I tiptoed up to the first door and tapped softly. I stood there shaking as somebody approached the door. "It's me," I breathed into the keyhole. "It's Zsuzsi."

The door opened a crack and Karoly's ashen face stared back at me. He seized my hand and unceremoniously pulled me inside the foyer. "Did anyone see you coming here?" His eyes were round and luminous with fear. I felt as limp as a rag doll and shook my head in a daze.

"Did everybody get away safely?"

"Thank God," I answered, adding, "I see you have gotten the point."

"Why else would you appear at my door at this hour of the night?"

In those few short moments, I heard the fear in his voice, telling me there might be trouble right here. "Is all well with you here?" I inquired. "Where is everyone?"

"Sleeping. Only I cannot seem to close my eyes. Oh, Zsuzsi," he cried, "this house is a Gehenna filled with Nazis!" He covered his eyes and began to sob. "A young man was shot dead here yesterday when they discovered that he was a Jew.

Oh, what an ordeal! They checked and rechecked our documents." Then he said with an expression of amusement and wonder on his face, "Can you believe it? We passed the test. But you must understand..." And he stopped speaking, as he choked back his tears and averted his gaze.

"Of course," I replied as I reached for the doorknob. I quickly fled the house in horror. "There is nowhere to go!" I mumbled to my family in a state of hysteria. "There is nowhere to go!"

"Do you mean to say that Karoly cannot accommodate us?" Iztvan asked, dumbfounded.

"A Jewish man was gunned down yesterday in that house!" I explained. "Karoly just told me. So what are we going to do?"

There was a long silence. Then Istvan declared decisively, "Why, we'll go back to Buda, of course."

"Go back to Buda?" I exclaimed. "After I told them that we were going to visit our parents for the holidays?" Then all at once, a new fear assailed me. "Erika," I cried passionately. "Anna. The mirror incident. It's impossible. Please, no. We can't go back."

55

"WELL DONE, LOLA," she congratulated herself smugly as she stepped into Theresa's apartment. She gave her friends a reassuring wink and walked up to the German. "Walter, she is coming. I will pick her up in about half an hour." Herr Krull did not respond. "Oh, Walter," Lola said sweetly, "at first she was reluctant to come, but you should have seen how her expression changed when I mentioned your name!"

The others began to laugh nervously. Lola looked closely at the recumbent figure and discovered that he was fast asleep. The beast! she thought to herself, hot tears forming in her eyes. I had to swallow my pride and grovel and beg her, and leave myself wide open to ridicule, all because of him! Angry and confused, she went to look for Theresa and found her sitting in the kitchen, exhausted from the events of the evening.

Theresa listened silently as Lola recounted the story and her current predicament. "I think you should go across the hall right now," Theresa advised her, "before the girls get all dressed up, and tell them not to come."

"No!" Lola cried fiercely. "I can't do it. Besides, it doesn't matter. I'm sure Zsuzsi will not come unless I pick her up."

"But what will you tell her tomorrow?"

"Well," Lola replied matter-of-factly, her voice now taking

on a more optimistic tone, "there is a saying: 'A rose speaks louder than words.' I'm sure a chunk of smoked ham speaks even louder."

Walter Krull awoke the next morning feeling refreshed and without the slightest hangover, and after properly thanking the hostess for her hospitality and the lovely party, he turned toward Lola. "Please tell your friends," he said, "that Walter Krull always remembers, and that he is looking forward to meeting them." He fished his car keys out of his vest pocket, and the next moment he was gone.

By seven o'clock, the men had left for work, leaving the two women alone in the house. Lola, armed with the side of smoked ham, strode confidently across the hall. "Zsuzsi!" she called. "It's me, Lola, bearing a peace offering." She waited a few seconds, and when there was no response, she added sweetly, "Be a good sport. Please don't be mad at me. Come on. Open that door and let's talk." When there was still no reply, she cursed softly and began to push the buzzer without letup.

"Theresa," she called from the hall. "Theresa, did you give them the spare key? You know, the one I used to keep hidden in the basement."

"No. It's in the shelter, hanging on the wall under the Fuehrer's picture."

Lola immediately headed for the shelter to get the key. She returned to the girls' door, more determined than ever to gain entrance. "Here I come," she shouted menacingly. "This is your last warning. If you don't answer, I will open the door myself." Silence greeted her, and she unlocked the door and marched inside.

To her utter surprise, there was not a sign of the girls. She ran into the bedroom. For a long minute she stood there mesmerized, unable to move, her eyes riveted to the stripped beds. From the corner of her eye she caught a glimpse of the half-open closet, where empty hangers taunted her without offering a clue. She began to scream hysterically, and she ran back to Theresa's house. Without a word of explanation, she pulled the startled woman by the hand and led her to the vacant apartment.

"They're gone!" Theresa exclaimed, horrified.

"They certainly are," Lola shouted as she began to rip open the drawers, looking for clues. A little paper bag landed soundlessly by her feet. She quickly lunged for it and gave it a vigorous shake. Tiny pieces of yellow cloth came fluttering out, landing on the rug. Both women looked at them, horror-struck.

"Yellow stars!" Lola cried.

"Yellow stars!" Theresa repeated, her face as white as a sheet. She bent down and started counting them out loud, "One, two, three, four, five. But there were only the two girls. Why five?" They looked at each other, puzzled. "Why did they have these?"

"There can be only one explanation," Lola said, more to herself than to her companion. "They're Jews!"

"Jews? How on earth could they be Jews?"

Their eyes locked for an instant, and then the women burst out laughing. "We, of all people, were harboring Jews!" Lola screamed with laughter. "And just think of it: me, setting up a date with Walter and Zsuzsi!"

Suddenly something clicked in Lola's mind, something so exciting that she had to clap her hands over her mouth so as not to cry out. "Sandor was right!" She began pacing the floor, her nerves raw, her heart racing a mile a minute. "Something is fishy about the girls you sold your condominium to," he had told her, "and it wouldn't surprise me a bit if they were of Jewish descent."

Lola had laughed it off. "According to you, brother dear, every stranger you meet is a Jew in hiding!"

"She'll be at the store tomorrow at four," he had said. "Come meet her."

"*This* girl? You dare suspect her?" she had retorted afterwards. "Why, she rather reminds me of our straight-nosed, blue-eyed German ancestors. What about her makes you think of those dark-eyed, olive-skinned, hook-nosed Semites?"

"It's not her looks," he had asserted heatedly, looking her straight in the eye, "but rather her words, how she phrased them. When she came to the store and asked for some cereal. 'Please,' she said, 'I have a six-month-old baby at home. It's not for me, but for my baby I ask.'"

"And what's so unusual about that? You make it sound as if only Jewish mothers feed their babies."

"Well, then, how shall I explain it? My friends and I used to go to the Keleti station to watch the trains transporting deportees through the city. The passengers would press their children's faces against the windows, screaming, 'Water! Water! Please, a drop of water. It's not for me. It is for my child.' I don't know what made them think that we would feel more sympathy for their offspring than for them."

"Nonsense." Lola had dismissed her brother's theory with a wave of her hand and she had never thought about it again. Now, however, she saw the whole incident in a new light. There is no doubt that they are Jews, she thought as she trembled with anticipation. Jews hiding out. I will hunt them down, and I surely won't leave one stone unturned until I find them, she vowed, her heart almost leaping out of her chest. It's not only my apartment I desire. It's more, much, much more. Why, if they can afford the grocery prices at my brother's store, they must be rich. They must be loaded! And Zsuzsi...she wears diamond earrings!

Then a new fear assailed her. How shall I handle Theresa, the only witness to their identity? she wondered. Theresa, with her unflinching loyalty to the Nazis, will be eager to do her patriotic duty and turn them in. How can I convince her not to report them before I get a chance to exploit them? Once I've extracted their riches, I don't care what happens to them. Andras will take care of them. Until then, I must somehow persuade her to remain silent. She let out a sigh of resignation. Well, if Theresa proves to be difficult, worse comes to worst, I'll simply have to offer her a share of the loot.

Suddenly Lola's train of thought was interrupted by Theresa's sobs. She ran to her. "Theresa, my dear, what's wrong?" she asked.

Theresa could only whisper, "The baby. My baby, what will become of her?"

So it's the baby, Lola thought with a mixture of satisfaction and delight. It won't be so hard after all to win her over. She'll never report them to the Party. Can I be so lucky that we share a common interest in shielding them, albeit for very different reasons? The thought danced within her mind. Then, putting a mask of surprise on her face, her eyes widened and she stared at Theresa. "Don't tell me you still care about them, knowing they are Jewish?" she asked, making her voice sound incredulous.

Theresa hid her face in her hands. "Yes, I'm afraid I do. I myself am astonished by my reaction, but I can't help it. Lola, please try to understand."

Fearful that her face would betray her joy, Lola looked down at the floor without speaking. As if deep in thought, she strolled over to the window and gazed out at the snowflakes fluttering down from a gray sky. How should I answer her? she asked herself. She laboriously brushed away some nonexistent lint from her skirt, thinking, This is the luckiest day of my life.

Theresa mistook her silence for refusal. She grabbed hold of Lola's hands. "This is all I ask of you," she implored her. "Don't tell. Please don't tell the men about ... about... about," she stammered, unable to bring herself to call the yellow star by its name. "You know, about the things we found," she finally blurted out.

"Well, my dear friend, this has to be the most difficult decision of my life," Lola began cunningly. "But I'll do it for you. Not only because you ask, but because I can't bear to see you suffering. You must understand that I do it with full knowledge that I am placing my future with the Party in your hands. You know as well as I do that shielding Jews is a crime against the nation and punishable by death."

"I know that this is a lot for me to ask of you," Theresa said, laughing and crying at the same time.

"But how could I say no to you when I am so indebted to you for all you've done for me, especially for introducing me to Andras and elevating me to the status of your elite, glamorous crowd?"

Theresa fell on Lola's shoulder. "I will ask Oscar to see to it that Andras gets a promotion at once," she whispered into her ear. "And rest assured, Lola, that even if the worst happens, I will swear on the Bible that I am the only one who knew."

Lola walked toward the door in a kind of drunken euphoria, gloating over this fortuitous turn of events and thinking, It's fortunate that she cannot see into my soul.

Theresa, her legs too weak to support her, remained slumped over in a chair. A thousand questions assailed her, demanding answers from her confused mind. Who were they? And, Lord in Heaven, where could those poor, frightened girls have gone? And what about the three extra sets of footprints in the snow under the window? Men's footprints, unmistakably men's! How on earth did the men learn that the girls were in trouble and needed help? A cry rose up in her throat, "And above all, is there a way I can find them? To assist them but...but without destroying Oscar — and myself — in the process?"

After hours of agonizing over the fate of the baby, sad at heart and drained of energy, she wearily placed her head on her arms at the dining-room table. Something moved under her arm and she absentmindedly picked it up. It was her string of rosary beads. She held them tightly, seeking comfort and strength from them. She started fingering the cold, shiny, black beads, offering a prayer for the two Jewish fugitive girls with the baby, who were hiding illegally from the authorities. She should have reported them to the police without delay, and offered to assist the authorities in every possible way, to help to capture them, to bring them to justice, to make sure the Jews, the *Jews* got what they deserved. But what do they deserve? And why do they deserve it? These questions plagued her, and then a terrible guilty feeling overcame her. How is it possible that this question never once arose in my mind all these years? Never once did I think of the horror, the pain, the injustice. And Zsuzsi, the poor, frightened mother, Zsuzsi...

The fire had long since gone out in the fireplace when Oscar arrived home to find his wife asleep by the table, her head resting on her folded arms.

"Theresa," he cried as he switched on the light. "Theresa, my dear, what's happened? What's wrong?"

Theresa lifted her head, her eyes red-rimmed in her pale face. "Darling," she mumbled, "I fell asleep and dreamed about you!"

"Oh," he said, rushing to her side and taking her hands in his own. "Your hands are freezing. There, there," he murmured, taking off his overcoat. "Let me bundle you up with this, and then I'll build a fire and bring you a cup of hot coffee." Soon the aroma of freshly brewed coffee filled the house, and Oscar returned to her side. "Drink it!" he ordered her, placing a mug in her hands. "It will warm you up." He sat opposite her, cradling his own cup in his hands.

They sat in silence for several minutes, both of them lost in their own thoughts. "Thank you, darling," Theresa finally said as she put her empty cup on the table.

She looks so pale, he thought, studying her face, but aloud he said, "And now, sweetheart, out with the dream!"

"Oh, it's really strange seeing you now," she said in a tremulous voice, rubbing her eyes. "It takes me time to sort out what is really happening and what is a dream. I dreamed of the time we first met. I could see myself at the Party meeting, sitting in the first row, gazing at the dashing officers stepping up on the platform. My heart skipped a beat. I racked my brain for a way to attract the attention of the guest speaker, without compromising myself in front of my friends. And then you unintentionally came to my rescue. You stood there tall and proud as you spoke, stealing my heart. 'Ladies and gentlemen,' you said, 'today's topic of discussion will be *Kristalnacht*.'

"It's funny," she said, managing a feeble smile, "but I could feel my hands become sore from applauding you, even in my dream. When the applause finally stopped, I heard myself asking naively, 'May I ask you, Aryan brother, what does *Kristalnacht* mean?'"

"And I will never forget how smitten I was by your radiant beauty. I remember thinking, That's how all Aryan girls should look! I talked only to you that night and I can recite every word I said. Want to hear?" he asked, straightening his shoulders and stepping up on an imaginary platform. "'*Kristalnacht*.' Well, the word *Kristal* means glass,'" he explained, gazing out at an imaginary audience. Then he turned to Theresa, who sat fidgeting in her chair, her face as pale as a mask of death. I hope she is not sick, he thought briefly. Nevertheless, he continued his speech. "'It happened in Germany...It will happen here, too. That will be the night of the glory of glories,'" he said, his voice dropping to a whisper. "'The police will secretly give us the signal, assuring us that they will look the other way, and we will force ourselves into Jewish homes and shops, breaking in through the doors and windows. The Jew and his property will be free to all!'"

Theresa jumped up as if bitten by a viper. "Stop! Stop! Stop!" she screamed, running from the room.

"I cannot stand your strange behavior!" Oscar cried, restraining his wife. "You must tell me what is going on!"

Theresa managed a shaky whisper. "I have found out today that our next-door neighbors are Jews!"

Tremendous relief flooded Oscar's entire being. She has nothing against me, after all, he said to himself. "Rest easy, my little patriot," he reassured her as he stroked her disheveled, golden tresses. "Big papa will take care of that."

A heartrending cry escaped from Theresa's lips. "No, no, no!" she screamed. "I don't want them to be harmed. I don't want them to be reported. If anything, anything should happen to the baby," she cried, crossing her chest, "may the good Lord forgive my sin, I will take my own life!"

Oscar stepped back and stared at her, wide-eyed with horror. "Don't tell me you still care for that brat, knowing she is a Jew?"

"Yes, Oscar," Theresa wept, "a hundred times yes, and you must help!"

"Why?" he asked, more astounded than angry. "Tell me, why must I help?"

"Because I love that child. She is the image of the children I have dreamed of having, but who have been denied to me by fate. Oh, Oscar, I love her with all the maternal love in me, which I would bestow on our own offspring."

Oscar didn't reply. He walked over to the fireplace, picked up a few pieces of firewood and tossed them into the hearth. He stood very straight, gazing into the flames, his back to her. The vision of a long-forgotten episode sprang into his mind.

They had just bought the condominium. Yes, this is the very spot where I was standing right after our wedding, he recalled, and I was talking about my ambitions, how far up in rank I could rise in the Party. And Theresa, her face flushed and her eyes shining, had said, "Darling, my only ambition, my greatest wish in life, is to have a half-dozen healthy and beautiful daughters and sons."

"Oh, Oscar," he heard her pleading now, "can you forgive them for their Jewishness? Can't you find the love in your heart?"

I reached my goal and far surpassed my wildest dreams, Oscar concluded silently. But my poor darling Theresa did not: there are no sons, no daughters for her — for *us*.

He was still standing with his back to Theresa, when she cried out, "You promised, you promised!"

Not knowing how to handle the situation, Oscar remained silent.

A fire burned in Theresa's eyes. "You promised!" she cried into his ears. "Here, recognize your own words: 'If you love somebody really and truly, then you love her family, and her friends become your friends. You love the house she lives in, the stones she walks on. Do I need to tell you, Theresa — I love whoever you love.'"

Suddenly there was a sharp knock at the door. It was the shoemaker delivering two pairs of priceless leather boots, a Christmas present for Theresa's two oldest nephews. Oscar took out his wallet, and, without flinching, paid an exhorbitant amount of pengos for the boots. Still stalling for time to commit himself, he held the shining, black boots before Theresa's eyes. "Can you imagine how proud the boys will be, showing these off to their friends?" he asked. "How grateful they will be for them."

"Yes," she said thoughtfully, her beautiful face bathed in love. "They are so good and pure, and, in our folly, we think we are the ones who mold the children's characters, when actually, it took a six-month-old baby to teach me that the opposite is true. Oh, Oscar, it was little Zsuzsi who made me realize the awful difference between individual Jews and all the masses thrown together under the same label, 'Jews.' Oscar," she said with tears running down her face, "I've found out, after so many years of being indifferent to their plight, that they are human beings with the same human needs as you and I. Oh, darling, if only...if only..." and her words were lost in a torrent of sobs.

56

Put not your trust in noblemen
Nor in the son of man, in whom there is no help!
Psalms 146:3

I SAT ON snow-covered debris in a gutted house, my family forming a circle around me to protect my baby from the icy draft as I nursed her. The howling wind raced through the broken windowpanes, snatching the words from our lips as we spoke them and making it virtually impossible to communicate among ourselves.

All at once, Joska shouted, "A plague! A plague!"

"What are you talking about?" I yelled at the top of my lungs, trying hard to make myself heard.

He approached me, then he bent down and cried directly into my ear, "A plague! You can invent one, of course! As far as I'm concerned," he added with a wave of his hand, "you may call it bubonic or black death. Take your pick."

I gazed at him, too stunned to answer.

"I don't understand what difference it makes," he said, frowning, "as long as you can convince that bunch of Nazis in Buda that it was a sudden outbreak of some kind of contagious disease that made us pack our bags and return to the house."

The others nodded their approval. Then my husband said

with great urgency, "We can make up the story on the way. Let's get out of here before we all get frostbite!"

"One more thing," Joska shouted. "I think I should become a ghost, at least upon our arrival, until we make sure that Lasi is still in the hospital, or, preferably, buried by now."

Harsh gusts of wind blew at my face, destroying any remaining opposition I had to their plan. I no longer cared what happened. I was bone-weary. "It's no use," I said, shivering with cold. "We can't stay here and we really shouldn't go back there, but if that's what all of you insist upon doing, then let's start moving."

We made our way to the bus stop in the howling wind. Within minutes, a bus arrived and we boarded. Crazed with fright, I tore open my coat to check on my baby, who was pressed tightly against me. I was in a state of perpetual panic, always wondering whether enough air was reaching her to keep her alive without the icy, north wind snuffing out her breath. I thought enviously of the kangaroo with its God-given pouch.

Disregarding our strict rules, Anna sat down on the empty seat beside me. She reached out to hold the baby's hand. "She's warm as toast," she whispered. "I'll be back. Just let me pass the information on to her papa." The next minute she was back. "Please don't send me away from you, Zsuzsi. I won't obey. I must have someone to talk to. Someone once told me," she continued in a melancholy voice, "'Be very careful with your wishes, for they may come true.' I never told you, Zsuzsi, how hard it was for me to walk away from the Dombalya Utca house. Oh, how I longed to run right back."

"You, too?" I replied, gazing at my sister. My disappointment was evident. "Then I know how you feel about going back," I added, feeling even more drained of energy.

"But your husband," she sighed with a trace of wonder in her tone. "Never before have I known a person with such undying faith."

Anna's remark reminded me of something Iztvan once

said: "It's easy to make a choice when there really is none. For when every road leads to a dead end, when every door in the world is locked, but we know about a seldom-used back road leading to a house to which we have the keys, then this is a clear sign that God wants us to be there. This must be the house from where He will free us, as He had decreed it from the very start."

But a disturbing thought stole into my mind, and I could not dismiss it. Will this house be the one we will emerge from free and unharmed, I wondered, or are we perhaps being lured there to meet our end?

As we alighted from the bus, we gazed out upon the vast snowfields, awestruck, for the raging storm had ceased, leaving behind it a white, picturesque, peaceful landscape.

"Look over there," Iztvan cried excitedly, pointing toward the distant horizon, which disappeared behind snow drifts in back of the house. "We're in luck! With all the snow swept behind the building, there is not a trace of it left to leave our footprints in while we walk toward the house!"

All I could think of was that not quite a thousand feet separated us from the formidable dwelling.

Anna tugged at my hand. "Zsuzsi," she said anxiously, "we must decide now. We must choose which lie sounds best."

"Anna, what can I say? I am utterly cold and tired. My mind is a blank."

"Well, snap out of it! We must do our homework. Can't you see we're almost there?"

The urgency of her voice shocked me to my senses. "All right," I said, trembling. "All right, then, let's talk."

"Any suggestions?" Iztvan asked.

We searched one another's eyes for an answer.

"Maybe we should go along with Joska's idea," I said. "I surely can't think of anything better."

"Scarlet fever then!" Anna exclaimed, letting out a long breath.

"Agreed!" we replied in unison, somewhat relieved.

"Anna is right!" I said decisively. "For even though the sickness is not always disabling, its victims are kept in a quarantine center for thirty days. It's enough to give people goosebumps even if one mentions it casually."

"Rifky," Anna said softly. "Remember Rifky, our niece?"

"How can I forget?" I replied. "I can still see how pathetic and forlorn she looked, standing there behind the window grate, her blond, tangled hair falling down over her scarlet-red face as she stretched out her little arms crying, 'Mommy! Mommy! Please take me home!' I still shudder, thinking about the trauma of tearing ourselves away from her when visiting hours ended. I can hear her bewildered cries ringing in my ears."

"And yet, Zsuzsi, oh, Zsuzsi, what we would give if only she were there now, with the promise of going home to her parents after those miserable thirty days of quarantine ended." And we both stood there weeping over the beautiful little girl.

I wasn't aware that Joska was watching us until I felt a hand on my shoulder. "We can't afford the luxury of tears with such pressing problems on our hands," he said angrily. Now calm down, Anna, and let me tell you a fairy tale to cheer you up. Once upon a time, in a faraway land called Szombathey, there lived a very learned and beloved Rabbi, his beautiful wife, and their large brood of kids. Do you know what this worthy woman did?"

"He is crazy," cried Anna, backing away from him, her eyes wide with horror.

"That's all we need now," I murmured, feeling ill.

"And do you know what this wonderful woman did?" Joska continued. "She hired Ilonka *neni*, the washerwoman, to do the laundry. You remember Ilonka *neni*, don't you?" His tone became deadly serious.

"Of course," I said.

"I assume you also remember her little girl, whom she took along with her to work?"

"Marta," Anna and I said together.

"Joska! What does all this have to do with us now?" Anna cried.

"Ah, but can't you see what a perfect candidate she is?"

"A candidate?" Anna asked haltingly. "A candidate for what?"

Joska shot a sidelong glance in her direction. "Think," he answered sharply. "Use your head!"

"You mean...you mean to make her the sick child whose illness caused us to panic and leave the town?"

"That's right."

"Iztvan! Oh, Iztvan," I exclaimed excitedly to my husband, who was walking toward us with my brother Lajos. "You must hear the brillant idea Joska just came up with!"

"The problem is solved," Anna declared. "We have the child. Imagine, someone we know from childhood, eliminating the need for our making up names, birthdays and such," she said, much relieved.

A murmur of approval escaped from our lips, and the overcast whiteness illuminated our impatient faces.

"Say that Mama discovered the rash on little Marta's face," Lajos advised us. "and to add credibility to your story, Zsuzsi, say that you and Anna watched while the van came to take her away to the quarantine center."

"Let me say something, too," Anna interjected. "We should also inform them right then and there that the medics told us this was not an isolated case of scarlet fever, but that it was actually the sixth such case reported since Saturday, when the epidemic first struck the town."

"Numbers are very important," Iztvan asserted. "If one of you says six cases, then both of you had better stick with the same number. Agree upon the important points and don't run into the danger of contradicting one another. Now you must decide when you left the town, and find answers to any other questions likely to crop up."

"We're almost there," Anna said, turning as white as the snow. "Why do we have to go through with all this?" she asked breathlessly, as she wiped tears from her eyes with the back of her hand. "Tell me, Zsuzsi, why did we have to leave here in the first place, if it was only to come running back?"

"Anna," I cried, gasping for breath, "Anna, I feel as though a hundred-pound weight has just been lifted from my shoulders. Oh, Anna, I see it clearly now. I am sure there is a reason for our coming back here. There is a reason hidden from our eyes!"

"You mean, as your husband says, that we must go back to Buda because that is where God wants to free us from?"

"Yes, Anna, yes. But please don't interrupt. Please let me talk. Let me get this off my chest. Oh, Anna, if you only knew how much I suffered, but now I see everything in an entirely different light. It was destiny, Anna. I never told you for fear you wouldn't understand, but there was much more to Karoly finding me crying in the vestibule, after Mrs. Teleki grabbed the money out of my hands and threw me out of her house. You have no idea how much I am still suffering and how many times I've begged for forgiveness for the folly I committed in a moment of despair when I no longer cared. Imagine, my endangering the lives of my husband and unborn child.

"But when Mrs. Teleki reneged on her promise to bring you out of the ghetto, and I knew that the ghetto was about to be evacuated, that was the last straw. It was as if I lost my mind. All the fight went out of me. All I craved was peace, yes, peace, peace forever. And then, precisely during this moment of vulnerability, I felt a hand on my shoulder. I turned my head and there stood the stranger. Thinking he was a Nazi, I blurted out to him what happened. I even told him my name and address. A form of suicide, the ultimate sin of the Jew." I looked up and gazed directly at my sister. "Yes, it was destiny. I can say it now, Anna. It was God's will that I said what I did to the stranger, because God knew that the stranger would have pity in his heart!"

Anna's green eyes opened wide and it seemed as if fire danced within them. "I kept something from you, as well, because I thought that *you* would not understand. I never wanted to leave the ghetto. I didn't want to leave Aunt Brandl during that hour of despair, no matter how much our sister Nechy begged me to leave. Then the stranger said calmly, 'Your sister is heavy with child and needs your help.'" Tears came rolling down her cheeks as she recalled the incident. "Zsuzsi," she murmured, "Karoly is no ordinary man. I think...I think he is a *tzaddik*."

57

> To shoot the innocent man in secret;
> Suddenly do they shoot at him, and fear not.
> *Psalms 64:5*

I STOPPED IN FRONT of the house, my heart throbbing, my legs about to buckle under me. Slowly, I opened the door. Silence greeted me in the dark, deserted hallway, and I nodded to the men, who then came following me on tiptoe, carrying their shoes in their hands.

"Here comes the hardest test," Anna whispered to me as we stopped on the first landing, our eyes riveted to the shadowy creatures ascending the stairs, silhouetted against the wall. Finally our ears picked up the sound of a door upstairs being opened quietly and then closed a moment later. Silence again. Anna and I remained motionless, our feet rooted to the floor. After waiting a considerable length of time, we heard no further movements in the house. We exhaled and fell upon each other's shoulders. "Thank God, the worst is over," I murmured gratefully.

Monika, who had been alerted to our arrival, was waiting for us behind the door to our apartment when we arrived. "Monika, you will never believe what we've been through," I said, sobbing with relief. "It was terrifying! Thank God we made it back here safely."

But Monika was not at all interested in our story. "Are you sure no one saw you turning toward the path?" she asked, her voice cold and flat.

I gazed at her, suddenly feeling unwelcome and utterly let down, and I tried again to make my point. "It was a miracle that we escaped. Oh, Monika, we were almost caught by the Nazis."

Without saying a word, Monika turned and hurried back to the window, where her husband and brother were taking turns looking out into the white night. The three of them began animatedly discussing something, completely disregarding our presence.

Abruptly, Uncle Yidel stood up and indicated to us that we should follow him into the kitchen. We immediately understood that he had something of great importance to say, for he was leading us to the only place in the house not connected by a wall to our neighbors' apartment.

Uncle Yidel sat down in a chair and stared at us for several moments without speaking. Then he began. "Monika believes we should not tell you," he whispered so softly that I had to strain my ears to hear him. "I must know," he said anxiously, "are you sure nobody saw you turn into the path?"

"One more word about this and I'll scream," I exclaimed. "How many times do we have to tell you? No! Absolutely not!"

"Zsuzsi, you must understand," he said calmly. "We are simply afraid. Only for this reason do I ask." He paused for a moment, and then the words came pouring out. "Iche and Geza were recognized by someone from our hometown just a block away from here, right before they would have turned onto this path!"

"Did they escape?" we asked, stunned by the news.

Uncle Yidel buried his face in his hands, and his voice came out in broken sobs. "No. The man was armed...an SS soldier. Poor boys. They didn't stand a chance. And they were almost here," he cried.

His words were followed by frozen silence.

"But only almost," he continued in hushed tones, "and

almost has no place in this life. Either you make it or you don't!"

"I can't believe it," I sobbed. "You are lying!"

Anna shook her head in disbelief, unable to utter a word. Suddenly the siren rang out and the house reverberated with the sound of footsteps.

I was stunned over the tragic loss of our beloved friends, which not only shocked me but intensified my distrust and fear of the Nazis we were about to face in the shelter. I walked toward the door with my baby and Anna. Uncle Yidel is right, I said to myself. Either you survive or you don't.

As I entered the shelter I collided with the old lady. "Zsuzsi!" she shrieked, and white as a sheet and visibly shaken, she immediately sank into her chair.

Ersabet was next to me in an instant. "When did you come back?"

Suddenly the room became very noisy, as everyone tried to outyell the others. "Why did you come back?" they all asked. I then told them our story in as calm a voice as I could manage.

Ersabet grabbed my hand. "Where is your brother Joska?" she demanded.

Hate engulfed me as I thought, *You* are asking me? You, of all people! He had to become a ghost for fear of your anti-Semitic son! I stared at her mutely as chills ran up and down my spine.

Anna found her voice first. "Oh, Joska?" she said casually, with a shrug of her shoulders. "He discovered the joys of being Mama's baby. I doubt that he will ever give it up."

Everyone burst out laughing. Then Ersabet pointed to her son. "He came home just a fortnight ago," she said, "and he was so disappointed that Joska wasn't here. They needed his hospital bed," she explained, "so they sent him home to recuperate."

"I am sorry," the lad replied faintly. "I was looking ver-ry much...uh...very much forward to his company."

By this time Maria had confronted Anna. She let out an

ear-shattering shriek. "Scarlet fever! Get away from me! Don't come near my baby!" Maria's face was white with fear. "Scarlet fever!" she shouted over and over, like a madwoman.

Then something happened. Something so familiar, a gesture I understood so well. Maria's trembling hands tightened protectively around the tiny little bundle in her arms as she pressed her infant to her chest. And, obeying an instinctive impulse to comfort her, I opened my mouth to speak. I wanted to cry out, "Maria, don't be frightened. It's not true. This story of scarlet fever is nonsense. We just made it up in order to protect ourselves."

Mr. Horvat, unintentionally, came to my rescue. "For the sake of peace, Zsuzsi, we will have to relocate you to the furthest corner of the shelter." Then, with a glint in his eyes he said quietly, "It's only Maria. She always blows things out of proportion. Remember what a laughingstock she made of herself over the incident with the mirrors? In a day or two she will relent and be ashamed, but now there is no use in making an issue of it."

"I don't care where I sit," I said, "as long as I can throw myself into a chair and get a little sleep. I haven't closed my eyes in the past twenty-four hours." I sank gratefully into the chair Mr. Horvat brought over for me.

Then, turning to my sister, he said, "Come, I'll help you move over there."

I sat there in a kind of a daze. My head was pounding as I watched my sister and Mr. Horvat carry over our belongings. Anna pulled two chairs between ours, and Mr. Horvat brought my bedroom dresser drawer and mounted it on top of the chairs. Bending over the baby as I lay her down, he cooed, "A wee little bed for a wee little girl." He turned to me and said in a fatherly tone, "I know how you feel being isolated here, but as I told you, probably in a day or two you can come back to your regular place."

"You are a fine man, Mr. Horvat," I managed to say, struggling to keep my eyes open.

I do not remember falling asleep, and I had no idea where I was when I awoke. My gaze rested upon the clock on the opposite wall, which was illuminated by a single light bulb wrapped in a dark cloth. That clock, which I had consulted so many times in the past, shocked me back to the present. The horrors of the past day had flooded my dreams during my brief, fitful sleep, but now, as I looked around at the familiar surroundings, I remembered that we had returned safely to the Dombalya Utca.

The baby stirred in her sleep. Bending over close to her, I whispered, "You and I are so lucky to be away from Theresa *neni*. She acted as if she were your mother, my darling, as if you weren't mine. Yes, that's how she made me feel. Oh, how terrifying it was!"

Suddenly, a faint, round circle of light appeared on the floor. By this time my eyes had grown accustomed to the darkness, and I could discern that it was the old lady carrying a flashlight. She stopped near Ersabet and tapped her on the shoulder, waking her up. She showed her an empty pillbox, and I understood that she was going upstairs to get her medication. Soon the circle of light disappeared from view, and the old lady was gone.

Jealousy and hatred assailed me. Oh, how different life is for her, I thought. She and her entire family are safely ensconced in the shelter, and she can come and go as she pleases, while I, whose family is compelled to sit out the raid unprotected, die a thousand deaths with each bomb blast. I felt like weeping, and yet I knew I had to be one of the last ones to leave the shelter, in order not to arouse their suspicions. Will I ever be able to live as she does? I wondered, choking back the tears. Will we ever be free?

When the air raid was over and we were able to escape the dark, dingy shelter, I was surprised to find that the sun was shining. And the realization dawned on me that the sun shines for me just as it does for everyone else. Happiness flooded me. This night of horror was behind us, and a prayer of thanks arose in my heart. Once more the good Lord had given us strength and wisdom.

"Anna," I whispered into my sister's ear, "we lived to see the morning! Perhaps this is not merely a new day, but a new beginning as well."

The atmosphere upstairs was heavy with anticipation. The ghosts looked at us, their eyes wide with fear. "How bad was it?"

"It was just fine," Anna said. "We have already become very adept at lying. Oh, if you had only seen the panic we created, you would have all had a good laugh."

They breathed a simultaneous sigh of relief, and their grim faces relaxed as if an unseen hand had suddenly erased all their cares.

"So it worked!" Joska marveled with barely concealed pride, and then burst out laughing.

"Let me tell you what Maria said," Monika laughed "and I'll leave it to your imagination to picture how she looked. 'No, no,' she shrieked. 'Don't come near me, and keep away from my son!'"

"How do you like that?!" Joska exclaimed, grinning from ear to ear.

Then the impossible happened, a thing which had never before happened in this room. The walls echoed our laughter from all four corners: "Ha, ha, ha! Ha, ha, ha!"

"Anna," I cried, smitten with fear as I looked at her white face. "Anna, what is wrong?"

Just as suddenly as it had come, the laughter froze on everybody's lips, and at that moment our brief carelessness ceased. The smell of impending danger hit our nostrils.

"No, no," my sister shook her head vigorously in protest. "No, nothing happened. Please relax. It's only me. I know it's silly but something just occurred to me." She spoke quickly now. "We were taught that lying is a sin and that 'the best of all lies in the world is the plain, old-fashioned truth.' Yet, we keep fabricating lie after lie, and what frightens me most is that we tell them looking straight into their eyes without flinching."

Hearty laughter followed Anna's words. "When you are summoned before the Golden Throne in the hereafter to answer for this particular sin," Joska remarked with a bitter chuckle, "remember that you will not be punished, but commended for your deeds."

"Oh, stop!" Monika cried, agitated. "I am not interested in your soul-searching. I have a much more pressing problem. It's the old lady. As soon as you left the house, she started pestering me, trying to start a conversation with me. It became a real challenge just to avoid her overtures. I don't know," she said in a low voice, "but I have the spooky feeling that she smells something. I am in mortal fear of her. She's not just a nosy old thing; she's brilliant and shrewd."

"Well, well, my dear," her husband Meir said, "I think she has met her match in you. You should have heard how Monika shook off the old lady when she came to our door one morning," he told us.

"That was her last attempt," Monika said fiercely, "and also the last straw for me. I answered the door, and there she was with a heavy sweater wrapped over her arm. 'Monika, I hope that it's not too much to ask of you. Please send this sweater together with your Christmas present to the fighting men at the front.'

"I responded coldly. 'And what's wrong with your daughter-in-law? Why can't Ersabet deliver it? Is she sick or something?' I gave her the army address, just to show her that I knew it by heart — I used to bring packages to the Army when I was staying in that Home — and then I slammed the door in her face.

"Nevertheless, the minute she left, I ran out to buy a Christmas tree, because I suspected that she was searching the corners of our room. The only thing they talked about in the shelter was Christmas, the coming of Christmas, and how to decorate their trees. And since we're on the subject, everyone keeps their tree in the front hall. Please Meir, help Yidel bring out the tree."

The next day brought gray skies and more snow. Anna's and Monika's faces were red from the cold as they burst into the house after their shopping trip. There was a happy sparkle in Anna's eyes as she showed off the generous amount of bread in her bag. "Not only that, but what a welcome I received in the store!"

"Yes, we got the 'white carpet' treatment," Monika added, pointing to the snowy field outside.

Just then, Uncle Yidel announced from his post at the window, "A stranger, a man, just turned into our path."

Monika leaped to the window and pushed her brother away from the spot. "To me it looks like a woman. Positively a woman, not a man. What do you say, Anna?" she asked, motioning her to the window.

Anna stood there for a long while. Even though her back was to me, I knew instinctively that the stranger meant trouble. Anna gripped the windowsill and fell against the pane with such force that her head nearly broke the glass. I began to shake even before she turned around, and I saw the ghastly expression on her face. When she spoke, her voice possessed the unnatural calm of profound terror. "It's Lola."

"Help!" I cried, feeling faint. "Take the baby from me. I can't hold her."

Iztvan ran to my side and took the baby out of my arms. "Lola?" he asked, pale as a ghost. "Is anyone with her?"

"She's alone," Anna replied, "but what difference does it make? I always had the feeling that she was the Angel of Death."

"Are you sure she's alone?" Iztvan repeated, his voice hoarse.

"Yes, yes."

"Good. Then we will take her prisoner, gag her and decide what to do with her later."

"No, no, no," I protested. "I don't want her to know about any of you being here. We have to be absolutely sure that neither Sandor nor Andras is coming to pick her up. As long as nobody knows about your presence here you still have a chance. Anna, you and Monika also hide under the bed."

"All right. It makes sense," Monika said obligingly, and she urged Anna to follow.

"Oh, be quiet," Anna snapped from the window. "I'm staying. Now get out of sight. She's almost at the front door."

The tension in the room was unbearable. "She won't leave here on her own two feet," Lajos vowed.

"We must take her by surprise, before she has time to make any noise," Iztvan advised us. "We must decide upon a code word to let us know when she's facing away from the bed."

"A code word. Fast," they demanded nervously before they disappeared under the bed.

"Don't worry," I said, adjusting the bedspread. "Relax. You'll be fine."

Then, something moved under the dustruffle, and Uncle Yidel appeared on the floor at the edge of the bed, huffing and puffing. Fear was written all over his face. "We can't see a thing from under here," he said through chattering teeth. "How will we know when the time is right?"

"A cue! Give us a cue! A password. Anything, anything, fast!"

From the corner of my eye I saw Anna clamp her hand across her mouth as a muffled cry escaped her lips. "I almost forgot," she said, and, racing across the room, she began hurling our clothes off the shelves, virtually throwing them into Yidel's startled face on the floor. "This is to stuff her mouth with," she said breathlessly.

Uncle Yidel's voice was cold and demanding. "Cue us!"

"I just heard the front door slam," Iztvan cried anxiously. "She's inside the building!"

"You'll know," I stammered, "you'll know when...when I say...your cue will be...it will be..."

"What?" my husband pressed me impatiently.

"Oh, I will say, yes, yes, I will say, 'Did you tell your husband you were coming here?'"

There was a brief and hurried exchange of words under the bed, and then I heard, "Agreed!"

I sucked in my breath and opened the door a crack to make sure that Lola wouldn't ring the wrong bell. "Oh, Lola," I greeted her cheerfully, trying to act natural and feigning surprise. "Welcome, Lola, welcome. Please come in."

"Lola! Did I hear right?" my sister cried, flying toward us and extending a hand.

Lola shot her an icy gaze, tilted her head up, and, with a haughty air, ignored her hand.

I remained staring at her, motionless, as if my feet had sunken into the earth. There was a brief silence between us, during which she regarded me through heavily lidded eyes. Then her eyes lit up, her mouth twisted into a grotesque smile and she spat a single word at me: "Jew!"

"Jew?" I cried indignantly. "Me, a Jew? You dare to call me a Jew?"

"Here, look at our papers!" Anna said brazenly, holding out her documents for Lola to see.

A broad smile appeared on Lola's smug face. "Credentials! Humph! Such official papers." She dismissed them with a shrug of her shoulders, and turned her head away from us.

"You're being very strange, Lola," I said in a small voice. I walked right up to her and looked directly into her eyes. "Tell me, Lola, what is this all about?"

"Why waste time?" she answered, and she held out a small brown bag.

My heart skipped a beat, and the very house seemed to sink beneath my quivering legs. "I don't know what you are implying, Lola," I said softly. "I don't know what this bag has to do with me!"

"Such a short memory you have. What a pity that you are so forgetful. Indeed, what a great pity. Perhaps I should refresh your memory," she continued, a shadow of triumph crossing her features. Before I knew what was happening, she ripped open the bag right over my head. One yellow star landed on my shoulder. "Just where it belongs," she sneered.

Paralyzed with fear, I stood there mutely, saying nothing.

"I am waiting," she taunted me. "Say something, or is your tongue stuck to the roof of your mouth?"

"Get out of here!" I whispered. "Right now!"

Without a moment's hesitation, she marched right into the apartment. I followed her as she moved about the room, watching her every move. She brazenly inspected every item, as if she were previewing a public auction. What frightened me most was that she didn't make the slightest effort to conceal her intentions. Suddenly, I realized that there was no hatred in Lola's eyes, only greed — fierce, all-consuming greed. And I knew that we were doomed, that she would stop at nothing to get what she wanted. My hands clenched into fists, and, fighting the urge to tear her to pieces right on the spot, I said in a small voice, "Level with me, Lola. Tell me what you want."

"Why," she answered, matter-of-factly, "everything, of course."

I stared at her, half-crazed with fear, trying to think of a way to steer her to the spot near the bed.

Anna tapped me on the shoulder. I noticed a flicker of impatience in her eyes. "Zsuzsi," she said in a mock whisper which could be heard for a mile. "Zsuzsi, your earrings. Quick, quick, take them off. Give them to me. Let me flush them down the toilet!" As she spoke, she pointed her finger toward the alcove behind Lola's back.

"Give me those earrings," Lola shrieked, livid with anger. "Don't you play tricks on me! Don't you dare!" She lunged for me, but I managed to escape her grasp. As she began to chase me, I maneuvered myself near the bed.

"Zsuzsi, this is the last thing we have from Mama, and you know it was a present from Papa to her!"

"I'll never give them to you, Lola, never!" I screamed as we ran around the bed. Then Anna signaled to me that Lola was at the designated spot. Sweat enveloped me from head to toe, and chills ran up and down my spine. I summoned all my strength and blurted out, "Your husband knows you came here?"

Ignoring my question, she snarled, "Give them to me!"

From the corner of my eye, I noticed the dustruffle fluttering and saw fingers inching out. Then, through a haze of confusion, I heard Lola say, "I have to go now. Come on, hurry up. My husband is waiting for me at Salasy's headquarters on Kor Utca." She grabbed the earrings from my hand and walked toward the window to inspect them in the light.

"She thinks they're worth a king's ransom, the swine," Anna whispered. Then, with an involuntary movement, Anna's hand shot up to her temple. "Oh, Zsuzsi, it just dawned on me. Those earrings are not the last things we have from Mama. No, Zsuzsi, they're not. Not while we still have her gift of gifts, not while we still have our life! Let's fight for it, Zsuzsi!" she declared, her eyes ablaze. "We must carry the torch and pass it down. This chain must never be broken!"

Then everything seemed to happen at once. My baby awoke from her nap, with a loud, happy gurgle, bringing me out of my state of panic. A horrifying picture flashed into my mind: SS men tearing her from my arms. I could hear the ice cracking on the River Danube....

Do something! Kill her! Don't let her get away! every atom in me cried, and then a newly-found strength surged within me. "Lola," I said calmly, grabbing her wet fur coat out of her hand and tossing it to Anna, "Lola, I have something of great importance to say." Then I pushed her roughly into a chair.

She remained seated for an instant, toying with her wristwatch. Then her mouth dropped open and she started to rise out of her chair. She looked at my face and all the blood drained from her cheeks, and she fell back, limp as a rag doll. For an instant, I thought she was going to faint. "Is it really four o'clock?" she shrieked suddenly, jumping to her feet again. "I must go!"

"All I'm asking for, Lola, is five minutes of your time," I told her with an air of authority. "This might turn out to be the most lucrative five minutes of your life."

I pointed to the snow-covered meadow beyond our window. My lips parted to speak, but my mind was completely blank. Then the words began to pour from my mouth:

"The Allied forces are around the corner and they will liberate us. It could be today. It could be tomorrow. Nobody can predict exactly when, but one thing is clear: Hitler and his followers' days are numbered. Hear, they are numbered. And so are yours. There were twenty-one of us, Lola, for your information. Nine couples, Anna, me and this child who went into hiding. And do you know what we did? Well, I'll tell you what we did. We went into the temple. We went there together. All twenty of us. To take an oath. A solemn oath. 'Whoever survives this nightmare, whoever remains alive, will be bound by the sacred duty to hound down and bring to justice those who murdered our brethren.' And do you know what else we did? Well, I'll tell you. We pricked our fingers with a needle and we each squeezed a drop of blood into a thimble. And dipping a pen into the blood, we signed our holy pact. Then we tore it to shreds and tossed it to the wind. Nobody knows the others' hiding places, for fear of your infamous torture tactics for extracting information. But we agreed to meet here, exactly a week after the liberation, and then, Lola, you will die a terrible death. And your death will be a poor exchange for ours, for we are already dead, dead in our souls. But Lola, you will die when the war is over, when this hideous bombing ends, and peace follows. Peace, glorious peace. When spring will come, and the acacia trees will blossom, and you will have everything to live for. It's your decision, Lola. It's all in your hands. Unless, of course, unless..." Out of breath, I was unable to continue.

A hushed silence descended upon the room. Abruptly, Lola jumped up as if shot from a cannon. "Give me my coat," she shrieked.

Anna rose slowly. She seemed dazed, too weak to stand, and she steadied herself against the arm of the chair. She made her way to the kitchen and returned, dragging Lola's coat behind her.

"Don't you dare sweep your dirty floor with my coat," Lola snarled, and, purple with rage, she grabbed the wet fur from my sister. There was murder in the small, hooded eyes. Spitting anti-Semitic slogans at Anna and me, she ran out the door.

I remained standing there, hypnotized by fear, staring at the door while Anna went to the window. Both of us were consumed by a single thought: Will she go to Mr. Horvat to report us?

After a seemingly endless period of time, a cry came forth from my sister's lips. "She's out of the house!" There was wonder in her voice. Gone was Anna's weary expression of a moment ago; her face was shining with triumph now. With a great leap she was next to the bed. "It's safe," she whispered, throwing herself to the floor. "Come on, everybody out!"

Monika emerged from the armoire. "Bravo!" she exclaimed, squeezing my hand. They all crowded around me. My husband's face was a mask of gray clay, but the brown eyes boring into my own were intensely alive. "Do you think she believed that rubbish? Do you think it frightened her at all?"

How should I know? I thought in bewilderment. I could not remember a single word I had said to Lola, although my family recalled my speech verbatim. How should I know if she was afraid or if she was simply angry? But I had detected a telltale pulse throbbing at her temple and also her desperate attempt to hide the slight trembling in her hands.

"Say something," my husband prodded me, "anything! Don't just look at me like that."

But my mind remained blank and my power of speech failed me. Still shaking from the ordeal, all I managed was a whisper. "I'm afraid."

"Afraid?" my husband cried, his face turning crimson. "Afraid? I never want to hear that word again." Then, composing himself, he added, "Fear is immobilizing, and right now we must gather all our resources and prepare for the confrontation ahead."

"My God, to lie there and let her go was torture," Lajos moaned pitifully.

"To let her go, when all I wanted to do was tear her apart with my bare hands," Uncle Meir snarled.

"Now I understand why you called her the 'Angel of Death,'" Uncle Yidel commented. "But I will clip her wings if it's the last thing I do." Then he charged past me, went into the kitchen and reappeared brandishing a bread knife. "There are five able-bodied men who will be ready for her if she returns, and give her the surprise of her life!"

By this time the other men had collected their weapons — scissors and knives from under the bed.

"And she had to find us now, after all we've been through," Anna moaned. As soon as the words were out of her mouth, an idea dawned on her, and her expression changed to one of great hope. "We are so paralyzed by fear that we never realized how the situation has changed," she said. "It's incredible that we still cringe in fear before the inhabitants of the shelter, when the only ones left are the women and two old men. Dr. Nagy and the dentist, our Nazi arch enemies, have left. The block overseer has been drafted, so who remains in the bunker? Only women and two old men — Maria's husband is well into his forties, and Janos must be at least fifty. If they try to help Lola and her Nazi cohorts, we can take precautions, lock them in the shelter and guard the exit doors."

"Shhh, quiet," somebody whispered, and we all pointed simultaneously toward the wall. Instantly, Anna's words froze on her lips, but there was excitement and hope in the air.

Then we heard the hateful voice of Salasy on the radio, and with it a sense of doom reentered our lives.

The baby, the baby, I silently cried, and, as if drawn by a magnet, I walked over to her crib. She slept peacefully, unaware of the danger. My hands trembled as I picked her up and I felt as though my legs were giving way. But somehow I made it to the Bitters' room, out of earshot of the horrifying, inciting, anti-Semitic slogans on the broadcast. I placed the sleeping child on the large double bed right next to the wall, and, driven by a sense of urgency, I pulled up a chair beside the night table, for I had a plan I had to see through.

Without so much as daring to glance at my baby, I collapsed into the chair. I rummaged feverishly through the pockets of my housedress and took out the two snapshots I had hidden there. I turned over one of the pictures and began to write.

Budapest. December 21, 1944. Ersabet: I can clearly see the SS men walking up the path toward the house. They are coming for us. When you read this, Ersabet, we or the SS will be dead. In any case, there will be no more secrets left surrounding our origin. I am aware of how passionately you hate Jews, but please, hear my cry. Please, please save our baby. You must understand, this is not between Gentiles and Jews. This is between two mothers' hearts. For I must confess that I, too, hate you and your Nazi son. Nevertheless, Ersabet, I swear to you that when he was stricken and you were so frightened and sad, my heart overflowed with pity for you, and, against my will, I found myself praying for the speedy recovery of your son. I hated myself for it, because he meant danger for us, but the heart of the mother in me felt your pain. Please, Ersabet, don't let the brutal murderers... please! It will be easy to hide her.

I turned over the photo and wrote on the picture. I had to summon all my strength because my hands were trembling so.

This is your father and mother. Your Jewish name is Faygele, after my mother. Oh, Faygele, we love you. We love you more than life itself. Please darling, our last wish, oh my Faygele, please be always and forever a Jew!

I will pin the photo onto the baby's shirt under her blanket, I said to myself, choking at the mere thought. I will ring Ersabet's bell and I will say, "Please watch her for a few minutes. Something came up. Anna is not home and I must take care of it." I must be careful to say it casually. Otherwise it will never work. And before she'll know what hit her, I'll thrust the baby into her arms and run out of the room. But the most important thing will be to immediately call her attention to the note on the baby's shirt. I'll call back from the door, "Please open the blankets. I overdressed her. Please take off her sweater right away." Then I'll go. Oh, Father in Heaven, please put pity into those stony hearts!

Suddenly an incident which happened in the Zuglo flashed into my mind. We had been sitting in the shelter talking, when Lola had turned to me with a perplexed expression on her face. "Zsuzsi, how on earth can Theresa be so naive, when it's an open secret and every school kid knows that Hitler uses the Jews as his personal liquid asset to finance his wars." Anna and I had joined in the laughter, all the while wanting to go for her jugular vein. You inhuman beast, I cried inwardly. Hitler, you can be proud of your followers. They learn fast and well.

My whole being exploded with hatred, and every part of me cried out for vengeance. Through my tears, I gazed at the picture on the night table, at the baby smiling confidently at her papa and mama, who were now unable to fulfill her expectations.

Through sheer force of will, I made my hand obey me as I scribbled in a frenzy, anxious to finish before they came for us.

Budapest. Dombalya Utca 5. There were nine Jews hiding under aliases here.

I painfully recorded everyone's names and birthdates and the towns each of us came from.

Among us is my seven-month-old little girl, Faygele. It's December 21, 1944, and we thought we had made it. Then a woman by the name of Lola Samos, residence Amerikas Utca 15-15, sought us out with the intention of turning us in to the Nazis. To rob. To kill. Please, whoever you are, avenge our deaths. Please. Revenge, revenge!!!

I stabbed at the picture until I was dizzy and the pen slipped out of my hand, landing under my chair. But as I tried to retrieve it, a pleasant warmth descended upon me, and gratefully, I sank deeper and deeper into my seat. I closed my eyes as the world turned black in front of me.

I don't know how long this blessed state of unconsciousness lasted. All at once I saw the two photographs on the nightstand. The strength of my anger surged through me, and with the ferociousness of a wild beast pouncing on its prey, I grabbed for the thumbtacks driven into Magda's shelves. My nails became broken and bloody, for the thumbtacks were rusty and deeply embedded into the wood.

I did not hear the door open, nor was I aware that my sister had entered the room until I heard her surprised and outraged cry. "Thumbtacks? So that is what you intend to stab the Nazis with, if they dare to come for us?"

With a start, I turned my head. "I need them," I mumbled, pointing to the photgraphs in my hand.

"You are mad," she said with an odd grin on her face which I knew only masked her own fear.

"You don't understand. It's urgent. I must secure one of the snapshots to the armoire." I tried to explain my plan to her, but under the gaze of shock in her eyes, I lost my train of thought and my words came out in an incoherent jumble.

"What you must do is assist us in our efforts to find a way out of this before the Nazis come back and tear down the doors," Anna interrupted me. "Every minute counts! Come." She picked up the baby and steered me unceremoniously toward the door.

"Leave me alone!" I shouted. "I must record something of great importance for generations to come."

"Generations?" she said, uncomprehending.

"Of course, generations. Didn't Hashem promise Avraham *Avinu* that his children would live on and on? But after what we have suffered, never again will we allow ourselves to be cast into the role of scapegoat for all the ills of the world."

"*Amen,*" Anna said. "Come, let's go!"

We stepped into the vestibule just in time to hear the announcement on the radio: "The world-famous opera of Bánk bán will be broadcast directly from the Hungarian National Opera House." Gone were the horrendous anti-Semitic slurs which had made me flee to the Bitters' room in despair just minutes before. I stood at the threshold, enchanted by the sounds of the hauntingly beautiful aria sung in a deep baritone.

Then, the music which had filled me with wonder only a moment ago began to enrage me. Flailing menacingly at the radio, I cried, "Anna, is there still a world out there, where people go to the opera and enjoy music and songs? Anna, is this a circus?"

Anna's face turned livid and she regarded me with eyes wide and staring. "A circus," she repeated. "Yes, it is a circus, like the ancient Roman circuses. It too rests upon the foundation of the mangled bodies of our martyred brethren. Only, you see, thanks to modern civilization, today's arena needn't be confined anymore to the dusty streets of Rome." Her eyes were ablaze. "Now the entire, vast continent of Europe has been transformed into one huge arena, in which, so conveniently for our enemies, we can be thrown right into the bloodthirsty Nazi beast's jaws!"

"I never thought of it that way before," I remarked, struck by the force of her words.

"Neither had I," she admitted, "but the facts speak for themselves. And just think, the whole world is watching the show without a word of protest."

The old Cain mentality of "Am I my brother's keeper?", I thought to myself as I frantically searched for the right spot on which to secure the snapshot. Finally, I tacked it to the roof of the armoire, sighing with relief at having finished my task.

Disgust was written all over my sister's face. "You act as though tacking that picture up were the only thing of any importance, when any moment now the Nazis may come for us! I don't know what's gotten into you, Zsuzsi. Is this the way you cope with mortal danger, by denying its existence?"

All at once, the gates of my tears opened. "Anna, our entire family has been killed. Remember, we are the last. And if, God forbid, it will be decreed that we, too, shall perish and we will join the ranks of our murdered brothers and sisters, then perhaps this snapshot will fall into the right hands. Otherwise, Anna, who will mourn for us? Who will know? Who will remember we ever lived? And Anna, there is a terrible force in our souls to be remembered after death, for I keep hearing our sisters and brothers begging me, I hear their pleas in the silence, I hear them crying in the wind, "Please do not forget me...do not ever forget us!"

Anna gazed at me, her face ashen. "In that case, Zsuzsi, let's write down every one of their names and paste them next to ours. We can use the few pieces of stationery that I brought along from Szombathely so we don't have to scribble on the few snapshots we have left."

58

Troubles have stretched my heart
O! Lead me out from my afflictions.
Psalms 25:17

December 21, 1944.
Dear Diary,

My name is Regina Klein *née* Einhorn. I live here with my family under the alias Zsuzsi Kovacs. My father used to call me Rivka Leah. To family and friends I am Leichi. More personal and informative details about us can be found on the back of a photograph in the armoire.

I desperately need a shoulder to cry on, an ear to hear the words which I cannot say to anyone. For you see, there is this unwritten law among us: *You must avoid spreading panic at all costs! Cheer and encourage each other and keep your fears to yourself.*

Now imagine our state of mind. Lola Samos just left us, I am frightened out of my wits and so is every one of us. But just hear us talk and see the feeble nods of approval with which we respond to each other's most outrageously bizarre schemes for saving ourselves! Then you will understand how desperately I need someone to whom I can express my true feelings.

My husband assures me that if the SS takes Anna and me away (I can't seem to convince Anna to hide under the bed when they come; Monika will — her husband is here), they will leave without searching our apartment. They will simply seal up the house in order to insure that no one loots the place before they return.

It's the same old story — blood and gold.

Will Ersabet hide my baby? Perhaps even Theresa will come along with the gang of SS executioners and convince the murderers to let her "do away with the baby," intending to save her. She could never let her be harmed. Never. She loves my baby with all her heart. But then again, Theresa will bring her up as one of her own. A Gentile.

Oh, don't let me think. I don't want to think. I can't.

My mind is wandering. My husband says that if the SS takes us away (but not the baby. No. Never. Ersabet will surely hide her), the men will slide down the back porch, using the heavy rope they secured to the railing the day we moved in here. They say that they will take the SS by surprise from behind and free us. They are confident that this will work, but I am terrified, crazed with fear, which floods me with guilt and self-loathing, for deep down I know that God will save our lives.

Uncle Yidel gave me and my sister each a folding pocket-knife and instructed us how and when to use it. Geza and Iche brought them for us, and the thought tears my heart. Poor boys, they were shot into the Danube a few days ago. Oh, what a dreadful way to die! I am horrified. Dear God, I must know that Ersabet will hide my baby. Please, someone, say it. I must hear it.

I hear my husband's footsteps. He will be terribly angry with me for being absent from the "consultation room," which I call the battleground.

The sirens have just sounded! I must run.

Dear Diary,

We just came upstairs and I rushed to tell you that no one in the shelter looked at us suspiciously. They haven't the faintest idea of what is going on up here. I must go now. The baby has fallen asleep on my shoulder. Her sweet little face is resting so peacefully next to mine. I have no words to describe the magnitude of my love, my pain. I can't take it anymore. I can't!

I am back, and I ask you: Can you imagine what would have happened if the air-raid siren had sounded when Lola was still here? She would have come down to the shelter with us! God is surely on our side!

The hamper is overflowing with the baby's laundry. I must hurry and wash.

Dear Diary,

It's 10:00 P.M., and a full six hours have passed since Lola stormed out to bring her henchmen. We stand by the window watching the path, and we are still in shock.

Dear Diary,

It's 11:00 P.M. We still haven't budged from the window. We tell each other, "Something must have happened to Lola, because she really meant business. She should have been back long ago. She knows only too well how quickly we disappeared from the Zuglo. Why would she give us time to repeat our escape?" The air is so thick with fear that one could almost slice it with a knife. All we can do is pray!

Dear Diary,

It's 12:00 midnight, and we still stand by our observation post, all ears and raw nerves, and each breeze outside makes us jump with the same maddening fear. Oh, this dreadful darkness! What havoc it plays with the imagination. I am not exaggerating when I say that no one on earth is entitled to define the word horror unless he has spent this night of horror here with us. To remain here, powerless to do anything. But we have no alternative. There is nowhere to go. Oh, if only morning would come.

December 22, 1944.
Dear Diary,

At last, the long night of misery is behind us. I just came up from the shelter, in time to see the sun rising over the meadow. Oh, what a relief to be able to look across the path and see that, in fact, there aren't any black-clad SS officers running to the house to arrest us, as I kept seeing in my mind's eye during this endlessly long horror of a night. It's morning! And we are still here!

Dear Diary,

It's 9:00 A.M., and Anna and Monika have just left the house to go shopping. Shopping. What a fancy word to use for going out in search of those loaves of clay we call "bread." Then again, I mustn't ridicule these loaves. After all, they keep us alive. Oh, I'll die a thousand deaths until I see them safely home with the bread. Now I'll go back to the window to wait for them.

Dear Diary,

It's 10:00. Where are they?

Dear Diary,

I am frantic. They have never been away for so long. It's already half past ten. I try so hard to push the thought out of my mind, but I can't. What if they bumped into Lola on the way? I am frantic. What shall I do?

Dear Diary,

It's 10:45 and they just turned onto the path. I can see from here that they are laden with packages. Who knows what the next second will bring? All I know is that I am ravenously hungry and I am going to eat as much bread as I can!

December 23, 1944, 11:00 P.M.
Dear Diary,

We are in the target zone! Bombs are raining from the skies over the meadow and all around the house. The fear for my husband and the others upstairs is driving me out of my mind. Since we rarely go upstairs anymore, I am writing this in the shelter bathroom behind closed doors.

The house is swaying! A bomb landed right next to the house!

Dear Diary,

11:53 P.M. I managed to go upstairs and check on my family. I saw them. They are fine, thank God. Here is what happened. At the sound of the explosion, I ran back to the baby in the shelter. My sister Anna was crazed with fright. We gazed at one another with eyes bulging, plagued by the same question: "Are they alright upstairs?"

"I have reached the limit of my endurance!" I cried, my voice drowned out by the screams of the others. "Anna, I must know of their welfare. I can't take it. It would kill me to lose them now, when the end is so near! We must find a way to warn them, to persuade them to come down here. They could easily take over this shelter."

"Zsuzsi, what are you doing?" she cried fearfully. "What's come over you?"

"Shhh. Quiet. Don't worry, I am not going mad. I am hiding this clean diaper for a reason. I have a plan. Do you think Janos will grant me permission to go upstairs to fetch a clean diaper for the baby?"

Anna's face lit up. "If you play your cards right, he might just let you. But wait a while, until the bombing eases up. Make your request during a period of relative calm."

Persuading Janos was not an easy task. Oh, what a fuss he made. But in the end I won. Let me describe what happened. I flew up the stairs, tearing into the apartment shouting, "Out with the emergency kit! Grab your knives and get ready to come down with me! Put on your coats! I won't hear of you staying here anymore, risking your lives. No, not at this stage," I cried, tears streaming down my face.

"Stop this! Stop this nonsense!" Uncle Yidel shouted, his face crimson. "You don't understand. Your husband won't tell you, so I will. Don't you wonder why the fighting has escalated around here? Well, I'll tell you why. The Allied forces are chasing the German brutes toward this open field! Right here! We are surrounded by the Nazis. We keep hearing their officers shouting out orders in their accursed language, right below this window."

"Why did you have to tell her?" my husband cried, angrily shoving Yidel aside. "Doesn't she have enough to worry about as it is?"

But Uncle Yidel was not to be crossed now. "This is the truth. The truth! And she should be made aware of it," he raged. "She thinks she came here to do us a favor, but she is endangering us!"

"Leave her alone!" my husband cried protectively. "Just leave her alone!"

"Zsuzsi, Yidel is right," my brother Lajos interjected through lips pale as clay. "Please keep our secret. Please do so even more carefully than before. For if even one of those bloodthirsty monsters should wander into the shelter, and they should point us out as Jews, he would murder us on the spot, for nothing but cruelty's sake. Believe me, the biggest service you could render us is not to call attention to us. So please, go right back downstairs. Don't forget why you came — take the diaper with you. And take heart, Zsuzsi. This won't last long. Everything will work out for the best. Just hope and pray and trust. Hashem is with us, you know."

Then, to my surprise, a smile lit up my husband's face and I noticed a trace of laughter in his dark brown eyes. "I almost forget to tell you the great news, Zsuzsi. According to the 'Voice of America,' all traffic between Buda and Pest has stopped, as of 9:00 P.M. last night!"

I wept with relief as the specter of Lola's return evaporated into thin air.

December 24, 1944, 9:00 P.M.
Dear Diary,

We just came upstairs. The International Red Cross has managed to secure a twenty-four-hour cease-fire on account of Christmas. Oh, the joy of being able to stay upstairs with my family! I am so excited!

December 24, 1944, 10:00 P.M.
Dear Diary,

It's clear to me that this twenty-four-hour period of peace and quiet is just the calm before the storm. I've no doubt that tomorrow the bombers will reappear, spewing their deadly cargo over our heads, but I don't want to think about it today, I don't want to remember this. I also know that after the cease-fire I must go back into the dreadful shelter, torn from my husband who, with the rest of them, is doomed to stay upstairs. But this, too, I don't want to remember. I do want to remember how our darling little girl snuggles up to her papa, and the look of joy on my husband's face. Yes, this I do want to remember. What good does it do to dwell on the fact that in a few hours from now, she will be separated from her father, forced to go into the bunker with me, so near to her papa and yet so unreachably far? So let me savor every hour, every minute, every second. Let me grab this pleasure with both hands while it lasts.

December 24, 1944, 11:45 A.M.
Dear Diary,

The old lady and Ersabet came to our house to see our Christmas tree! Luckily we had one, and even luckier, we displayed it in the foyer, so we didn't have to invite them inside! That's all we would have needed. The old lady invited us to go with them to midnight Mass. We declined. I hope it won't arouse her suspicions. We told her that Monika was acting up and we were afraid to leave her alone in the house in her disturbed mental state. No sooner had we made our apologies when Monika began to thrash her arms about wildly. "I don't believe!" she screamed. "Why should I when he killed my family? All my family is dead!"

The old lady tried to pacify her. "You must forgive, Monika. You must forget. On a night like this you cannot bear grudges against the 'Savior,' for you know that this night signifies peace on earth and love among mankind."

Perhaps she would still be here preaching if not for the church bells ringing out at midnight. When she heard them, she left in a hurry.

By the time she finally left us, we were keyed up and angry with her. "The old hypocrite," Monika cried through tears of rage. "Maybe I should have asked her where peace and love can be found. For I can't find it in the hearts of her people, who are killing us without cause."

Lord in Heaven, I cried to myself. Let these rumors about the gas chambers not be true.

"Where is this love that she speaks of?" Monika asked derisively. "Certainly not among the guards in the labor camps. It surely didn't find its way into the hearts of the brutal Nazis guarding the ghettos. Nor can it live in the hearts of the tyrants marching innocent people to the banks of the Danube River to be shot into the sinister waters below," she wept.

"Hypocrite! Liar!" Monika raged on. "She would sing a different song if she were in our shoes. How low she has sunk, how she must deceive herself to talk about love among mankind at times like these," she spat, reeling around so her back faced the Christmas tree. "But then again, there is still hope," she sighed, "as long as there are people of such caliber as Karoly and Magda. Oh, if everyone were like them, the embodiment of compassion and love, there would be no need to preach about it."

December 26, 1944, 9:00 A.M.
Dear Diary,

Through the grace of God we've made it! Can you believe it? We are FREE! FREE! FREE! We were liberated by the Russian forces last night at precisely 1:57 A.M., December 26, 1944!

I alternate between euphoria and the deepest despair. One moment I feel like shouting to the four corners of the world, "I am a Jew and I am free!" while the next moment I am weeping uncontrollably, thinking, How can I rejoice in our good fortune while in Pest, beyond the banks of the Danube River, the war still rages. The Lovag Utca, the ghetto sheltering the rest of my loved ones, is still in the brutes' hands. As the ancient proverb says, "A Jew can never be completely happy." But right now, I hear laughter. Something is going on in the next room. Let me see....Would you believe it? Our little daughter is entertaining the whole gang. She is flying from hand to hand and squealing with laughter.

December 28, 1944, 2:00 A.M.
Dear Diary,

I am weary beyond description, but sleep is impossible. I walk around in a dreamlike state watching my family sleeping peacefully. I look outside, savoring the quietude of the great open field under the window. There are no words to describe the joy in my heart. So why this great urgency in me to write tonight? Perhaps it is plain, old-fashioned guilt, for abandoning this journal at the time of good tidings. Whatever the reason, I feel driven by an inner force.

"If all the seas were ink and all the grasses quills," I could not write enough of the horrors we went through, nor could I write down all the miracles which God sent to us, which we have witnessed with our own eyes. Oh, what torture it is not knowing what is going on in the Lovag Utca and the ghetto. If only they were here with us!

Forgive me for jumping from subject to subject, but it's so hard to concentrate. Now I must record this most fascinating ending to our story.

During the last days of the siege, people in the shelter continuously ran around screaming, crazed with fright. I don't know how it happened, but Ersabet and the old lady ended up sitting right next to us. From time to time, my gaze fell upon Ersabet, who sat there, her face distorted with fright, rapidly telling her rosary beads and crossing her chest from time to time.

Then it happened. The house took a direct hit.

I heard the awesome sound of crumbling bricks, and with it crumbled my well-planned house of cards. Jacob and my brothers and uncles screamed in me. I completely lost control, and out of my mouth issued forth the age-old testament of the eternal Jew: *Shema Yisrael!* Then, in a shocked daze, I felt a hand clasp over my mouth, and the amazed whisper of the connecting words penetrated my ears: *Hashem Elokeinu, Hashem Echad*! I spun around to the source of these words, and I found myself looking at Ersabet.

For a moment the world seemed to recede as we stared at each other in mutual shock. Ersabet found her voice first. "You! You of all people!" she gasped. "You? Zsuzsi? Our despised source of perpetual fear! You, with your horde of Nazi boyfriends?"

"Nonsense!" I said through chattering teeth. "Stop this right now! My husband, my brothers — five men altogether — are hiding upstairs!"

Ersabet gazed at me in utter shock. She signaled with her eyes toward the bathroom. "Go in and lock the door. Wait there. I'll send help."

All this transpired under the cover of the blessed uproar, and no one noticed our little drama being played out right under their noses.

She continued, "Just keep up the pretenses for Maria and

her husband," Ersabet said. "They are dangerous."

Anna reached for the baby. Her voice shook terribly as she said, "Please, leave her with me."

"Thanks, Anna," I replied, swallowing my tears. "I know you love her just as I do, and I know you will take the best care of her if something happens and I don't come back."

I don't remember how I got into the bathroom, but there I was, pacing the floor with the fierceness of a wild beast that had just been caught and caged. I didn't notice when the opposite wall noiselessly slid open and I only became aware of someone's presence by the sound of his gasping for breath. "Shhh," Janos hissed. "Just give me your hand and I'll lead you. Be quiet or they might overhear us."

He held my limp hand as I followed him up the steps. "Zsuzsi," he whispered, "I, too, am a fugitive with a price on my head."

"Where are you taking me? Please hurry. They may need my help, and time is running out."

"Now we are above the secret chamber where Dr. Nagy and his son Laslo and the dentist are hiding," Janos explained.

"Let's hurry!"

He switched on the light, and, to my amazement, I found myself in his apartment. "Let me go to them!" I pleaded.

"First I have to make sure it is safe for you," he said, pressing his ear to the wall. "I think it has stopped raining brick."

"Open the door!" I cried, shoving him aside, and out I ran into the dusty darkness, my eyes tearing, choking with sobs and carrying in my mind's eye a picture of their mangled bodies strewn across the floor. By the time I made it upstairs over the debris, my hands and feet were bloody and cut up. Nevertheless, when I somehow fit the key into the keyhole and forced the door open, all fear of what I might find inside turned into prayer and hope, and in my mind reverberated the Priestly Benediction with which my father used to bless us children every Friday night:

May the Lord bless you and keep you.
May the Lord make his face to shine upon you
And be gracious unto you.
May the Lord turn His Countenance to you
And grant you Peace!

Despite my mood of optimism, I was not prepared for what followed. I walked into the room, bloody and overwhelmed, unable to utter a sound, and my brother ran up to me. "Talk!" he shouted at me. "What happened to you?" I just gazed at him, eyes bulging in shock. "Talk!" he shrieked, shaking me.

"Don't you know? The apartment on the other side of the wall has been hit! Not a window is left intact, not a door is left on its hinge, and the roof over the main bathroom has caved in!"

"The explosions were so constant," my husband replied, "that we were unable to hear it. Besides, we were too busy praying!"

Nevertheless, within fifteen minutes they were downstairs in the secret chamber, with only a thin wall separating us from the bunker. For the first time in seven months, I breathed a sigh of relief. Jacob, I thought jubilantly, we are together, just as the Rebbe said we would be. And finally, my eyes closed and I slept.

I don't know how long I had been asleep when I felt a tap on my shoulder. "Zsuzsi," Janos said softly. I looked into his jubilant face. "Zsuzsi, I don't want you to sleep through this. I don't want you to miss this most beautiful sound we've longed so much to hear. Listen! The soldiers are running toward this house, and the orders they are shouting are in a tongue we do not understand. They are our liberators."

"*Baruch Hashem!*"

A tribute to Karcsi Bitter
Who appeared on our horizon one dark dreary night
And rekindled in an instant
The belief in mankind in our faltering minds.
"I am a Gentile," he said, "and you are Jews,
But fear not, my brothers. I have come to help."
And not even the Almighty Lord in Heaven
Would thwart such humane excellence.
Today we gather here to thank him
And spread the word for everyone to hear,
How one man and his beautiful young wife
Hid thirteen Jews and saved their lives.
Please tell me, anyone, tell me, I implore!
How does one thank them for risking their lives?
What can one say to such selfless, noble friends?

Epilogue

Jewish 'children' thank Christian rescuer

By ROBERT LANE

I entered this world on a beautiful spring day, a world of madness, where thousands of my brethren were being slaughtered in the biggest blood bath in history. The reason for their senseless slaughter, only one - being born a Jew!

The words open a letter of thanks that Feige Klein Goldenberg stood clutching last night as she and her relatives waited in the International Arrivals Building at Kennedy Airport. They were written to the man who saved Feige and her entire family from certain death at the hands of the Nazis.

Shortly after 7 p.m., the man, 64-year-old Karol Bitter, a Hungarian Catholic, walked through the swinging doors of the Customs area into the arms of the Jewish family he calls "his children."

BITTER'S TRIP to the United States — a gift of thanks from Feige's father, Jacob — was arranged after years of searching for Bitter ended in another reunion in Budapest last spring.

"We lost touch with him after the 1956 Hungarian Revolution," Jacob said. "We made a point of finding him again during a trip to Hungary."

At that first reunion, Klein, who lives with his family in Borough Park, Brooklyn, asked Bitter if he would accept a gift. "He told us the best gift we could give him was a trip to the United States so he could see his children," Klein said.

The odyssey that led to yesterday's reunion began in May 1944, when Bitter happened upon a young Jewish mother-to-be crying bitterly in the hallway of an apartment house in Nazi-occupied Budapest. Hungary was an ally of Germany in World War II and the Jews in Budapest were on the run. The woman, Feige's mother Rifka Leah, was in despair over the apparently fruitless efforts she was making to save her family members who were scattered throughout Hungary.

RIFKA AND JACOB had found a way to obtain false identification papers that would help them and other relatives elude the Nazis. They needed two things: a way to transport the rest of the family to Budapest and a place to hide them once they arrived.

For the next five months, Bitter took the family under his wing, bringing relatives of the Kleins, who posed as Christians, into the safety of an apartment he rented for them in Budapest.

By the time Soviet soldiers liberated the Hungarian capital, Bitter had managed to bring together and care for 13 members of the family in that one apartment.

All of those memories were written down in the letter of thanks from Feige.

from the New York Daily News

NEWS

HOWARD GOLDEN

PRESIDENT, BOROUGH OF BROOKLYN
BOROUGH HALL, BROOKLYN, N.Y. 11201

PRESS CONTACT: GINA HOLMES 643-7784/875-9047

November 20, 1980 FOR IMMEDIATE RELEASE 80-126

GOLDEN HONORS HUNGARIAN RESCUER OF THIRTEEN JEWS DURING WORLD WAR II

Brooklyn Borough President Howard Golden today honored Karoly Bitter, a Hungarian citizen who saved the lives of thirteen Jews in Nazi-occupied Hungary during World War II.

Bitter has spent the past three weeks in the United States visiting Brooklyn residents Jacob and Regina Klein and nine other Hungarian Jews whom Bitter and his wife Magda personally rescued and protected from the Nazis. At great personal risk, the Bitters provided shelter and forged new identities for those in danger. At one point, Bitter rescued two members of Klein's family from a ghetto.

"Karoly Bitter's extraordinary courage in the face of the horrors of the Nazi regime is an example of heroism of the highest order. He risked his life, and the lives of his own family, so that innocent people--strangers--could be saved. His compassion and selflessness should serve as lessons for us all," Golden said.

"Nine Brooklyn residents and their families owe their very existence to Karoly Bitter. I join them when I express my heartfelt thanks and deepest admiration," he added.

Karoly Bitter's first visit to the United States climaxes a remarkable story of human compassion. After losing touch with Bitter for many years, Jacob and Regina Klein journeyed to Hungary in search of the man who had approached them on a Budapest street shortly after the Nazi invasion and, sensing their distress, immediately invited them into the safety of his home.

Upon finding Bitter in Budapest, the Kleins invited him to come to the United States for a long-awaited reunion with those he sheltered.

GENE KAPPOCK DAILY NEWS

Reunited with man who saved his family

Karol Bitter (left) is embraced by Jacob Klein during reunion at Kennedy Airport last night. Bitter, a Hungarian Catholic, hid Klein, who is Jewish, and his family from the Nazis in Budapest in 1944. The thankful Kleins, who live in Borough Park, Brooklyn, arranged for Bitter to travel to the U.S. to see his children.

ED MOLINARI DAILY NEWS

An emotional rescue

Brooklyn Borough President Howard Golden (center) honors silver-haired Karoly Bitter, a Hungarian citizen who saved the lives of 13 Jews in Nazi-occupied Hungary during World War II. Bitter has spent the past three weeks in the U.S. visiting Brooklyn residents Jacob and Regina Klein and nine other Hungarian Jews who Bitter and his wife rescued and protected from Nazis.

Glossary

The following glossary provides a partial explanation of some of the Hebrew, Yiddish and German words and phrases used in this book. The spelling and explanations reflect the way the specific word is used herein. Often, there are alternate spellings and meanings for the words.

AVINU: our father.
BAR MITZVAH: a Jewish boy of 13, the age at which he assumes religious obligations.
BARUCH HASHEM: "Thank God!"
BOCHUR: a young man; a YESHIVA student.
BRIS: lit., convenant; the ritual of circumcision.
BUBBIE: (Y.) a grandmother.
CHAVRUSA: lit., company, society; a partner in Torah study.
CHAZAL: Hebrew acronym for "our Sages, of blessed memory."
CHUPPAH: the wedding canopy; the wedding ceremony.
CHUTZPAH: audacity; impertinence.
DAVEN: (Y.) to pray.
DAYAN: a religious judge.
EICHAH: The Book of Lamentations.
ERETZ YISRAEL: the Land of Israel.
EREV SHABBOS: Sabbath eve.
GABBAI: a secretary or treasurer of a synagogue.
GALUS: the Exile; the Diaspora.
GAN EDEN: the garden of Eden.
GAON: a very learned man; a genius.
HASHEM: God.
HASHGACHAH: Divine Providence.
HATZLACHAH: success.
JUDENREIN: (G.) free of Jews.
KEHILLAH: a Jewish community; congregation.
KINDERLACH: (Y.) children.
KITTEL (Y.) a white cloak worn during prayer on ROSH HASHANAH and other holy days.

KOHEN, KOHANIM: member(s) of the priestly tribe.
L'CHAIM: "To life!"; a toast.
LATKES: (Y.) potato pancakes.
MA'ARIV: the evening prayer service.
MASHIACH: the Messiah.
MATZAH, MATZOS: unleavened bread.
MAZAL: luck; fortune.
MAZEL TOV: lit., good luck; "Congratulations!"
ME'ARAS HA-MACHPELAH: the Cave of Machpelah, burial place of the Patriarchs.
MIDRASH: collection of homiletic teachings of the Sages.
MIKVAH: ritual bath.
MUSAF: additional prayers appended to SHACHARIS on SHABBOS, ROSH CHODESH and Festivals.
PESACH: Passover.
REBBE: (Y.) rabbi; Torah teacher.
REBBETZIN: (Y.) the wife of a rabbi.
RIBBONO SHEL OLAM: Master of the Universe.
ROSH CHODESH: the beginning of the Hebrew month.
ROSH HASHANAH: the Jewish New Year.
SEFER, SEFARIM: sacred book(s).
SHABBOS: the Sabbath.
SHACHARIS: the morning prayer service.
SHALOM: lit., peace; a traditional Jewish greeting.
SHALOM ALEICHEM: lit., "Peace be with you," a traditional Jewish greeting.
SHEMA YISRAEL: lit., Hear O Israel, the opening words of the fundamental Jewish prayer which proclaims the unity of God.
SHIDDUCH: a marital match; matchmaking.
SHOCHET: a ritual slaughterer.
SHOFAR: a ram's horn, sounded in SHUL on the High Holy Days.
SHUL: (Y.) a synagogue.
SIDDUR: a prayer book.
SIMCHAH: happiness; a joyous occasion.
TACHRICHIM: burial shrouds.
TALLIS: a prayer shawl.
TALMID, TALMIDIM: student(s).
TALMID CHACHAM: a scholar; a learned man.
TEFILLIN: phylacteries.
TEHILLIM: The Book of Psalms.
TZADDIK: a righteous, pious man; a holy man.
YERUSHALAYIM: Jerusalem.
YESHIVA: an academy of Torah and Talmud study.
YOM TOV: a Jewish festival.
ZOLL ZEIN MIT MAZEL: (Y.) "May [this occasion] be accompanied by good fortune."

THE FELDHEIM REMEMBRANCE SERIES

To a generation that never knew war, the horrors of even the recent past seem remote. A generation that bears no scars of war can have no memory of war. In an era of peace and plenty, it is hard to recall times of strife and deprivation; in an era of spiritual revival, remembrance dims of a time when the Jewish People faced the threat of spiritual and physical annihilation.

The Remembrance Series is a special collection of works that chronicle the survival of our People and our Faith throughout the war years, when cities were devastated, countless Jewish communities were virtually obliterated, and six million of our brethren perished. The eyewitness accounts recorded in this series recreate the vibrance of Jewish communal life and the spirit of our Nation in that tragic period of desolation and turmoil.

"Remember what Amalek did to you on your way out of Egypt" and all that Amalek-incarnate did.

Remember the power of the Almighty, for both destruction and salvation are in His hands.

Remember the valor of our martyrs and the heroism of our survivors, for they were put to the ultimate test.

Remember — for the Holocaust is a part of our history we dare not forget.